The
STEVENSON
COMPANION

Robert Louis Stevenson

The STEVENSON

COMPANION

SELECTED AND ARRANGED

WITH AN INTRODUCTION BY

JOHN HAMPDEN

MEDILL McBRIDE COMPANY
NEW YORK

Printed in Great Britain

CONTENTS

Letters

Novels

Illustrations

ROBERT LOUIS STEVENSON

HIS LIFE AND WORK

I

ROBERT Louis Stevenson knew how to tell a story—no more accomplished master of narrative has yet used the English tongue, or the Scots—and for this reason, if no other, he has always kept a certain number of enthusiastic admirers, young and old. But for a generation or so more literary-minded readers have relegated him to the nursery or the classroom, and that is a very odd fate indeed for the writer whom Henry James valued as 'a whole province of one's imagination', and whose magnificent fragment, *Weir of Hermiston*, is the only novel in our literature which can be placed close beside *Wuthering Heights*.

Stevenson's friends were partly to blame: they made him into a Cult. Even before he left England his personality had begun dangerously to overshadow his work, and his wanderings among the South Sea Islands, his remote, romantic burial, completed the legend. For twenty years after his death, despite Henley's denunciation of the picture of him as a 'Seraph in Chocolate', the sentimental eulogies and the Stevensoniana multiplied until many readers were nauseated, so that the reaction, when it came, was more contemptuous than the usual post-mortem devaluation from which nearly every writer suffers. But it is now fifty-five years since Stevenson died and like many other nineteenth-century authors he is being appreciated afresh.

He certainly offers not only quality but quantity and variety. The latest collected edition of his works, the Tusitala, runs to thirty-five volumes, and comprises seventeen novels and *nouvelles* (several written in collaboration), many short stories, two books for boys, five plays (all written in collaboration), five travel books, two volumes of poems in English and Scots, a biography, a family history, two scientific papers, a descriptive and historical account of Edinburgh, prayers, fables, some forceful pamphlets on South Sea politics, a remarkable

variety of essays—critical, historical, biographical and
'familiar', various other items, and five volumes of letters to
his family and friends. His versatility was due not only to a
natural restlessness but to an artist's delight in experimenting
in new media, and his copiousness has none of that hasty
facility which marred so many Victorian novels; he was
incapable of slovenly work. He is in fact the most accomplished
as well as the most versatile of Scottish men of letters, and
everything he wrote carries the impress of his personality.

Nearly all his best work carries the impress of his nationality
also. England, though he made many friends in it, was always
a foreign country to him—far more foreign than France. He
learned a great deal from English literature, he learned still
more from French, and much of his life was spent in wandering
across Europe, the United States and the South Seas in search
of health, but he remained essentially a Scot. All that was
fundamentally good and bad in him was moulded finally
during his 'covenanting childhood' in Edinburgh.

He was born in that 'Athens of the North' eighteen years
after the death of Sir Walter Scott, on November 13th, 1850.
For three generations his family had been great engineers,
whose light-houses in particular had given them an inter-
national reputation. They were not only inventors, owing as
much to creative imagination as to the mathematics and
physics which they taught themselves, but pioneers, travelling
on horseback or in small ships, working against physical
hardship and danger among half-barbarous people on remote
Scottish coasts. They were also devout Presbyterians and
leading citizens of an intellectual, dour little metropolis in
which respectability was apt to be regarded as the highest
virtue. Louis's mother, Margaret Isabella Balfour, was 'a
daughter of the manse' and grand-daughter of a well-known
Professor of Moral Philosophy. She was very pretty and
vivacious. Louis's father, Thomas Stevenson, had a lively
imagination, a temperament alternating between gaiety and
despondency, a lifelong habit of putting himself to sleep by
making up adventure stories, and a nice sense of words. (He
said that he regarded life as a shambling sort of omnibus
which was taking him to his hotel.) He had also rigid religious
beliefs. All the powers of environment were united to make
Robert Louis Stevenson into a civil engineer, an elder of the

kirk, and a circumspect burgess of Edinburgh. By temperament he was an artist, a heretic and a vagabond. It was only after years of agonising struggle that he freed himself, and he might never have succeeded but that he was fortunate in his friends and in his discovery of France.

II

Louis was an only child.* His mother being often unwell, his childhood was ruled by his nurse, Alison Cunningham, whom he later made famous as 'Cummy'. She gave herself devotedly to tending his frail little body and his immortal soul. She could be gay enough, she had a native sense of poetry and drama and told him unforgettable tales of the Covenanters, but she gave him coffee as a cure for sleeplessness and filled his infant imagination with the fires of hell. 'When he had a touch of fever at night', Stevenson wrote of himself in 'A Chapter of Dreams', 'the night-hag would have him by the throat and pluck him, strangling and screaming, from his sleep. . . . Hell gasped for him; and he would awake clinging to the curtain-rod with his knees to his chin.' A cabinet made by Deacon Brodie stood in his nursery, and Cummy enlarged on the story of that respected city counsellor and cabinet-maker who was also leader of a notorious gang of burglars until caught and hanged in 1788. The idea of a double life, of respectability as a façade for crime, was so deeply rooted in Stevenson's childish mind that it became a recurrent theme in his work, for all his life he remained vividly conscious of his childhood.

His attendance at Edinburgh Academy and other schools was much broken up by his mother's convalescences in southern England, southern France and elsewhere, and by his own ill-health. He nearly died of 'gastric fever' at the age of eight, and suffered much from bronchial troubles and 'nervous excitability'. At the age of twelve he accompanied his parents on a Grand Tour of France, Italy and Germany and fell in

* He was christened Robert Lewis Balfour Stevenson. The third name he dropped himself; the second was altered to 'Louis' by the family, from dislike of a man named Lewis, but the Scottish pronunciation was retained. The initials 'R.L.S.', which became world-famous, he began to use regularly for his contributions to the *Cornhill Magazine*.

love with France at first sight, but it was six years before he could improve the acquaintanceship. At seventeen he entered Edinburgh University to study engineering under Professor Fleeming Jenkin, and Mrs Jenkin has recorded how she first met him, when she found Mrs Stevenson, apparently alone sitting in the firelight one winter afternoon of 1868:

'Suddenly from out of a dark corner came a voice peculiar, vibrating; a boy's voice I thought at first . . . I listened in perplexity and amazement. Who was this son who talked as Charles Lamb wrote? This young Heine with the Scottish accent? I stayed long, and when I came away the unseen converser came down with me to the front door. . . . I saw a slender, brown, long-haired lad with great dark eyes, a brilliant smile, and a gentle, deprecating bend of the head. . . . I asked him to come and see us, and ran home. As I sat down to dinner I announced, 'I have made the acquaintance of a poet!' From that day forward our affection and our admiration for him, and our delight in his company, grew.'

If Stevenson had conformed he would probably have been an exemplary citizen and civil engineer. (In 1871 he won the Silver Medal of the Royal Scottish Society of Arts with a paper 'On a New Form of Intermittent Light for Lighthouses' —presumably to show that he could do it.) But it was impossible for him to conform. He was born to be a writer. At the age of six, before he could write at all, he dictated 'A History of Moses'. The deliberate truancies and evasions of his schoolboy and undergraduate days masked a steady purpose which he described later in a famous passage of his essay on 'A College Magazine':

'All through my boyhood and youth, I was known and pointed out for the pattern of an idler; and yet I was always busy on my own private end, which was to learn to write. I kept always two books in my pocket, one to read, one to write in. As I walked, my mind was busy fitting what I saw with appropriate words. . . . It was not so much that I wished to be an author (though I wished that too) as that I had vowed that I would learn to write. . . .

'And yet this was not the most efficient part of my training. . . . It only taught me (so far as I have learned them at all) the lower and less intellectual elements of the art, the choice of the essential note and the right word: things that to a happier constitution had perhaps come by nature. . . . So that there was perhaps more profit, as there was certainly more effort, in my secret labours at home. Whenever I read a book or a passage that particularly pleased me . . . I must sit down at once and set myself to ape that quality. . . . I have thus played the sedulous ape to Hazlitt, to Lamb, to Wordsworth, to Sir Thomas Browne, to Defoe, to Hawthorne, to Montaigne, to Baudelaire and to Obermann. . . . *Cain*, an epic, was (save the mark!) an imitation of *Sordello*: *Robin Hood*, a tale in verse, took an eclectic middle course among the fields of Keats, Chaucer and Morris: in *Monmouth*, a tragedy, I reclined on the bosom of Mr Swinburne. . . . Even at the age of thirteen I had tried to do justice to the inhabitants of the famous city of Peebles in the style of the *Book of Snobs*. So I might go on for ever through all my abortive novels, and down to my later plays. . . . It is the great point of these imitations that there still shines beyond the student's reach his inimitable model . . . and it is a very old and a very true saying that failure is the only highroad to success. I must have had some disposition to learn; for I clearsightedly condemned my own performances. . . .'

III

Stevenson's parents and their Edinburgh friends knew nothing of this intense self-discipline, or discounted it as trivial. They saw only a lazy schoolboy who grew into a disreputable undergraduate and became a moral and religious outcast. Their harsh creed and narrow social convention, and the smug hypocrisy which he often detected, or thought he detected, among the godly, became intolerable to the growing writer. He had to escape or die, and the only escape he could see was that suggested by Deacon Brodie. He found his way into the terrible slums which lay so close behind the prim façade of Edinburgh's 'New Town' and soon made himself at home among thieves and prostitutes. They called him 'Velvet Coat', petted and made a fuss of him. He was not only 'seeing life' and collecting 'copy', taking his penny note-book with him everywhere: something in him responded dangerously to the fascination of evil, rejoicing in the uninhibited ease of movement which it brought him. His religious beliefs went with his moral and social code. A number of his undergraduate friends thought and behaved in similar fashion without raising open scandals. Stevenson flaunted his defiance, going to formal dinner parties in disreputable bohemian clothes, talking freely about his heresies and about the advantages of a 'double life'.

A climax came, if Edinburgh traditions are true, when he fell in love with a young and beautiful Highland girl, Kate Drummond, whose passionate devotion appealed to both his youthful idealism and his newly awakened sensuality. Thomas Stevenson was confronted suddenly by a son who wanted to marry a prostitute. The father won. The girl was left in her brothel. Stevenson suffered a moral and sexual defeat which must have been as shattering to him as the whole episode was to his parents. Thereafter his double life was lived more discreetly, and according to tradition his sordid sexual adventures continued at least until the eve of his marriage: but he could not escape the all-seeing eye of the Scottish Jehovah, who bore such a terrible resemblance to the Scottish Satan, nor free himself from a painful consciousness of the 'war in the members.' This and the Brodie theme found expression repeatedly in his work—he was always one of the most autobiographical of writers—and these adolescent experiences marked him apparently for the rest of his life. Almost to the end he remained immature in some respects: it is significant that only in the last and greatest of his novels, *Weir of Hermiston*, did he succeed in creating women who were completely alive and real. He was nearing the end when he wrote, 'If I had to begin again . . . I believe I should try to honour sex more religiously. The worst of our education is that Christianity does not recognize and hallow sex. . . . It is a terrible hiatus. . . .'

Meanwhile he continued to give intermittent attention to his engineering classes. In 1868 he spent some weeks at harbour works at Anstruther and Wick, and next year accompanied his father on a tour of inspection in the *Pharos*, a steamship belonging to the Board of Northern Lights. In 1870 the building of the deep-sea lighthouse of Dhu Heartach took him to the little island of Earraid, where David Balfour was wrecked when *Kidnapped* came to be written sixteen years later. But in 1871, less than a month after winning the Silver Medal, he announced that he would not become an engineer. Thomas Stevenson refused to accept authorship as a career, so they compromised on law, and Louis did well enough to get himself called to the Scottish Bar in 1875. He practised half-heartedly for a few months, before he gave himself finally to literature.

For Thomas Stevenson the worst shock of all came in 1873.

'The thunderbolt has fallen with a vengeance now,' wrote Louis to his friend Baxter. . . . 'My father put me one or two questions as to beliefs, which I candidly answered. I really hate all lying so much now—a new-found honesty that has somehow come out of my late illness . . . but if I had foreseen the real hell of everything since, I think I should have lied, as I have done so often before. . . . And now they are both ill, both silent. . . . They don't see either that my game is not the lighthearted scoffer; that I am not (as they call me) a careless infidel. . . . I am as honest as they can be in what I hold. . . .

'O Lord, what a pleasant thing it is to have just *damned* the happiness of (probably) the only two people who care a damn about one in the world.'

It was bitter enough for Thomas Stevenson that his beloved only son should have disgraced the family and renounced the family's high calling; it was infinitely worse that he should have become a 'horrible atheist', destined to eternal torment. For Louis the bitterness lay not only in the suffering he had caused (he loved his parents) but in his own position: ill-health, lack of qualifications, and perhaps lack of courage kept him still dependent on his father—with £1 a month as pocket-money.

It might have gone very ill with Stevenson if the same year, 1873, had not brought also the beginnings of deliverance. He had like-minded friends in Charles Baxter, Walter Ferrier, and notably his cousin Bob, R. A. M. Stevenson, later a brilliant art critic, who presently taught Louis to think and drink and appreciate French art. They were often partners in elaborate hoaxes and practical jokes, for there was even then more gaiety than gloom in Louis. And Professor Jenkins' household provided him with a congenial circle in which he could talk as he liked. But he needed to escape, physically and mentally, from Edinburgh, for he had come now to hate that 'inclement city' as much as he loved it. The climate he hated without qualification, and it would have killed him in a few years if he had remained. Yet he never ceased to realize how much he owed to Edinburgh, and to his Scottish birth and upbringing, in terms of love and learning and in his conscious-ness of 'the fragility and unreality of that scene in which we play our uncomprehended parts'.

'Nor must we omit,' he wrote in *The Foreigner at Home*, 'the sense of the nature of his country and his country's history gradually growing in the child's mind from story and from observation. A Scottish child hears much of shipwreck, outlying iron skerries, pitiless breakers and great sea-lights; much of heathery mountains, wild clans and hunted Covenanters. Breaths come to him in song of the distant Cheviots and the ring of foraying hoofs. He glories in his hard-fisted forefathers. . . . Poverty, ill-luck, enterprise, and constant resolution are the fibres of the legend of his country's history.'

That history was very vivid, very close to him and very dear. Everything that was best in his future work was to be rooted in it. Moreover he longed all his life to be a man of action, he was never so much alive as on board a ship, and never grew out of a desire to be a soldier. In his own imagination he wore always the *panache* of romantic adventure, but without losing his humility as an artist or his gentleness and friendliness as a man. This sense of romance had been strongly nourished by his country's and his family's history, as he well knew, but henceforward he loved Scotland most when he was far away, and it must have been with an overwhelming sense of release that he set out in July 1873 to visit a cousin who was married to the Rector of Cockfield, Suffolk, though he could not have guessed how decisive that visit was to be. Most probably he left Edinburgh in the adolescent despair of his own 'Vanquished Knight':

> I have left all upon the shameful field,
> Honour and Hope, my God, and all but life. . . .

IV

At Cockfield Stevenson was warmly welcomed, particularly by his cousin's guest, Mrs Frances Sitwell. He was often strongly attracted by young children, and more than once by women older than himself who were unhappy. Mrs Sitwell, then thirty-four, was living apart from her husband and had a ten-year-old son. She was also a remarkable woman. When she died in 1924, J. L. Garvin wrote 'Beauty like hers was genius. . . . Divining intuition like hers was genius.' She summoned immediately to Cockfield her friend Sidney Colvin, whom she was later to marry, and who, although only twenty-eight, was already Slade Professor of Fine Art at Cambridge, with a growing reputation as a literary critic. There developed rapidly between these two and Stevenson an intimate friendship which was continued all his life. Until his marriage he poured out his hopes and troubles to Mrs Sitwell in a long series of letters. Colvin introduced him during the next few years to most of the leading critics and editors of the day, secured his admission to the Savile Club, a great meeting-place of writers, and gave him harbourage in Trinity College, Cambridge, and later in the Keeper's House at the British Museum. Sir Sidney Colvin's *Memories and Notes* includes a vignette of the emaciated stripling of twenty-three, with fair hair and brilliant dark eyes, who made such an impression at Cockfield:

'He seemed, this youngster, already to have lived and seen and felt and dreamed and laughed and longed more than others do in a life-time. He showed himself moreover full of reading, at least in English and French—for his Latin was shaky and Greek he only got through translations. . . . Pure poetic eloquence (coloured always, be it remembered, by a strong Scottish accent), grave argument and criticism, riotous streaks of fancy, flashes of nonsense more illuminating than wisdom, streamed from him inexhaustibly as he kindled with delight at the delight of his hearers . . . till all of us seemed to catch something of his own gift and inspiration. This power of inspiring others has been noted by many of those who knew Stevenson later as an especial and distinguishing mark of his conversation. As long as he was there you kept discovering with delight unexpected powers in yourself. . . .

'He comprised within himself, and would flash on you in the course of a single afternoon, all the different ages and half the different characters of man, the unfaded freshness of a child, the ardent outlook and adventurous day-dreams of a boy, the steadfast courage of manhood, the quick sympathetic tenderness of a woman, and already, as early as the mid-twenties of his life, an almost uncanny share of the ripe life-wisdom of old age. He was a fellow of infinite and unrestrained jest and yet of infinite earnest, the one very often a mask for the other; a poet, an artist, an adventurer; a man beset with fleshly frailties, and despite his infirm health of strong appetites and unchecked curiosities; and yet a profoundly sincere moralist and preacher and son of the Covenanters after his fashion, deeply conscious of the war within his members, and deeply bent on acting up to the best he knew.'

So he remained, except for a growing strength of character and purpose, until his death. But in uncongenial company he was often a different person, aggressive because he was ill at ease, a foolish *poseur* or practical joker. Miss Blantyre Simpson, giving an Edinburgh view, says that many who knew him slightly agreed with a janitor's description of him as 'Yon daft laddie'. 'He attitudinized in his twenties as a sparkling, flighty speaker, and those of his own years had no patience with his sudden raptures, his almost hysterical sensitiveness over a sad story or a too realistic drama.' They noted also that (although not conceited) he could not bear ridicule; his naïve vanity was defenceless against it.

Henceforward however it mattered far less to him what Edinburgh thought. The cage-door had opened, never to close again entirely. He returned in September 1873, to an unhappy mother and a father who was often reduced to silence or hysteria by his 'atheism', but he wrote, with Mrs Sitwell's encouragement, an essay on 'Roads' which had been planned at Cockfield, and with Colvin's recommendation it was accepted by the London *Portfolio*. This was his first appearance in a national periodical, and the first piece of writing for which he was paid. He had begun his career.

V

In October 1873 Stevenson went to London, intending to read for the English Bar, but by this time his health was so bad that Mrs Sitwell and Colvin insisted on his seeing a well-known doctor, who diagnosed 'nervous exhaustion with a threat of phthisis' and told him to spend the winter, alone, on the Riviera. *Ordered South* describes how miserably he passed his first months at Mentone—the only occasion on which he ever allowed himself to write like an invalid—but he soon recovered in spirit and to some extent in body. For four years thereafter France was his spiritual home. He visited England and Scotland and Germany, and passed his final examination as a Scottish Advocate. In Edinburgh in February 1875 he was introduced by Leslie Stephen to that boisterous cripple, W. E. Henley, who became one of his most intimate friends. But in France he found for the first time the mental and physical climate which he so profoundly needed, sunshine, freedom, and a mode of living to which all his instincts responded. 'There is something, or there seems to be something, in the very air of France that communicates the love of style,' he wrote in 'Fontainebleau'. 'Precision, clarity, the cleanly and crafty employment of material, a grace in the handling, apart from any value in the thought, seem to be acquired by the mere residence. . . . The air of Paris is alive with this technical inspiration. . . .' And years later he said, 'Wherever I meet a Frenchman I am at home.' He now learned to speak French fluently and expressively, though not always correctly. He read more widely than ever in French literature, learning much from contemporary writers—George Sand, Flaubert, Daudet, Musset, Maupassant and Baudelaire among them. Sainte Beuve he admired as much as he disliked Chateaubriand. The serenity, the broad humanity of Michelet captivated him altogether. Among older writers Montaigne in particular appealed to him—as a fellow rebel against Calvinism, but still more as a supreme master of the familiar essay, which he was now assiduously practising. The results of this French influence were strikingly apparent. His first published essay in literary criticism dealt with 'Victor Hugo's Romances' (1874). His first contribution to the Encyclopedia Britannica (1875) was an article on Béranger. His first published short story (1877), *A Lodging for the Night*, was an imaginary incident in the life of François Villon. His first book, *An Inland Voyage* (1878) described how he and his friend Sir Walter Simpson, a fellow Advocate, paddled their canoes up the Sambre and down the Oise. (Characteristically, Stevenson looked so disreputable by the time they reached Châtillon-sur-Loire that the Commissary clapped him into gaol). His third book was *Travels with a Donkey in the Cevennes*. During these five years, however, he wrote also on many subjects outside France, including one of his best short stories, *Will o' the Mill* (1878) and the essays, mannered but much admired, which were later collected in *Virginibus Puerisque*. For Stevenson was never *deraciné*. He might be summed up as a Scottish writer who learned to write like a Frenchman but never ceased to be a Scot.

He saw a good deal of the Riviera coast and of Montmartre. Presently he and his stimulating cousin, R. A. M. Stevenson (their luggage consisting of greatcoats and toothbrushes) joined a colony of painters at Grez, a picturesque riverside village in the Forest of Fontainebleau. It was blessed with an old inn and a very amenable inn-keeper. There Stevenson lived, probably for the first and last time, a life as carefree as it was joyous. There one summer evening in 1876, returning late, he saw through a window of the lamp-lit dining-room a stranger who had just arrived, and his heart told him that he must marry her. He vaulted over the window-sill into the room.

The stranger proved to be a Mrs Fanny Van de Grift Osbourne, an American of Swedish-Dutch descent, who had left an unfaithful husband in California and was scraping a living as a journalist while she studied art. She was about twelve years older than Stevenson, 'slight, with delicately moulded features and vivid eyes gleaming from under a mass of dark hair', by no means without humour, but grave and very determined. Her son and daughter adopted Stevenson at once, while the love between him and Fanny deepened rapidly. But he had never been able to earn his own living, and though his relationship with his parents was improving he knew that they would be outraged by his wanting to marry another man's wife. How was he to keep a wife and family?

For two years they shared a precarious happiness in Grez, Paris and London. Stevenson's essays, reviews and stories were now appearing fairly frequently (but not very profitably) in the *Cornhill*, *Academy* and other literary journals, and the initials R.L.S. were becoming familiar to discriminating readers, who were then, as always, a small minority. When in London he enjoyed the company of Colvin and Mrs Sitwell, Henley, Andrew Lang, Edmund Gosse, Leslie Stephen and others. George Meredith, whose work he revered, he met in April 1878, while staying with his parents at Burford Bridge. When Henley began, with the weekly *London*, his remarkable career as an editor, Stevenson contributed a number of essays, and helped to kill the journal with his *New Arabian Nights*—for those impudent fantasies of Prince Florizel took some years to find an admiring public.

In the autumn of 1878, Fanny decided that she must return to California, to come to some final settlement with her husband, and she at least seems to have thought that her parting from Stevenson was final. He sought solace in his journey through the Cevennes: 'And yet even while I was exulting in my solitude I became aware of a strange lack. I wished a companion to lie near me in the starlight, silent and not moving, but ever within touch. For there is a fellowship more quiet even than solitude, and which, rightly understood, is solitude made perfect.'

For the second time in his life Stevenson had to face a supreme test, and this time he did not fail. When news came in the summer of 1879 that Fanny could and would divorce her husband, but was seriously ill, he asked no help from his father and would not listen to his friends. On August 7th he sailed for New York in the emigrant ship *Devonia*.

VI

The physical hardships of that voyage can be inferred from the uncomplaining pages of *An Amateur Emigrant*, yet Stevenson contrived, in his desperate need of money, to write a short novel, *The Story of a Lie*. ('The handwriting is not good because of the ship's misconduct,' he told Colvin.) An emigrant train took him to San Francisco, and while it snorted across Nebraska he perched dangerously on the roof of a coach to write to Henley: 'Peace of mind I enjoy with extreme serenity; I am doing right; I know no one will think so; and don't care. My body however is all to whistles. . . . What it is to be ill in an emigrant train let those declare who know.'

Fanny had recovered from her illness when he found her, but his own health was alarming. For the first and last time in his life he had to struggle against dire poverty, living on a few cents a day, writing desperately for money, but still incapable of hasty work and entirely dependent on the far-distant London market. In seven months, despite repeated illnesses, he wrote *The Amateur Emigrant*; *Across the Plains*; a few poems, several descriptive or critical essays, three quarters of a novel which he abandoned, dissatisfied with it; the beginnings of 'Prince Otto'; and *The Pavilion on the Links*. This last was a short novel of adventure with a Scottish setting, which epitomises neatly in anticipation most of John Buchan's romances. Stevenson regarded it as mere 'carpentry', 'blood and thunder', and was surprised that the august *Cornhill* accepted it; but it marked a definite advance in narrative skill,

a growing strength derived from growing economy of word
and incident.

Meanwhile his strength was failing. In September he set
out on a camping expedition (his usual recipe for health) into
the Santa Lucia Mountains, and after lying for two nights
'under a tree in a sort of stupor' he was rescued by 'a mighty
hunter of bears'. In December he had pleurisy. ('I have to
get money *soon*, or it has no further interest for me,' he wrote
to Henley; 'I am nearly through my capital.') By February
he believed that he was going to die, but characteristically
used the last of his strength to tend his landlady's dying child.
For six weeks he was very dangerously ill, 'on the verge of a
galloping consumption', and was nursed by Fanny, who had
now secured her divorce and was formally engaged to him.
Yet 'however ill he might be,' wrote one of his San Francisco
friends, 'or however anxious had been his vigils, he was always
gay, eloquent and boyish, with the peculiar youthfulness of
spirit that was destined to last him to the end.' He was not
only learning to write but learning to live. 'My spirits have
risen *contra fortunam*,' he wrote to Henley in January; 'I will
fight this out, and conquer.' The story of Kate Drummond was
not to be repeated. If he did not kill himself in the attempt he
would marry Fanny. He married her on May 19th, 1880. He
might perhaps have died first, but when the news of his illness
and his approaching marriage reached his father it brought a
cable in reply: 'Count on 250 pounds annually.' After agonising
for seven months Thomas Stevenson had relented at last,
ironically too late to save him from the tuberculosis which had
threatened so long; and now the prodigal must come home,
bringing his wife and her twelve-year-old son, Lloyd Osbourne.
The emotional relief must have been as great as the financial;
some months earlier he had written of his father, 'Since I have
gone away, I have found out for the first time how I love that
man: he is dearer to me than all, except Fanny.'

The honeymoon was spent at a deserted mining camp in the
mountains fifty miles north of San Francisco, which Stevenson
described later in *The Silverado Squatters*. Fanny and Lloyd
nearly died of diphtheria, but all three were sufficiently
recovered by July to set out for New York. On August 17th
1880 they landed at Liverpool, where they were met by
Stevenson's parents and Sidney Colvin.

VII

Fanny Stevenson brought all her tact and charm to bear, so successfully that she made a complete conquest of Stevenson's father and mother, and these four and Lloyd Osbourne were soon united in an affectionate intimacy which was broken only by death. Colvin and others of Stevenson's friends accepted Fanny as best they could. Henley was always jealous; he and Stevenson quarrelled in 1887, and never recovered their old intimacy. Henley was one of those who failed to realize that Fanny was not being merely possessive when she turned them away because they had colds, or cut conversations short when Stevenson's doctor had set a strict limit of fifteen minutes. But she was fighting for her husband's life. From his return to Britain until his first Pacific voyage eight years later he was sick as he had never been before, repeatedly at the point of death from haemorrhage or congestion of the lungs, or so dangerously exhausted that he had to lie in bed for days at a time, forbidden to speak, with his right arm in a sling to stop his dangerous gesticulations. Sciatica and ophthalmia provided variations. It must be partly to Fanny's credit that he lived until he was 44, to the surprise of many of his doctors, and certainly his work improved rapidly after his marriage.

There are few more difficult undertakings for a woman than marriage with an artist. If he is something of a genius, so much the worse for her. If he is an invalid it is worse still. Fanny's own health was not good, and suffered from some of the climates which benefited Stevenson. She was woman enough to need conventional comfort and security far more than he did, and his nomadic, improvident habits must have added acutely to the strain. All the available evidence seems to show that she responded nobly. How deeply their marriage satisfied them both is of course far more difficult to estimate. The artist and the puritan in Stevenson were so much at odds, he had been for so long ill-adjusted and immature, that only the right woman could bring him to integration and maturity. The artist who had come to see life steadily and see it whole appears only in his last work, *Weir of Hermiston*. It may be a reflection on his marriage that he took fourteen years to reach that point; it may be the supreme tribute to Fanny that he reached it at all. He praised her often and said more than once that he could not have made a better marriage. There seems no reason to doubt his sincerity, and the dedication of *Weir of Hermiston* is the noblest tribute which could be paid her.

Fanny's difficulties began at once. Two August visits to the Highlands made it quite plain that Stevenson dare no longer live in Scotland, even in summer. Twice they wintered in Davos, where he enjoyed tobogganing, endless *kriegsspiels* with Lloyd, and long conversations with John Addington Symonds, until the climate made Fanny ill. From September 1882 until July 1884 they lived in the south of France, spending a few supremely happy months in the magical beauty of Hyères. Then they moved to Bournemouth, and occupied for over two years the villa which Stevenson renamed Skerryvore, after one of his family's noblest achievements in lighthouse building. Here his health was so bad that he lived for the most part 'like a weevil in a biscuit', but with some excursions—to Dorchester to stay with Thomas Hardy, to London to meet Browning and Burne-Jones, for example. Visitors were numerous, the most exhausting being Henley, who collaborated with him in a series of plays which were to make their fortunes but had a well-merited lack of success. The only visitor who was always welcome to both Fanny and Stevenson was Henry James, and each of the novelists soon found in the other his only ideal critic, who would often disagree but never fail to understand. The Master's two essays are still among the best criticisms of Stevenson yet written.

When he was well enough he talked as brilliantly as ever, casting the old spell over his listeners, but it was largely because he was often too ill to get up that he wrote so much. There was nothing paradoxical in this. Apparently he suffered little severe pain, his energy was always psychic rather than physical (if that distinction can be made), and bed reduced interruptions while curbing his intense restlessness.

Like the rest of his writing career, these seven years were littered with new projects, begun in great enthusiasm and sometimes not abandoned until after weeks or months of hard work. A history of the Highlands, biographies of Wellington and Hazlitt and several stories were among these derelicts. But his achievements were notable. The essays included 'Talk and Talkers', 'A Penny Plain and Twopence Coloured' (which celebrated his life-long enjoyment of toy-theatres),

'Old Mortality' and 'Fontainebleau', and his first attempts to define his position as a writer of fiction: 'A Gossip on Romance', 'A Note on Realism' and 'A Humble Remonstrance'. He published many more poems than in previous years, and *A Child's Garden of Verses* appeared in 1885. *Thrawn Janet*, the acknowledged masterpiece among his short stories, was written in 1881, and was followed by *Markheim* and *Olalla*. *The Merry Men*, also written in 1881, was his most serious attempt in the *nouvelle* so far, but he failed to complete any full-length romance until a drawing of an island, made casually by Lloyd Osbourne, started him on *Treasure Island*. As a serial in *Young Folks* it was ill received. But its appearance in book form in December 1883 not only brought Stevenson an advance of £100 on account of royalties, which delighted him, but his first approach to popular success—although only about five or six thousand copies were sold in the first twelve months.

Yet it was after all a *nouvelle*, not a novel, which made him famous: *The Strange Case of Dr Jekyll and Mr Hyde*. It was written and completely rewritten in six days' feverish concentration, during the winter of 1885, and it swept Britain and America in a few months: the general public as well as the critics were convinced that a new writer of power and originality had arrived. *Kidnapped* followed in 1886, a novel begun as another story for boys which developed of its own volition into the most adult novel he had written so far. It confirmed his popularity, and his financial problem was solved, but although he had never lowered his standard he could not escape misgivings.

'What the public likes,' he wrote to Edmund Gosse in 1886, 'is work (of any kind) a little loosely executed; so long as it is a little wordy, a little slack, a little dim and knotless, the dear public likes it; it should (if possible) be a little dull into the bargain. I know that good work sometimes hits; but, with my hand on my heart, I think it is by an accident. And I know also that good work must succeed at last; but that is not the doing of the public; they are only shamed into silence or affectation. . . . There must be something wrong in me, or I would not be popular.'

By 1886 Stevenson was utterly weary of the battle for life which he was slowly losing in his bedroom at Skerryvore. 'I wish to die in my boots,' he wrote later. 'No more Land of Counterpane for me.' In May 1887 his father's death, a terrible blow, destroyed the one tie which could keep him in Britain. In August the party of five (Stevenson's mother and a French maid included) sailed from London for New York. It was the faithful Colvin who saw them off, and their farewell presents included a case of champagne from Henry James.

VIII

When the author of *Travels with a Donkey* arrived in New York in 1879 his one day there was spent, walking the streets under a deluge of rain, in the vain attempt to get commissions from editors. The author of *Dr Jekyll and Mr Hyde*, *Kidnapped* and *Treasure Island* was met at the quayside by a posse of newspaper men; for not only were all three novels being widely read, in pirated or authorized editions, but a dramatization of 'Jekyll and Hyde', with Richard Mansfield in the lead, was having a sensational success on Broadway. Stevenson was sought out by editors and publishers with offers which seemed enormous, but he was too sincere an artist to fall a victim of self-conceit. He had immediate need of the money, however, for he was escaping again, this time from the life of an invalid. The racketty voyage across the Atlantic, on a cargo ship loaded with matches, horses and apes, had revived all his inherited love of the sea.

'Wealth is only useful for two things: a yacht and a string quartette,' he wrote to Bob Stevenson from Saranac in October 1887. 'I was so happy on board that ship . . . [although] we had the beastliest weather and many discomforts. . . . I had literally forgotten what happiness was, and the full mind—full of external and physical things, not full of cares and labours and rot about a fellow's behaviour. My heart literally sang. . . . It is worth having lived these last years, partly because I have written some better books, which is always pleasant, but chiefly to have had the joy of this voyage. . . . I know a little about fame now; it is no good compared to a yacht. . . .'

Thanks to the American publishers and £3,000 inherited from his father, the yacht was now a possibility. The winter of 1887–88 the party spent in arctic discomfort at Saranac in the

Adirondacks, where Stevenson began *The Master of Ballantrae*, and wrote the first of twelve monthly essays for Scribner's Magazine: 'A Chapter on Dreams', 'The Lantern Bearers', 'Beggars', etc. And during 1887–88 Chatto & Windus published *Underwoods*, his first volume of serious poetry, Longmans published *A Memoir of Fleeming Jenkin*, his only biography, and Cassells *The Black Arrow*—a piece of 'tushery' which deserved its author's poor opinion of it.

He amused himself at Saranac and Manasquan by beginning to revise Lloyd Osbourne's first novel, *The Wrong Box*; playing a penny whistle, which had superseded his clumsy but ardent piano-strummings, and revelling with Lloyd in Findlay's *Sailing Directories of the World*. Fanny found at San Francisco the yacht they needed, a small fore-and-aft schooner: the *Casco*, Captain Otis. They chartered her and sailed on June 28th, 1888, for the Marquesas, some three thousand miles away. 'The first experience can never be repeated', wrote Stevenson. 'The first love, the first sunrise, the first South Sea island, are memories apart, and touched a virginity of sense.' The island world took him by the heart. The inexhaustible beauty of mountain, beach and atoll, the vast expanse of ocean, the sudden deadly menace of tempest or hidden reef, the handsome Polynesians (for whom he had the same instinctive sympathy that he had for children) with their legends, nobilities and savageries, the nomad life, the incessant physical activity—in all these things Stevenson realized the fascination which had haunted him since 1875, when a visitor to his father's house had talked of the beauty of the South Seas.

So the Stevensons went on and on, though the schooner proved dangerously unseaworthy, to the Paumotus, Tahiti (where he nearly died) and Honolulu, where they paid off the *Casco* and spent Christmas with Fanny's daughter, Mrs Isobel Strong, and her family, who were living there. 'I never knew the world was so amusing,' wrote Stevenson, 'We had grown so used to sea life that no one wearied, except Fanny who is always ill.' And a year later even she 'wearied, the last time we were ashore, to get afloat again'.

In Honolulu he finished *The Master of Ballantrae* and *The Wrong Box*, and continued the descriptive articles which were afterwards abridged to make *In the South Seas*. He had written already 'The Song of Rahero' and 'The Feast of Famine', which appeared next year in *Ballads*. Mrs Thomas Stevenson returned to Scotland, expecting the others to follow a year later, and they set out in the schooner *Equator* for a second cruise, which lasted from June to December 1889, taking them to the Gilbert Islands and finally to the Samoan island of Upolu. Stevenson fell in love with the island and the Samoans, and wrote there his first Island story, *The Bottle Imp*. He bought three hundred acres of forest land and arranged for a small wooden house to be built, intending to stay there occasionally.

During 1890 he paid two visits to Sydney, and both of them made him seriously ill, despite a long voyage between on the S.S. *Janet Nicoll* to New Caledonia, the Gilbert Islands and the Marshalls.

'I must tell you plainly,' he wrote to Henry James in August 1890, 'I can't tell Colvin—I do not think I shall come to England more than once, and then it'll be to die. . . . I am sorry about seven or eight people in England, and one or two in the States. And outside of that I simply prefer Samoa. . . . I was never fond of towns, houses, society, or (it seems) civilisation. . . . The sea, islands, the islanders, the island life and climate, make and keep me truly happier.'

So October 1890 found Stevenson and Fanny installed in their Samoan estate, which they named Vailima (Five Waters). It was six hundred feet above the sea and three miles from the port of Apia. There was no road. They worked strenuously, clearing, weeding and bringing up supplies, and were soon spending money extravagantly. The estate never paid its way, as it might have done under efficient management. A much larger house was built, a staff of a dozen Samoan servants was got together, Mrs Thomas Stevenson, Mrs Strong and her son joined the household, and Lloyd Osbourne brought some of the Skerryvore furniture from England. The *Vailima Letters*, which Stevenson wrote monthly to Colvin, describe his life in detail. As always he was still actor-manager in the thrilling drama of Robert Louis Stevenson, but no longer 'on the road' and cast now for his final rôle as Laird of Vailima. Like Scott at Abbotsford he was the chief of the clan, keeping open house for all comers.

The comers were numerous, and some of them well known.
Many books had to be ordered from England for the large
but always inadequate library. Casks of wine had to come from
France. The estate had to be tended. Though his income was
about £4,000 a year Stevenson soon found himself once more
labouring desperately for money: but as always never too
short of it to help any friend or acquaintance who was in need.

The Samoans, who named him Tusitala, Teller of Tales,
quickly learned to love and trust him. He responded with a
passionate interest in their politics and their wrongs. Since
July 1889 Samoa had been a condominium of Britain,
Germany and U.S.A. There were endless local bickerings and
gross mismanagement by the two governors, a German and a
Swede. Stevenson set out to get them recalled, writing a series
of letters to *The Times*, whereupon they tried to get him
deported. The Tauchnitz edition of his *Footnote to History*
(1892), which deals with Samoan affairs, was ordered by the
German Government to be burnt. In the end Stevenson won,
but the governors were not withdrawn until 1893, and meanwhile, as he had feared, there was a rebellion against their
puppet king, and the rebels were defeated. When Stevenson
secured the release of the rebel chiefs from prison, they showed
their gratitude (though they intensely disliked labour of this
kind) by making a road to Vailima with their own hands. He
named it 'the Road of Loving Hearts'.

Politics, farming, entertaining, household affairs, occasional
illnesses, and the vigorous outdoor life which he so much
loved, made alarming claims on the writer's time, but in these
last four years he wrote *The Wrecker* and *The Ebb Tide* (both
with Lloyd Osbourne), *The Beach of Falesá*, *The Isle of Voices*,
Catriona, *St Ives* (completed by Quiller-Couch), *A Family of
Engineers* (unfinished), *A Footnote to History*, essays, poems,
fables, prayers, and the unfinished *Weir of Hermiston*. Towards
the end his resolution and gaiety began to fail. Writer's
cramp added to his difficulties, though his step-daughter
Mrs Strong acted as amanuensis, and 1893 was darkened by
Fanny's ill-health and his own, and still more by the fear that
his creative powers were failing. Next year, however, the
Edinburgh Edition of his works, planned by Colvin and Baxter,
promised financial relief, and he received many other tokens
of the esteem in which both he and his work were held, for

'R.L.S.' was now a world-famous author, and to many young writers an almost legendary hero. From the late spring until September he laboured wearily at *St Ives*. Then he gave it up for *Weir of Hermiston*, which had been put aside in the previous year, and suddenly found himself working, consciously and delightedly, with such power as he had never known before. This he knew was to be his masterpiece, and Fanny and Lloyd Osbourne confirmed his judgment. On December 3rd he was talking gaily to her when suddenly he cried out and fell unconscious. He died that evening. Next day the Samoans cut a path through the forest and carried his coffin to the grave on the narrow summit of Mount Vaea above Vailima.

Engraved on the tomb was the Requiem which he had written for himself:

> Under the wide and starry sky,
> Dig the grave and let me lie.
> Glad did I live and gladly die
>   And I laid me down with a will.
>
> This be the verse you grave for me;
> *Here he lies where he longed to be;*
> *Home is the sailor, home from sea,*
>   *And the hunter home from the hill.*

IX

A piece of literature, like any other work of art, must finally be enjoyed and judged by its intrinsic merit, without respect to the personality of the author or the circumstances of composition, and it is fortunate that Stevenson no longer stands, as he stood for so long, between his readers and his books. His life story has however been told here at some length not only because it is interesting in itself but because a knowledge of it can quicken appreciation of his work. This is far more true of him than of most other novelists—of his friend Henry James, of Trollope or of Dickens, for example. He is one of the most persistently autobiographical of authors. His egotism permeated everything he wrote—deliberately and histrionically in his lesser work: subliminally in his greatest. His essential Scottishness must be understood by the English reader, because it was the most persistent and powerful force in that fierce mêlée of impulses which made him an artist from childhood, yet prevented him from becoming a mature artist almost until his death.

This failure to find a satisfactory métier combined with his intense interest in style and craftsmanship to make him always restless. He attempted every literary form in turn, and it is the extraordinary variety, much more than the quantity of his work, which has made the editing of this book very difficult, for many widely varying selections are possible. Some critics long believed that he would be remembered mainly as an essayist. There can be little doubt now, however, that it is his novels and tales which will not only continue to attract the majority of his readers, but will secure him a permanent place in the history of English literature. It is generally admitted also that *Weir of Hermiston* is his supreme achievement, and that *Thrawn Janet* and *The Beach of Falesá* rank very high—judgments with which the editor warmly agrees. Who does not know these three does not know Stevenson. They deserve the large proportion of the book which they occupy, but the necessary limit of length has prevented the editor from including more than one other piece of fiction. *The Master of Ballantrae*, *The Ebb Tide* and *The Suicide Club* have been passed over regretfully, with some shorter stories: the allegory of *Will o' the Mill*, the macabre tale of *Tod Lapraik*, the masterly *tour de force* of *The Sire de Maletroit's Door* and two powerful *nouvelles*, *Dr Jekyll and Mr Hyde* and *The Merry Men*. *A Lodging for the Night* here represents Stevenson's historical fiction.

The remaining space permits little more than reminders that his essays and travel-books are numerous, and had, or have, a multitude of enthusiastic readers, that he wrote a little poetry and much charming verse, in both English and Scots, and that he is among the best of our letter-writers. Many categories of his work have been left entirely unrepresented, because they would merely have crowded out more interesting things.

X

Stevenson took to essay-writing as naturally as many young writers take to verse. His Scottish passion for detail, his invalid sensitiveness to the daily physical impacts of life, his delight in *le mot juste* and the well-turned phrase, his egotism, lack of originality and love of moralising, all led him into the familiar essay, while his acute interest in literary craftsmanship led to the critical essay. Moreover both these forms were still widely popular and much respected, so that there were good prospects of publication in the august, influential reviews of the day and later in collected volumes.

As an essayist he developed rapidly. 'Roads' and his other earliest efforts are undistinguished enough, but three or four years later he was making his first reputation, a *succès d'estime*, in the *Cornhill Magazine* with 'Walking Tours', 'On Falling in Love', 'An Apology for Idlers' and the other essays afterwards collected in *Virginibus Puerisque* (1881). This became one of his most famous books, and for the next thirty years or more his essays commanded a large, enthusiastic public. Many were over-valued then, partly for their optimistic brightness and a bohemianism which wore a grand air of escape and rebellion without threatening to become inconvenient or disreputable. Moreover Stevenson was much given to preaching, and his contemporaries enjoyed being preached at by such a picturesque vagabond. Nowadays the more mannered of the essays make the reader feel uncomfortable: the sedulous ape is so obviously looking in vain for something to write about, and jauntily trying to conceal his failure under a flamboyant cloak of words. But the less pretentious of them are not likely to be forgotten. They have a measured movement of feeling and phrase which is very attractive, and the best succeed admirably in the particular province of the familiar essay, that of setting ordinary things in a new light, because of Stevenson's skill in recapturing the sensations of boyhood and early manhood. They can be represented in this volume only by 'Old Mortality' (1884) and 'The Lantern Bearers' (1888)—the latter somewhat blemished by its last two sections, the former a shapely piece of work in the central tradition of the English essay. Similar qualities will be found in 'A Penny Plain and Twopence Coloured', 'A Chapter on Dreams', 'The Manse' and 'The Foreigner at Home', for example, or 'Ordered South', 'Talk and Talkers' and 'Fontainebleau'. There is much of interest also, at least to the reader concerned with the technicalities of writing, in 'A Humble Remonstrance', 'A Note on Realism', 'A Gossip on Romance', and other studies in criticism.

The transition from essays to 'travel' was natural. Stevenson's first published book *An Inland Voyage* (1878) was a string of essays, mannered, self-conscious and sometimes coy. *Travels with a Donkey in the Cevennes* (1879) was made on the same model, but it is more accomplished and sensitive. Stevenson's only human companion on this journey was the unseen Fanny, who had left him for California, and the thought of her supplies a more serious undertone. It is probably his most popular work, after the novels and *A Child's Garden of Verses*, and for many readers still it is one of the most delectable of travel-books. The chapter given here, *A Night among the Pines*, is characteristic of it, and of Stevenson at twenty-eight. Though he had not yet learned to use words without obtruding them often between the reader and the scene, or to forego the bravura phrase even when it was merely distracting, he had learned to see the world with his own eyes. We might say of this book as the *Saturday Review* had already said of *Picturesque Notes on Edinburgh* (1878), 'It speaks for itself; it is captivating and irritating; it keeps the attention awake; it sketches in pictures; in two words, it is never commonplace. . . .'

The Silverado Squatters was written in 1882, after his marriage and his narrow escape from death in California, and its greater maturity is the measure of its author's. It is no less deft and sensitive than the *Travels*, but less elegant and self-centred—decidedly a book to be read in its entirety by anyone who enjoys 'The Act of Squatting'.

In style and treatment these two passages are 'early' and 'middle' Stevenson. The third is 'late': 'The King of Apemama', a chapter from *In the South Seas* (1889-90), which book contains a long account of Tembinok' and his island, and is written in prose that has shed its airs and graces. The matter needs no embellishment and is given none. The style, as plain and grave as it is objective and vivid, is approaching that of *Weir of Hermiston*.

The earliest of Stevenson's extant verses is a 'songstry', as he called it, which he crooned to himself in bed and his unseen father wrote down:

'Had not an angel got the pride of man
No evil thought, no hardened heart
    would have been seen
No hell to go to, but a heaven so pure . . .

B

He was then six years old, and very much aware of hell. He went on making verses, which were sometimes poetry, all the rest of his life, though they did not begin to appear in print until he was thirty and acquiring a reputation as a prose-writer. His first collection (dedicated to Cummy) was *A Child's Garden of Verses*, begun in 1881 and published in 1885— a book without precedent in English, for it was not written *about* children: it tried to present the world which Stevenson saw when a child, and succeeded to a remarkable degree. Its grace and skill and unaffected charm brought it an immediate popularity which still continues.

Several volumes of verse followed—*Underwoods*, in English and Scots (1887), *Ballads* of the South Seas and Scotland (1891), *Songs of Travel*, a posthumous collection (1895)—and the unexpected *New Poems* of 1916. All except the last have much the same facility and charm. Stevenson described himself to Henley as 'a kind of prose Herrick, divested of the gift of verse', and a good deal of his verse is simply the work of an accomplished prose-writer who is acquiring metrical skill. He wrote a few delightful songs, however, and when deeply moved—by the death of Mrs Sitwell's son, by a memory of Scotland—he was capable of poetry which is hauntingly beautiful. *New Poems* are different. They were unknown until the Bibliophile Society of Boston, U.S.A., printed them from the holographs in 1916. They lack his distinctive accent and skill, but they show more spontaneous feeling, are more often touched with poignancy or bitterness, than his later work, for they were the product of his unhappy youth and early amours. The interest of most of them is more biographical than literary. They are represented here by the alcaics addressed to H. F. Brown.

Nearly all the best of Stevenson's poems in English appear in this volume. Those in Scots a Sassenach editor, like myself, may enjoy but can hardly presume to judge, and the Scottish reader will seek out for himself if he does not know them already. They are said to follow Fergusson rather than Burns. To an English ear they have a more sinewy strength, a livelier humour, a more realistic approach than his English verse. 'The Spaewife' is praised by Stevenson's latest Scottish critic, Mr Daiches, for 'an originality which few Scots poems of the nineteenth century possess.'

He wrote a great many letters, partly because he was so often separated from his closest friends. Sir Sidney Colvin edited successive editions devotedly, but not always accurately or wisely, so that they make Stevenson appear more egotistic and less broadly human than he was in reality. Colvin's comment on them is worth quotation:

'What he could do as an artist we know. I remember Sir John Millais, a shrewd and very independent judge of books, calling across to me at a dinner-table, "You know Stevenson, don't you?" and then going on, "Well, I wish you would tell him from me, if he cares to know, that to my mind he is the very first of living artists. I don't mean writers merely, but painters and all of us. Nobody living can see with such an eye as that fellow, and nobody is such a master of his tools." But in his letters, excepting a few written in youth and having more or less the character of exercises, and a few in after years which were intended for the public eye, Stevenson the deliberate artist is scarcely forthcoming at all. He does not care a fig for order or logical sequence or congruity, or for striking a key of expression and keeping it, but becomes simply the most spontaneous and unstudied of human beings. He has at his command the whole vocabularies of the English and Scottish languages, classical and slang, with good stores of the French, and tosses and tumbles them about irresponsibly to convey the impression or affection, the mood or freak of the moment; pouring himself out in all manner of rhapsodical confessions and speculations, grave or gay, notes of observation and criticism, snatches of remembrance and autobiography, moralising on matters uppermost for the hour is his mind, comments on his own work or other people's, or mere idle fun and foolery.

'By this medley of moods and manners, Stevenson's letters at their best come nearer than anything else to the full-blooded charm and variety of his conversation. . . .'

Many of them are obviously the letters of a professional writer, and it is when the essayist or the moralist intervenes that they are least attractive, but when the novelist sketches in, sometimes with great skill, a scene, an incident or a character, they have an extraordinary fascination. The selection in this book is perforce very inadequate. The letters need to be read extensively and the reader who turns to a volume of them may well find it very difficult to put down.

XI

Stevenson had written many short stories, most of them now lost without trace, before the first to appear in print was published in the *Temple Bar* magazine of October 1877: *A Lodging for the Night*. This is not unworthy to represent the historical fiction which he continued to write until his death. Its weakness is its inconclusiveness. It reads like the opening chapter of a novel, and it does not come to an end, it peters out. That may be because, quite literally, Stevenson's strength failed him; his imaginative impulses often failed from sheer lack of physical vitality to support them. But in this case they were vigorous until Seigneur and thief began to moralise together, and had been nourished by some two years' consideration of the theme. The scene of the murder, Villon's outcry—'What right has a man to have red hair when he is dead?'—and above all Villon's flight through the snow-covered streets, strike indelibly upon the reader's imagination. They are as unforgettable as that famous scene, written ten years later, in which the Master of Ballantrae and his brother fought by candlelight in the long shrubbery, with the blackness of the frost-bound night like a roof over their heads. Stevenson had suddenly begun to find himself, and the extraordinary thing is that this stark, objective story, with its skilled economy of phrase and effect, was written while he still went on spinning out of his egotism the bright artificial webs of his earlier essays. His new-found power was confirmed by the publication in the *Cornhill* for January 1878 of *Will o' the Mill*, a story completely different in tone and substance, which Mr V. S. Pritchett has recently appraised as 'that moving allegory of the wisdom and tragedy of the passive life.'

Unfortunately temperament, circumstance and inadequate vitality combined to keep Stevenson from the steady application which might have made him a great novelist. It was another eight years before his first adult novel appeared (if *Prince Otto* can be called adult), and meanwhile the stories and *nouvelles* were outnumbered by the essays and travel-books.

Thrawn Janet was written in the Highlands in 1881, the year of *Treasure Island*, *The Body Snatcher* and *The Merry Men*. It has a quality without precedent in Stevenson's work, or indeed in

Scottish literature apart from the best of Sir Walter Scott. For the first time since mastering the techniques of narration and atmosphere he had found a theme which was not only entirely, instinctively congenial but moved him to the depths because it touched the sense of evil which was so strong in him. The virtuoso was completely lost in the artist, who speaks in this story with the authentic, unmistakable note of profound imaginative power. He knew what he had done. He wrote later to Colvin, 'If I had never written anything but [*Tod Lapraik* in *Catriona*] and *Thrawn Janet*, still I'd have been a writer.' But he would not or could not avoid incessant changes of key, indeed he delighted in new transpositions of his style and the grand manner of *Thrawn Janet*, echoed at intervals in other novels and tales, was never fully resumed until he began *Weir of Hermiston* twelve years later.

This constant preoccupation with form and style marks him off from most British novelists. So many of them have adopted, deliberately or unconsciously, the principle stated by Lewis Carroll, 'Take care of the sense and the sounds will take care of themselves', and many have been equally careless of construction, with Dickens and Scott among the worst offenders. Stevenson was a stylist and craftsman in the French rather than the English manner, a votary of the art of letters like Henry James and Flaubert, for whom literature was a sacred calling to be followed with anguish and strenuous endeavour, to be rewarded by rare moments of insight and achievement. As a stylist Stevenson matured early. As a man he matured late, particularly in his attitude to women, because his adolescent frustrations had delayed his development, and he long evaded his major problem by concentration upon tales of adventure in which he refused to face the full psychological and social implication of his characters' relationships. But in the end he brought to the adult interpretation of life a rare technical equipment—a great narrative skill, remarkable limpidity and adaptability of style, and that artist's eye for significance in both form and detail which Millais had recognized.

Though he did not succeed in completing any long tale before *Treasure Island* he had by that time published a number of *nouvelles*. The shorter form was easier for him, since it did not demand so prolonged an effort, but it has also its distinctive literary value, as George Eliot, Trollope, Henry James, Conrad and others have shown. Two *nouvelles* at least must be ranked very high in the Stevenson canon: *The Strange Case of Dr Jekyll and Mr Hyde* (1886) and *The Beach of Falesá* (1892). The former is less masterly in execution than *Thrawn Janet*, but more significant: it is perhaps the most forceful presentation in literature of that duality in man's nature of which Stevenson himself was so painfully aware. As G. K. Chesterton says, it has 'the outside excitement that belongs to Conan Doyle with the inside excitement that belongs to Henry James'. *The Beach of Falesá* is startlingly different from everything else he wrote, and not least from his other South Sea stories, the perfectly managed apologue of *The Bottle Imp* and the slighter folk-tale of *The Isle of Voices*. It is an astonishing thing that the author of *Treasure Island* and *The Master of Ballantrae* could see Falesá so clearly and consistently through the eyes of this commonplace Englishman with the rough-and-ready sense of honour, the easy-going vulgarity of mind. The whole tale is as perfectly integrated (but in how different a key!) as *Thrawn Janet*; the romance of adventure has gained adult significance, and Stevenson has succeeded most persuasively in his declared aim, 'to get out the facts of life as clean and naked and sharp as I could manage it'.

Yet he had not written his masterpiece. None of his novels is satisfactory as a whole—for the enchanting *Treasure Island* cannot be classed as a novel. In all of them his vitality had failed here and there, so that the characterization flickered, the structure broke and had to be patched—though there are fine and unforgettable things in *Kidnapped*, *The Wrecker* and *The Ebb Tide*, and magnificent things in *The Master of Ballantrae*, and the first and last must rank high in any reckoning of English historical fiction.

But *Weir of Hermiston* is in a different category, as Stevenson himself knew well. Whether he would have flagged in this also, whether it would have declined in its latter half as sadly as did *The Master of Ballantrae*, it is now impossible to say, for here the indecipherable alchemy of genius was involved. We can see, however, that the elements in the alembic were of the kind which had always produced Stevenson's most powerful work: his memories of Edinburgh, city and university, the law school, the 'Speculative', the savage romance of Scotland's past, the haunted beauty of the Pentlands and Lammermuirs, Cummy's devotion and eloquence (for she was half the older Kirstie), the judge who hanged Deacon Brodie (for Lord Braxfield was the prototype of Hermiston), his intense aware-ness of evil, his hatred of cruelty, and above all his first love and his estrangement from his father—the two things which had moved him far more deeply than anything else in life. Fiction, history and autobiography were woven together— 'Intent on my own race and place I wrote.' Once again he was moved to the depths, as he had been in *Thrawn Janet* and *Dr Jekyll and Mr Hyde*, but he was now a much healthier and more experienced man, a more mature and practised artist, than in those two earlier tales. Though a mannered writer still, he had found a grand manner at last.

'The plot is not good, I fear,' he wrote to S. R. Crockett, 'but Lord Justice-Clerk Hermiston ought to be a plum.' The plot was later summarized by his amanuensis, Isobel Strong, with whom he had discussed it fully: Archie and Kirstie are still in love, but he avoids her after the stormy interview with which the book breaks off, and she allows herself to be seduced by Frank Innes and finds that she is with child. The elder Kirstie, having discovered this, accuses Archie, who gets the truth from Kirstie and promises to protect her. After a violent quarrel he kills Frank beside the Weaver's Stone (as fore-shadowed in the Introduction); he is arrested for the murder and tried by his father, who sentences him to death. The Four Black Brothers, learning the whole story from the elder Kirstie, gather their followers and break into the gaol. Archie is rescued and escapes to America with Kirstie, while his father, broken by the strain of the trial, collapses and dies.

Stevenson could have had only one reason for saying that the plot was not good: it must have been incredible to him, as it is to us, that Hermiston would be allowed to try his own son, yet the whole book as far as we have it is moving towards this tremendous climax, with no apparent possibility of evading it. In the consciousness of his newly found maturity Stevenson might have tried to make it credible, and Hermiston takes so powerful a hold upon the reader's imagination that as he grew in stature even this might have been believed of him. We are already willing to believe that no extremity, no human emo-tion, not even his profound, inhibited love for his son, could turn him aside, and that no one would be capable of barring his way.

Stevenson died before he had to face this challenge, however, and in these first nine chapters there is no narrative weakness, while the characterization shows a creative power, a psychological courage and insight, which he had never achieved before. Frank Innes, it is true, is little more than a puppet, because Stevenson is not interested in what he is but only in what he does. All the rest have the breath of life in them. The Black Brothers and their kin are taken direct from the canny, half-tamed life of the Border, only a few generations removed from war and civil war, as he had seen it through Cummy's eyes and his own. The two Kirsties are real women, the first to appear in his pages. It was not that 'There arose before him the curtains of boyhood, and he saw for the first time the ambiguous face of woman as she is', but that he dared at last to write what he had learned from his own first tragic love. Archie also is made, with a ruthless sympathy, from the stuff of his own ineffectual, rebellious youth. The tragedy of father and son—unlike as the two fathers were—had been proved upon his own pulses. The Braxfield who had put an end to Deacon Brodie, like the wrath of Jehovah, was transfigured by the power of genius into Hermiston, bestial and obscene, majestic in his incorruptible authority, steadfastly mounting 'the great bare staircase of his duty, uncheered and undepressed'—one of the greatest creations in the splendid portrait-gallery of our literature. As fully as in a Shakespearean tragedy, character has become destiny, character so moulded by Scottish history, the wynds of Edinburgh and the wild Border hills, that people, story, and setting are one and the whole movement of life takes on the terrible inevitability of fate. When Stevenson broke off dictation, an hour or two before death struck him down as dramatically as he himself could have wished, only half the book was written and none of it finally revised. Nevertheless it is one of the masterpieces of literature, surpassed in truth and tragic power by very few novels written in our tongue.

JOHN HAMPDEN

1949

A STEVENSON BIBLIOGRAPHY

(1)

The dates are those of first publication in book form. Nearly all Stevenson's writings appeared first in periodicals—notably *The Portfolio, Macmillan's Magazine, Fortnightly Review, Cornhill Magazine, London, Pall Mall Gazette, Longman's Magazine, Scribner's Magazine* and *Illustrated London News*. Only the more important works are named.

1878   *An Inland Voyage*

1879   *Edinburgh: Picturesque Notes*
       Travels with a Donkey

1881   *Virginibus Puerisque*

1882   *Familiar Studies of Men and Books*

1882   *New Arabian Nights* (and other stories)

1883   *The Silverado Squatters*
       Treasure Island

1885   *Prince Otto*
       A Child's Garden of Verses
       The Dynamiter (with F. Van de G. Stevenson)

1886   *The Strange Case of Dr Jekyll and Mr Hyde*
       Kidnapped

1887   *The Merry Men* (and other stories)
       Underwoods (poems)
       Memories and Portraits (essays)

1888   *The Black Arrow*
       The Master of Ballantrae

1889   *The Wrong Box* (with Lloyd Osbourne)

1890   *The South Seas* (privately printed: published as *In the South Seas*, 1896)
       Father Damien: an open letter to Rev. Dr Hyde
       Ballads

1892   *Across the Plains* (essays)
       The Wrecker (with Lloyd Osbourne)
       A Footnote to History
       Three Plays (with W. E. Henley)

1893   *Island Nights' Entertainments*
        Catriona (previously serialized as *David Balfour*)

1894   *The Ebb Tide* (with Lloyd Osbourne)

Posthumously published

1895   *The Amateur Emigrant*
        Vailima Letters (written to Sidney Colvin, 1890–94)

1896   *Weir of Hermiston* (unfinished)

1896   *Songs of Travel*
        Four Plays (*Three Plays* plus *Robert Macaire*)

1898   *St Ives* (the last six chapters by A. T. Quiller-Couch)
        (New York edition, 1897)

1899   *Letters of Robert Louis Stevenson to his Family and
        Friends*, edited by Sydney Colvin

1903   *Essays and Criticisms*

1905   *Prayers written at Vailima*
        Tales and Fantasies

1911   *Lay Morals and other papers*

1912   *Memoirs of Himself* (unfinished: privately printed)
        Records of a Family of Engineers (unfinished)

1916   *Poems, hitherto unpublished* (Boston, U.S.A.)

1918   *New Poems*

1894–8 *Edinburgh Edition*, edited by Sir Sidney Colvin. 28
        volumes, followed by various other collected editions.

1923–4 *Tusitala Edition*, with introductions by Lloyd
        Osbourne (13 of them new), F. Van de G. Stevenson
        and Sir Sidney Colvin. 35 vols. Index.

A Bibliography of the Works of Robert Louis Stevenson, by W. F. Prideaux, revised by Mrs L. S. Livingston, 1917; *The Cambridge Bibliography of English Literature*, edited by F. W. Bateson; *The Life of Robert Louis Stevenson*, by Graham Balfour, 1901; the official biography, including bibliography. *Robert Louis Stevenson*, by J. A. Steuart, 1924; a critical biography. *An Intimate Portrait of R.L.S.*, by Lloyd Osbourne, New York, 1924; see also his introductions to the Tusitala Edition. *The True Stevenson*, by G. S. Hellman, Boston, U.S.A., 1925; 'A Study in Clarification', mainly of Stevenson's wild youth. *R. L. Stevenson*, by Janet Adam Smith, 1937; *Robert Louis Stevenson*, by Lettice Cooper, 1947; two admirable short lives. *Memories and Notes*, by Sir Sidney Colvin; which includes a chapter on R.L.S., a character study with many reminiscences. *A Chronicle of Friendships*, by Will H. Low, 1908; much about R.L.S. in France and U.S.A., by an intimate friend, an American painter. *With Stevenson in Samoa*, by H. J. Moors, 1911; written from close personal knowledge. *Stevensoniana*, edited by Sir John A. Hammerton, revised edition, 1910; a compendium of anecdotes and appreciations. 40 illustrations. *R. L. Stevenson*, by Frank Swinnerton, revised edition, 1924; *Robert Louis Stevenson*, by G. K. Chesterton, 1927; *Robert Louis Stevenson*, by David Daiches, 1948; three stimulating critical studies, differing much in style and approach. *Robert Louis Stevenson* (1887) and *The Letters of Robert Louis Stevenson* (1900), by Henry James; these are two critical essays which have been reprinted, with the correspondence between the two authors, etc., in *Henry James and Robert Louis Stevenson*, 'a record of friendship and criticism', edited with an introduction by Janet Adam Smith, 1948.

Stevenson's Dedication to

Weir of Hermiston

TO MY WIFE

I saw rain falling and the rainbow drawn
On Lammermuir. Hearkening I heard again
In my precipitous city beaten bells
Winnow the keen sea wind. And here afar,
Intent on my own race and place, I wrote.
    Take thou the writing: thine it is. For who
Burnished the sword, blew on the drowsy coal,
Held still the target higher, chary of praise
And prodigal of counsel—who but thou?
So now, in the end, if this the least be good,
If any deed be done, if any fire
Burn in the imperfect page, the praise be thine.

Stories

*

A LODGING FOR THE NIGHT
from
New Arabian Nights

THRAWN JANET
from
The Merry Men

A LODGING FOR THE NIGHT

A Story of Francis Villon

It was late in November 1456. The snow fell over Paris with rigorous, relentless persistence; sometimes the wind made a sally and scattered it in flying vortices; sometimes there was a lull, and flake after flake descended out of black night air, silent, circuitous, interminable. To poor people, looking up under moist eyebrows, it seemed a wonder where it all came from. Master Francis Villon had propounded an alternative that afternoon, at a tavern window: was it only Pagan Jupiter plucking geese upon Olympus? or were the holy angels moulting? He was only a poor Master of Arts, he went on; and as the question somewhat touched upon divinity, he durst not venture to conclude. A silly old priest from Montargis, who was among the company, treated the young rascal to a bottle of wine in honour of the jest and the grimaces with which it was accompanied, and swore on his own white beard that he had been just another irreverent dog when he was Villon's age.

The air was raw and pointed, but not far below freezing; and the flakes were large, damp, and adhesive. The whole city was sheeted up. An army might have marched from end to end and not a footfall given the alarm. If there were any belated birds in heaven, they saw the island like a large white patch, and the bridges like slim white spars, on the black ground of the river. High up overhead the snow settled among the tracery of the cathedral towers. Many a niche was drifted full; many a statue wore a long white bonnet on its grotesque or sainted head. The gargoyles had been transformed into great false noses, drooping towards the point. The crockets were like upright pillows swollen on one side. In the intervals of the wind, there was a dull sound of dripping about the precincts of the church.

The cemetery of St John had taken its own share of the snow. All the graves were decently covered; tall white housetops stood around in grave array; worthy burghers were long ago in

bed, benightcapped like their domiciles; there was no light
in all the neighbourhood but a little peep from a lamp that
hung swinging in the church choir, and tossed the shadows to
and fro in time to its oscillations. The clock was hard on ten
when the patrol went by with halberds and a lantern, beating
their hands; and they saw nothing suspicious about the
cemetery of St John.

Yet there was a small house, backed up against the cemetery
wall, which was still awake, and awake to evil purpose, in
that snoring district. There was not much to betray it from
without; only a stream of warm vapour from the chimney-top,
a patch where the snow melted on the roof, and a few half-
obliterated footprints at the door. But within, behind the
shuttered windows, Master Francis Villon the poet, and some
of the thievish crew with whom he consorted, were keeping
the night alive and passing round the bottle.

A great pile of living embers diffused a strong and ruddy
glow from the arched chimney. Before this straddled Dom
Nicolas, the Picardy monk, with his skirts picked up and his
fat legs bared to the comfortable warmth. His dilated shadow
cut the room in half; and the firelight only escaped on either
side of his broad person, and in a little pool between his outspread feet. His face had the beery, bruised appearance of the
continual drinker's; it was covered with a network of congested
veins, purple in ordinary circumstances, but now pale violet,
for even with his back to the fire the cold pinched him on the
other side. His cowl had half fallen back, and made a strange
excrescence on either side of his bull neck. So he straddled,
grumbling, and cut the room in half with the shadow of his
portly frame.

On the right, Villon and Guy Tabary were huddled together
over a scrap of parchment; Villon making a ballade which he
was to call the 'Ballade of Roast Fish', and Tabary spluttering
admiration at his shoulder. The poet was a rag of a man, dark,
little, and lean, with hollow cheeks and thin black locks. He
carried his four-and-twenty years with feverish animation.
Greed had made folds about his eyes, evil smiles had puckered
his mouth. The wolf and pig struggled together in his face.
It was an eloquent, sharp, ugly, earthly countenance. His
hands were small and prehensile, with fingers knotted like a
cord; and they were continually flickering in front of him in

violent and expressive pantomime. As for Tabary, a broad, complacent, admiring imbecility breathed from his squash nose and slobbering lips: he had become a thief, just as he might have become the most decent of burgesses, by the imperious chance that rules the lives of human geese and human donkeys.

At the monk's other hand, Montigny and Thevenin Pensete played a game of chance. About the first there clung some flavour of good birth and training, as about a fallen angel; something long, lithe, and courtly in the person; something aquiline and darkling in the face. Thevenin, poor soul, was in great feather: he had done a good stroke of knavery that afternoon in the Faubourg St Jacques, and all night he had been gaining from Montigny. A flat smile illuminated his face; his bald head shone rosily in a garland of red curls; his little protuberant stomach shook with silent chucklings as he swept in his gains.

'Doubles or quits?' said Thevenin.

Montigny nodded grimly.

'*Some may prefer to dine in state*,' wrote Villon, '*On bread and cheese on silver plate*. Or—or—help me out, Guido!'

Tabary giggled.

'*Or parsley on a golden dish*,' scribbled the poet.

The wind was freshening without; it drove the snow before it, and sometimes raised its voice in a victorious whoop, and made sepulchral grumblings in the chimney. The cold was growing sharper as the night went on. Villon, protruding his lips, imitated the gust with something between a whistle and a groan. It was an eerie, uncomfortable talent of the poet's much detested by the Picardy monk.

'Can't you hear it rattle in the gibbet?' said Villon. 'They are all dancing the devil's jig on nothing, up there. You may dance, my gallants, you'll be none the warmer! Whew! what a gust! Down went somebody just now! A medlar the fewer on the three-legged medlar-tree!—I say, Dom Nicolas, it'll be cold tonight on the St Denis Road?' he asked.

Dom Nicolas winked both his big eyes, and seemed to choke upon his Adam's apple. Montfaucon, the great grisly Paris gibbet, stood hard by the St Denis Road, and the pleasantry touched him on the raw. As for Tabary, he laughed immoderately over the medlars; he had never heard anything more light-hearted; and he held his sides and crowed. Villon fetched him a fillip on the nose, which turned his mirth into an attack of coughing.

'Oh, stop that row,' said Villon, 'and think of rhymes to "fish." '

'Double or quits,' said Montigny doggedly.

'With all my heart,' quoth Thevenin.

'Is there any more in that bottle?' asked the monk.

'Open another,' said Villon. 'How do you ever hope to fill that big hogshead, your body, with little things like bottles? And how do you expect to get to heaven? How many angels, do you fancy, can be spared to carry up a single monk from Picardy? Or do you think yourself another Elias— and they'll send the coach for you?'

'*Hominibus impossibile*,' replied the monk, as he filled his glass.

Tabary was in ecstasies.

Villon filliped his nose again.

'Laugh at my jokes, if you like,' he said.

'It was very good,' objected Tabary.

Villon made a face at him. 'Think of rhymes to "fish," ' he said. 'What have you to do with Latin? You'll wish you knew none of it at the great assizes, when the devil calls for Guido Tabary, clericus—the devil with the hump-back and red-hot finger-nails. Talking of the devil,' he added in a whisper, 'look at Montigny!'

All three peered covertly at the gamester. He did not seem to be enjoying his luck. His mouth was a little to a side; one nostril nearly shut, and the other much inflated. The black dog was on his back, as people say, in terrifying nursery metaphor; and he breathed hard under the gruesome burden.

'He looks as if he could knife him,' whispered Tabary, with round eyes.

The monk shuddered, and turned his face and spread his open hands to the red embers. It was the cold that thus affected Dom Nicolas, and not any excess of moral sensibility.

'Come now,' said Villon—'about this ballade. How does it run so far?' And, beating time with his hand, he read it aloud to Tabary.

They were interrupted at the fourth rhyme by a brief and fatal movement among the gamesters. The round was completed, and Thevenin was just opening his mouth to claim another victory, when Montigny leaped up, swift as an adder, and stabbed him to the heart. The blow took effect before he had time to utter a cry, before he had time to move. A tremor or two convulsed his frame; his hands opened and shut, his heels rattled on the floor; then his head rolled backward over one shoulder with the eyes wide open; and Thevenin Pensete's spirit had returned to Him who made it.

Every one sprang to his feet; but the business was over in two twos. The four living fellows looked at each other in rather a ghastly fashion; the dead man contemplating a corner of the roof with a singular and ugly leer.

'My God!' said Tabary; and he began to pray in Latin.

Villon broke out into hysterical laughter. He came a step forward and ducked a ridiculous bow at Thevenin, and laughed still louder. Then he sat down suddenly, all of a heap, upon a stool, and continued laughing bitterly as though he would shake himself to pieces.

Montigny recovered his composure first.

'Let's see what he has about him,' he remarked; and he picked the dead man's pockets with a practised hand and divided the money into four equal portions on the table. 'There's for you,' he said.

The monk received his share with a deep sigh, and a single stealthy glance at the dead Thevenin, who was beginning to sink into himself and topple sideways off the chair.

'We're all in for it,' cried Villon, swallowing his mirth. 'It's a hanging job for every man jack of us that's here—not to speak of those who aren't.' He made a shocking gesture in the air with his raised right hand, and put out his tongue and threw his head on one side, so as to counterfeit the appearance of one who has been hanged. Then he pocketed his share of the spoil, and executed a shuffle with his feet as if to restore the circulation.

Tabary was the last to help himself; he made a dash at the money, and retired to the other end of the apartment.

Montigny stuck Thevenin upright in the chair, and drew out the dagger, which was followed by a jet of blood.

'You fellows had better be moving,' he said, as he wiped the blade on his victim's doublet.

'I think we had,' returned Villon, with a gulp. 'Damn his fat head!' he broke out. 'It sticks in my throat like phlegm.

What right has a man to have red hair when he is dead?' And he fell all of a heap again upon the stool, and fairly covered his face with his hands.

Montigny and Dom Nicolas laughed aloud, even Tabary feebly chiming in.

'Cry baby,' said the monk.

'I always said he was a woman,' added Montigny, with a sneer. 'Sit up, can't you?' he went on, giving another shake to the murdered body. 'Tread out that fire, Nick!'

But Nick was better employed; he was quietly taking Villon's purse, as the poet sat, limp and trembling, on the stool where he had been making a ballade not three minutes before. Montigny and Tabary dumbly demanded a share of the booty, which the monk silently promised as he passed the little bag into the bosom of his gown. In many ways an artistic nature unfits a man for practical existence.

No sooner had the theft been accomplished than Villon shook himself, jumped to his feet, and began helping to scatter and extinguish the embers. Meanwhile Montigny opened the door and cautiously peered into the street. The coast was clear; there was no meddlesome patrol in sight. Still it was judged wiser to slip out severally; and as Villon was himself in a hurry to escape from the neighbourhood of the dead Thevenin, and the rest were in a still greater hurry to get rid of him before he should discover the loss of his money, he was the first by general consent to issue forth into the street.

The wind had triumphed and swept all the clouds from heaven, only a few vapours, as thin as moonlight, fleeting rapidly across the stars. It was bitter cold; and by a common optical effect, things seemed almost more definite than in the broadest daylight. The sleeping city was absolutely still: a company of white hoods, a field of little Alps, below the twinkling stars. Villon cursed his fortune. Would it were still snowing! Now, wherever he went, he left an indelible trail behind him on the glittering streets; wherever he went he was still tethered to the house by the cemetery of St John; wherever he went he must weave, with his own plodding feet, the rope that bound him to the crime and would bind him to the gallows. The leer of the dead man came back to him with a new significance. He snapped his fingers as if to pluck up his own spirits, and, choosing a street at random, stepped boldly forward in the snow.

Two things preoccupied him as he went: the aspect of the gallows at Montfaucon in this bright windy phase of the night's existence, for one; and for another, the look of the dead man with his bald head and garland of red curls. Both struck cold upon his heart, and he kept quickening his pace as if he could escape from unpleasant thoughts by mere fleetness of foot. Sometimes he looked back over his shoulder with a sudden nervous jerk; but he was the only moving thing in the white streets, except when the wind swooped round a corner and threw up the snow, which was beginning to freeze, in spouts of glittering dust.

Suddenly he saw, a long way before him, a black clump and a couple of lanterns. The clump was in motion, and the lanterns swung as though carried by men walking. It was a patrol. And though it was merely crossing his line of march, he judged it wiser to get out of eyeshot as speedily as he could. He was not in the humour to be challenged, and he was conscious of making a very conspicuous mark upon the snow. Just on his left hand there stood a great hotel, with some turrets and a large porch before the door; it was half-ruinous, he remembered, and had long stood empty; and so he made three steps of it and jumped in to the shelter of the porch. It was pretty dark inside, after the glimmer of the snowy streets, and he was groping forward with outspread hands, when he stumbled over some substance which offered an indescribable mixture of resistances, hard and soft, firm and loose. His heart gave a leap, and he sprang two steps back and stared dreadfully at the obstacle. Then he gave a little laugh of relief. It was only a woman, and she dead. He knelt beside her to make sure upon this latter point. She was freezing cold, and rigid like a stick. A little ragged finery fluttered in the wind about her hair, and her cheeks had been heavily rouged that same afternoon. Her pockets were quite empty; but in her stocking, underneath the garter, Villon found two of the small coins that went by the name of whites. It was little enough; but it was always something; and the poet was moved with a deep sense of pathos that she should have died before she had spent her money. That seemed to him a dark and pitiable mystery; and he looked from the coins in his hand to the dead woman, and back again to the coins, shaking his head over the riddle of man's life. Henry V of England, dying at Vincennes just after he had conquered France, and this poor jade cut off by a cold draught in a great man's doorway, before she had time to spend her couple of whites—it seemed a cruel way to carry on the world. Two whites would have taken such a little while to squander; and yet it would have been one more good taste in the mouth, one more smack of the lips, before the devil got the soul, and the body was left to the birds and vermin. He would like to use all his tallow before the light was blown out and the lantern broken.

While these thoughts were passing through his mind, he was feeling, half mechanically, for his purse. Suddenly his heart stopped beating; a feeling of cold scales passed up the back of his legs, and a cold blow seemed to fall upon his scalp. He stood petrified for a moment; then he felt again with one feverish movement; and then his loss burst upon him, and he was covered at once with perspiration. To spendthrifts money is so living and actual—it is such a thin veil between them and their pleasures! There is only one limit to their fortune—that of time; and a spendthrift with only a few crowns is the Emperor of Rome until they are spent. For such a person to lose his money is to suffer the most shocking reverse, and fall from heaven to hell, from all to nothing, in a breath. And all the more if he has put his head in the halter for it; if he may be hanged to-morrow for that same purse, so dearly earned, so foolishly departed! Villon stood and cursed; he threw the two whites into the street; he shook his fist at heaven; he stamped, and was not horrified to find himself trampling the poor corpse. Then he began rapidly to retrace his steps towards the house beside the cemetery. He had forgotten all fear of the patrol, which was long gone by at any rate, and had no idea but that of his lost purse. It was in vain that he looked right and left upon the snow: nothing was to be seen. He had not dropped it in the streets. Had it fallen in the house? He would have liked dearly to go in and see; but the idea of the grisly occupant unmanned him. And he saw besides, as he drew near, that their efforts to put out the fire had been unsuccessful; on the contrary, it had broken into a blaze, and a changeful light played in the chinks of door and window, and revived his terror for the authorities and Paris gibbet.

He returned to the hotel with the porch, and groped about upon the snow for the money he had thrown away in his

childish passion. But he could only find one white; the other
had probably struck sideways and sunk deeply in. With a
single white in his pocket, all his projects for a rousing night
in some wild tavern vanished utterly away. And it was not
only pleasure that fled laughing from his grasp; positive discomfort, positive pain, attacked him as he stood ruefully
before the porch. His perspiration had dried upon him; and
though the wind had now fallen, a binding frost was setting in
stronger with every hour, and he felt benumbed and sick at
heart. What was to be done? Late as was the hour, improbable
as was success, he would try the house of his adopted father,
the chaplain of St Benoît.

He ran there all the way, and knocked timidly. There was no
answer. He knocked again and again, taking heart with every
stroke; and at last steps were heard approaching from within.
A barred wicket fell open in the iron-studded door, and emitted
a gush of yellow light.

'Hold up your face to the wicket,' said the chaplain from
within.

'It's only me,' whimpered Villon.

'Oh, it's only you, is it?' returned the chaplain; and he
cursed him with foul unpriestly oaths for disturbing him at
such an hour, and bade him be off to hell, where he came from.

'My hands are blue to the wrist,' pleaded Villon; 'my feet
are dead and full of twinges; my nose aches with the sharp air;
the cold lies at my heart. I may be dead before morning. Only
this once, father, and before God I will never ask again!'

'You should have come earlier,' said the ecclesiastic coolly.
'Young men require a lesson now and then.' He shut the wicket
and retired deliberately into the interior of the house.

Villon was beside himself; he beat upon the door with his
hands and feet, and shouted hoarsely after the chaplain.

'Wormy old fox!' he cried. 'If I had my hand under your
twist, I would send you flying headlong into the bottomless pit.'

A door shut in the interior, faintly audible to the poet down
long passages. He passed his hand over his mouth with an oath.
And then the humour of the situation struck him, and he
laughed and looked lightly up to heaven, where the stars
seemed to be winking over his discomfiture.

What was to be done? It looked very like a night in the
frosty streets. The idea of the dead woman popped into his

imagination, and gave him a hearty fright; what had happened to her in the early night might very well happen to him before the morning. And he so young! and with such immense possibilities of disorderly amusement before him! He felt quite pathetic over the notion of his own fate, as if it had been some one else's, and made a little imaginative vignette of the scene in the morning when they should find his body.

He passed all his chances under review, turning the white between his thumb and forefinger. Unfortunately he was on bad terms with some old friends who would once have taken pity on him in such a plight. He had lampooned them in verses, he had beaten and cheated them; and yet now, when he was in so close a pinch, he thought there was at least one who might perhaps relent. It was a chance. It was worth trying at least, and he would go and see.

On the way, two little accidents happened to him which coloured his musings in a very different manner. For, first, he fell in with the track of a patrol, and walked in it for some hundred yards, although it lay out of his direction. And this spirited him up; at least he had confused his trail; for he was still possessed with the idea of people tracking him all about Paris over the snow, and collaring him next morning before he was awake. The other matter affected him very differently. He passed a street corner, where, not so long before, a woman and her child had been devoured by wolves. This was just the kind of weather, he reflected, when wolves might take it into their heads to enter Paris again; and a lone man in these deserted streets would run the chance of something worse than a mere scare. He stopped and looked upon the place with an unpleasant interest—it was a centre where several lanes intersected each other; and he looked down them all one after another, and held his breath to listen, lest he should detect some galloping black things on the snow or hear the sound of howling between him and the river. He remembered his mother telling him the story and pointing out the spot, while he was yet a child. His mother! If he only knew where she lived, he might make sure at least of shelter. He determined he would inquire upon the morrow; nay, he would go and see her too, poor old girl! So thinking, he arrived at his destination —his last hope for the night.

The house was quite dark, like its neighbours; and yet after a few taps, he heard a movement overhead, a door opening, and a cautious voice asking who was there. The poet named himself in a loud whisper, and waited not without some trepidation, the result. Nor had he to wait long. A window was suddenly opened, and a pailful of slops splashed down upon the doorstep. Villon had not been unprepared for something of the sort, and had put himself as much in shelter as the nature of the porch admitted; but for all that, he was deplorably drenched below the waist. His hose began to freeze almost at once. Death from cold and exposure stared him in the face; he remembered he was of phthisical tendency, and began coughing tentatively. But the gravity of the danger steadied his nerves. He stopped a few hundred yards from the door where he had been so rudely used, and reflected with his finger to his nose. He could only see one way of getting a lodging, and that was to take it. He had noticed a house not far away, which looked as if it might be easily broken into, and thither he betook himself promptly, entertaining himself on the way with the idea of a room still hot, with a table still loaded with the remains of supper, where he might pass the rest of the black hours, and whence he should issue, on the morrow, with an armful of valuable plate. He even considered on what viands and what wines he should prefer; and as he was calling the roll of his favourite dainties, roast fish presented itself to his mind with an odd mixture of amusement and horror.

'I shall never finish that ballade,' he thought to himself; and then, with another shudder at the recollection, 'Oh, damn his fat head!' he repeated fervently, and spat upon the snow.

The house in question looked dark at first sight; but as Villon made a preliminary inspection in search of the handiest point of attack, a little twinkle of light caught his eye from behind a curtained window.

'The devil!' he thought. 'People awake! Some student or some saint, confound the crew! Can't they get drunk and lie in bed snoring like their neighbours? What's the good of curfew, and poor devils of bell-ringers jumping at a rope's end in bell-towers? What's the use of day, if people sit up all night? The gripes to them!' He grinned as he saw where his logic was leading him. 'Every man to his business, after all,' added he, 'and if they're awake, by the Lord, I may come by a supper honestly for this once, and cheat the devil.'

He went boldly to the door and knocked with an assured hand. On both previous occasions, he had knocked timidly and with some dread of attracting notice; but now when he had just discarded the thought of a burglarious entry, knocking at a door seemed a mighty simple and innocent proceeding. The sound of his blows echoed through the house with thin, phantasmal reverberations, as though it were quite empty; but these had scarcely died away before a measured tread drew near, a couple of bolts were withdrawn, and one wing was opened broadly, as though no guile or fear of guile were known to those within. A tall figure of a man, muscular and spare, but a little bent, confronted Villon. The head was massive in bulk, but finely sculptured; the nose blunt at the bottom, but refining upward to where it joined a pair of strong and honest eyebrows; the mouth and eyes surrounded with delicate markings, and the whole face based upon a thick white beard, boldly and squarely trimmed. Seen as it was by the light of a flickering hand-lamp, it looked perhaps nobler than it had a right to do; but it was a fine face, honourable rather than intelligent, strong, simple, and righteous.

'You knock late, sir,' said the old man, in resonant, courteous tones.

Villon cringed, and brought up many servile words of apology; at a crisis of this sort, the beggar was uppermost in him, and the man of genius hid his head with confusion.

'You are cold,' repeated the old man, 'and hungry? Well, step in.' And he ordered him into the house with a noble enough gesture.

'Some great seigneur,' thought Villon, as his host, setting down the lamp on the flagged pavement of the entry, shot the bolts once more into their places.

'You will pardon me if I go in front,' he said, when this was done; and he preceded the poet upstairs into a large apartment, warmed with a pan of charcoal and lit by a great lamp hanging from the roof. It was very bare of furniture: only some gold plate on a sideboard; some folios; and a stand of armour between the windows. Some smart tapestry hung upon the walls, representing the crucifixion of our Lord in one piece, and in another a scene of shepherds and shepherdesses by a running stream. Over the chimney was a shield of arms.

'Will you seat yourself,' said the old man, 'and forgive me

if I leave you? I am alone in my house to-night, and if you are to eat I must forage for you myself.'

No sooner was his host gone than Villon leaped from the chair on which he had just seated himself, and began examining the room, with the stealth and passion of a cat. He weighed the gold flagons in his hand, opened all the folios, and investigated the arms upon the shield, and the stuff with which the seats were lined. He raised the window curtains, and saw that the windows were set with rich stained glass in figures, so far as he could see, of martial import. Then he stood in the middle of the room, drew a long breath, and retaining it with puffed cheeks, looked round and round him, turning on his heels, as if to impress every feature of the apartment on his memory.

'Seven pieces of plate,' he said. 'If there had been ten, I would have risked it. A fine house, and a fine old master, so help me all the saints!'

And just then, hearing the old man's tread returning along the corridor, he stole back to his chair, and began humbly toasting his wet legs before the charcoal pan.

His entertainer had a plate of meat in one hand and a jug of wine in the other. He set down the plate upon the table, motioning Villon to draw in his chair, and, going to the sideboard, brought back two goblets, which he filled.

'I drink to your better fortune,' he said, gravely touching Villon's cup with his own.

'To our better acquaintance,' said the poet, growing bold. A mere man of the people would have been awed by the courtesy of the old seigneur, but Villon was hardened in that matter; he had made mirth for great lords before now, and found them as black rascals as himself. And so he devoted himself to the viands with a ravenous gusto, while the old man, leaning backward, watched him with steady, curious eyes.

'You have blood on your shoulder, my man,' he said.

Montigny must have laid his wet right hand upon him as he left the house. He cursed Montigny in his heart.

'It was none of my shedding,' he stammered.

'I had not supposed so,' returned his host quietly. 'A brawl?'

'Well, something of that sort,' Villon admitted, with a quaver.

'Perhaps a fellow murdered?'

'Oh, no, not murdered,' said the poet, more and more confused. 'It was all fair play—murdered by accident. I had no hand in it, God strike me dead!' he added fervently.

'One rogue the fewer, I dare say,' observed the master of the house.

'You may dare to say that,' agreed Villon, infinitely relieved. 'As big a rogue as there is between here and Jerusalem. He turned up his toes like a lamb. But it was a nasty thing to look at. I dare say you've seen dead men in your time, my lord?' he added, glancing at the armour.

'Many,' said the old man. 'I have followed the wars, as you imagine.'

Villon laid down his knife and fork, which he had just taken up again.

'Were any of them bald?' he asked.

'Oh yes, and with hair as white as mine.'

'I don't think I should mind the white so much,' said Villon. 'His was red.' And he had a return of his shuddering and tendency to laughter, which he drowned with a great draught of wine. 'I'm a little put out when I think of it,' he went on. 'I knew him—damn him! And then the cold gives a man fancies—or the fancies give a man cold, I don't know which.'

'Have you any money?' asked the old man.

'I have one white,' returned the poet, laughing. 'I got it out of a dead jade's stocking in a porch. She was as dead as Cæsar, poor wench, and as cold as a church, with bits of ribbon sticking in her hair. This is a hard world in winter for wolves and wenches and poor rogues like me.'

'I,' said the old man, 'am Enguerrand de la Feuillée, seigneur de Brisetout, bailly du Patatrac. Who and what may you be?'

Villon rose and made a suitable reverence. 'I am called Francis Villon,' he said, 'a poor Master of Arts of this university. I know some Latin, and a deal of vice. I can make chansons, ballades, lais, virelais, and roundels, and I am very fond of wine. I was born in a garret, and I shall not improbably die upon the gallows. I may add, my lord, that from this night forward I am your lordship's very obsequious servant to command.'

'No servant of mine,' said the knight; 'my guest for this evening, and no more.'

'A very grateful guest,' said Villon politely; and he drank in dumb show to his entertainer.

'You are shrewd,' began the old man, tapping his forehead, 'very shrewd; you have learning; you are a clerk; and yet you take a small piece of money off a dead woman in the street. Is it not a kind of theft?'

'It is a kind of theft much practised in the wars, my lord.'

'The wars are the field of honour,' returned the old man proudly. 'There a man plays his life upon the cast; he fights in the name of his lord the king, his Lord God, and all their lordships the holy saints and angels.'

'Put it,' said Villon, 'that I were really a thief, should I not play my life also, and against heavier odds?'

'For gain, but not for honour.'

'Gain?' repeated Villon, with a shrug. 'Gain! The poor fellow wants supper, and takes it. So does the soldier in a campaign. Why, what are all these requisitions we hear so much about? If they are not gain to those who take them, they are loss enough to the others. The men-at-arms drink by a good fire, while the burgher bites his nails to buy them wine and wood. I have seen a good many ploughmen swinging on trees about the country, ay, I have seen thirty on one elm, and a very poor figure they made; and when I asked some one how all these came to be hanged, I was told it was because they could not scrape together enough crowns to satisfy the men-at-arms.'

'These things are a necessity of war, which the low born must endure with constancy. It is true that some captains drive over hard; there are spirits in every rank not easily moved by pity; and indeed many follow arms who are no better than brigands.'

'You see,' said the poet, 'you cannot separate the soldier from the brigand; and what is a thief but an isolated brigand with circumspect manners? I steal a couple of mutton chops, without so much as disturbing people's sleep; the farmer grumbles a bit, but sups none the less wholesomely on what remains. You come up blowing gloriously on a trumpet, take away the whole sheep, and beat the farmer pitifully into the bargain. I have no trumpet; I am only Tom, Dick, or Harry;

I am a rogue and a dog, and hanging's too good for me—
with all my heart; but just you ask the farmer which of us he
prefers, just find out which of us he lies awake to curse on cold
nights.'

'Look at us two,' said his lordship. 'I am old, strong, and
honoured. If I were turned from my house to-morrow, hun-
dreds would be proud to shelter me. Poor people would go
out and pass the night in the streets with their children, if I
merely hinted that I wished to be alone. And I find you up,
wandering homeless, and picking farthings off dead women
by the wayside! I fear no man and nothing; I have seen you
tremble and lose countenance at a word. I wait God's summons
contentedly in my own house, or, if it please the king to call
me out again, upon the field of battle. You look for the gallows;
a rough, swift death, without hope or honour. Is there no
difference between these two?'

'As far as to the moon,' Villon acquiesced. 'But if I had been
born lord of Brisetout, and you had been the poor scholar
Francis, would the difference have been any the less? Should not
I have been warming my knees at this charcoal pan, and would
not you have been groping for farthings in the snow? Should
not I have been the soldier, and you the thief?'

'A thief!' cried the old man. 'I a thief! If you understood
your words, you would repent them.'

Villon turned out his hands with a gesture of inimitable
impudence. 'If your lordship had done me the honour to
follow my argument!' he said.

'I do you too much honour in submitting to your presence,'
said the knight. 'Learn to curb your tongue when you speak
with old and honourable men, or some one hastier than I may
reprove you in a sharper fashion.' And he rose and paced the
lower end of the apartment, struggling with anger and anti-
pathy. Villon surreptitiously refilled his cup, and settled himself more comfortably in the chair, crossing his knees and
leaning his head upon one hand and the elbow against the
back of the chair. He was now replete and warm; and he was
in nowise frightened for his host, having gauged him as justly
as was possible between two such different characters. The
night was far spent, and in a very comfortable fashion after
all; and he felt morally certain of a safe departure on the
morrow.

'Tell me one thing,' said the old man, pausing in his walk. 'Are you really a thief?'

'I claim the sacred rights of hospitality,' returned the poet. 'My lord, I am.'

'You are very young,' the knight continued.

'I should never have been so old,' replied Villon, showing his fingers, 'if I had not helped myself with these ten talents. They have been my nursing mothers and my nursing fathers.'

'You may still repent and change.'

'I repent daily,' said the poet. 'There are few people more given to repentance than poor Francis. As for change, let somebody change my circumstances. A man must continue to eat, if it were only that he may continue to repent.'

'The change must begin in the heart,' returned the old man solemnly.

'My dear lord,' answered Villon, 'do you really fancy that I steal for pleasure? I hate stealing, like any other piece of work or of danger. My teeth chatter when I see a gallows. But I must eat, I must drink, I must mix in society of some sort. What the devil! Man is not a solitary animal—*Cui Deus fœminam tradit*. Make me king's pantler—make me abbot of St Denis; make me bailly of the Patatrac; and then I shall be changed indeed. But as long as you leave me the poor scholar Francis Villon, without a farthing, why, of course, I remain the same.'

'The grace of God is all-powerful.'

'I should be a heretic to question it,' said Francis. 'It has made you lord of Brisetout and bailly of the Patatrac; it has given me nothing but the quick wits under my hat and these ten toes upon my hands. May I help myself to wine? I thank you respectfully. By God's grace, you have a very superior vintage.'

The lord of Brisetout walked to and fro with his hands behind his back. Perhaps he was not yet quite settled in his mind about the parallel between thieves and soldiers; perhaps Villon had interested him by some cross-thread of sympathy; perhaps his wits were simply muddled by so much unfamiliar reasoning; but whatever the cause, he somehow yearned to convert the young man to a better way of thinking, and could not make up his mind to drive him forth again into the street.

'There is something more than I can understand in this,'

he said at length. 'Your mouth is full of subtleties, and the devil has led you very far astray; but the devil is only a very weak spirit before God's truth, and all his subtleties vanish at a word of true honour, like darkness at morning. Listen to me once more. I learned long ago that a gentleman should live chivalrously and lovingly to God, and the king, and his lady; and though I have seen many strange things done, I have still striven to command my ways upon that rule. It is not only written in all noble histories, but in every man's heart, if he will take care to read. You speak of food and wine, and I know very well that hunger is a difficult trial to endure; but you do not speak of other wants; you say nothing of honour, of faith to God and other men, of courtesy, of love without reproach. It may be that I am not very wise—and yet I think I am—but you seem to me like one who has lost his way and made a great error in life. You are attending to the little wants, and you have totally forgotten the great and only real ones, like a man who should be doctoring a toothache on the Judgment Day. For such things as honour and love and faith are not only nobler than food and drink, but indeed I think that we desire them more, and suffer more sharply for their absence. I speak to you as I think you will most easily understand me. Are you not, while careful to fill your belly, disregarding another appetite in your heart, which spoils the pleasure of your life and keeps you continually wretched?'

Villon was sensibly nettled under all this sermonizing. 'You think I have no sense of honour!' he cried. 'I'm poor enough, God knows! It's hard to see rich people with their gloves, and you blowing in your hands. An empty belly is a bitter thing, although you speak so lightly of it. If you had had as many as I, perhaps you would change your tune. Any way I'm a thief—make the most of that—but I'm not a devil from hell, God strike me dead. I would have you to know I've an honour of my own, as good as yours, though I don't prate about it all day long, as if it was a God's miracle to have any. It seems quite natural to me; I keep it in its box till it's wanted. Why now, look you here, how long have I been in this room with you? Did you not tell me you were alone in the house? Look at your gold plate! You're strong, if you like, but you're old and unarmed, and I have my knife. What did I want but a jerk of the elbow and here would have been you with the cold steel in your bowels, and there would have been me, linking in the streets, with an armful of gold cups! Did you suppose I hadn't wit enough to see that? And I scorned the action. There are your damned goblets, as safe as in a church; there are you, with your heart ticking as good as new; and here am I, ready to go out again as poor as I came in, with my one white that you threw in my teeth! And you think I have no sense of honour—God strike me dead!'

The old man stretched out his right arm. 'I will tell you what you are,' he said. 'You are a rogue, my man, an impudent and a black-hearted rogue and vagabond. I have passed an hour with you. Oh! believe me, I feel myself disgraced! And you have eaten and drunk at my table. But now I am sick at your presence; the day has come, and the night-bird should be off to his roost. Will you go before, or after?'

'Which you please,' returned the poet, rising. 'I believe you to be strictly honourable.' He thoughtfully emptied his cup. 'I wish I could add you were intelligent,' he went on, knocking on his head with his knuckles. 'Age, age! the brains stiff and rheumatic.'

The old man preceded him from a point of self-respect; Villon followed, whistling, with his thumbs in his girdle.

'God pity you,' said the lord of Brisetout at the door.

'Good-bye, papa,' returned Villon, with a yawn. 'Many thanks for the cold mutton.'

The door closed behind him. The dawn was breaking over the white roofs. A chill, uncomfortable morning ushered in the day. Villon stood and heartily stretched himself in the middle of the road.

'A very dull old gentleman,' he thought. 'I wonder what his goblets may be worth.'

THRAWN JANET

THE Reverend Murdoch Soulis was long minister of the
moorland parish of Balweary, in the vale of Dule. A severe,
bleak-faced old man, dreadful to his hearers, he dwelt in the
last years of his life, without relative or servant or any human
company, in the small and lonely manse under the Hanging
Shaw. In spite of the iron composure of his features, his eye
was wild, scared, and uncertain; and when he dwelt, in private
admonition, on the future of the impenitent, it seemed as if
his eye pierced through the storms of time to the terrors of
eternity. Many young persons, coming to prepare themselves
against the season of the Holy Communion, were dreadfully
affected by his talk. He had a sermon on 1st Peter, v. and 8th,
'The devil as a roaring lion,' on the Sunday after every
seventeenth of August, and he was accustomed to surpass
himself upon that text both by the appalling nature of the
matter and the terror of his bearing in the pulpit. The children
were frightened into fits, and the old looked more than usually
oracular, and were, all that day, full of those hints that Hamlet
deprecated. The manse itself, where it stood by the water of
Dule among some thick trees, with the Shaw overhanging it
on the one side, and on the other many cold, moorish hill-tops
rising toward the sky, had begun, at a very early period of Mr
Soulis's ministry, to be avoided in the dusk hours by all who
valued themselves upon their prudence; and guidmen sitting
at the clachan alehouse shook their heads together at the
thought of passing late by that uncanny neighbourhood.
There was one spot, to be more particular, which was regarded
with especial awe. The manse stood between the highroad
and the water of Dule, with a gable to each; its back was
towards the kirktown of Balweary, nearly half a mile away; in
front of it, a bare garden, hedged with thorn, occupied the
land between the river and the road. The house was two stories
high, with two large rooms on each. It opened not directly on
the garden, but on a causewayed path, or passage, giving on
the road on the one hand, and closed on the other by the tall

willows and elders that bordered on the stream. And it was this strip of causeway that enjoyed among the young parishioners of Balweary so infamous a reputation. The minister walked there often after dark, sometimes groaning aloud in the instancy of his unspoken prayers; and when he was from home, and the manse door was locked, the more daring schoolboys ventured, with beating hearts, to 'follow my leader' across that legendary spot.

This atmosphere of terror, surrounding, as it did, a man of God of spotless character and orthodoxy, was a common cause of wonder and subject of inquiry among the few strangers who were led by chance or business into that un-known, outlying country. But many even of the people of the parish were ignorant of the strange events which had marked the first year of Mr Soulis's ministrations; and among those who were better informed, some were naturally reticent, and others shy of that particular topic. Now and again, only, one of the older folk would warm into courage over his third tumbler, and recount the cause of the minister's strange looks and solitary life.

Fifty years syne, when Mr Soulis cam' first into Ba'weary, he was still a young man—a callant, the folk said—fu' o' book-learnin' an' grand at the exposition, but, as was natural in sae young a man, wi' nae leevin' experience in religion. The younger sort were greatly taken wi' his gifts and his gab; but auld, concerned, serious men and women were moved even to prayer for the young man, whom they took to be a self-deceiver, and the parish that was like to be sae ill-supplied. It was before the days o' the moderates—weary fa' them; but ill things are like guid—they baith come bit by bit, a pickle at a time; and there were folk even then that said the Lord had left the college professors to their ain devices, an' the lads that went to study wi' them wad hae done mair an' better sittin' in a peatbog, like their forbears of the persecution, wi' a Bible under their oxter an' a speerit o' prayer in their heart. There was nae doubt onyway, but that Mr Soulis had been ower lang at the college. He was careful and troubled for mony things besides the ae thing needful. He had a feck o' books wi' him—mair than had ever been seen before in a' that presby-tery; and a sair wark the carrier had wi' them, for they were a'

like to have smoored in the De'il's Hag between this and
Kilmackerlie. They were books o' divinity, to be sure, or so
they ca'd them; but the serious were o' opinion there was little
service for sae mony, when the hail o' God's Word would
gang in the neuk o' a plaid. Then he wad sit half the day and
half the nicht forbye, which was scant decent—writin', nae
less; an' first they were feared he wad read his sermons; an'
syne it proved he was writin' a book himsel', which was surely
no' fittin' for ane o' his years an' sma' experience.

Onyway it behoved him to get an auld, decent wife to keep
the manse for him an' see to his bit denners; an' he was
recommended to an auld limmer—Janet M'Clour, they ca'd
her—an' sae far left to himsel' as to be ower persuaded. There
was mony advised him to the contrar, for Janet was mair than
suspeckit by the best folk in Ba'weary. Lang or that, she had
had a wean to a dragoon; she hadna come forrit[1] for maybe
thretty year; and bairns had seen her mumblin' to hersel' up
on Key's Loan in the gloamin', whilk was an unco time an'
place for a Godfearin' woman. Howsoever, it was the laird
himsel' that had first tauld the minister o' Janet; an' in thae
days he wad hae gane a far gate to pleesure the laird. When
folk tauld him that Janet was sib to the de'il, it was a' superstition by his way o' it; an' when they cast up the Bible to him
an' the witch of Endor, he wad threep it doun their thrapples
that thir days were a' gane by, an' the de'il was mercifully
restrained.

Weel, when it got about the clachan that Janet M'Clour was
to be servant at the manse, the folk were fair mad wi' her an'
him thegither; an' some o' the guidwives had nae better to
dae than get round her door-cheeks and chairge her wi' a' that
was ken't again' her, frae the sodger's bairn to John Tamson's
twa kye. She was nae great speaker; folk usually let her gang
her ain gate, an' she let them gang theirs, wi' neither Fair-
guid-een nor Fair-guid-day; but when she buckled to, had
a tongue to deave the miller. Up she got, an' there wasna
an auld story in Ba'weary but she gart somebody lowp for it
that day; they couldna say ae thing but she could say twa to
it; till, at the hinder end, the guidwives up an' claught haud
of her, an' clawed the coats aff her back, and pu'd her doun
the clachan to the water o' Dule, to see if she were a witch or

[1] 'To come forrit'—to offer oneself as a communicant.

no, soom or droun. The carline skirled till ye could hear her
at the Hangin' Shaw, an' she focht like ten; there was mony
a guidwife bure the mark o' her neist day an' mony a lang
day after; an' just in the hettest o' the collieshangie, wha suld
come up (for his sins) but the new minister!

'Women,' said he (an' he had a grand voice), 'I charge you
in the Lord's name to let her go.'

Janet ran to him—she was fair wud wi' terror—an' clang to
him, an' prayed him, for Christ's sake, save her frae the cum-
mers; an' they, for their pairt, tauld him a' that was ken't, an'
maybe mair.

'Woman,' says he to Janet, 'is this true?'

'As the Lord sees me,' says she, 'as the Lord made me, no'
a word o't. Forbye the bairn,' says she, 'I've been a decent
woman a' my days.'

'Will you,' says Mr Soulis, 'in the name of God, and before
me, His unworthy minister, renounce the devil and his works?'

Weel, it wad appear that when he askit that, she gave a
girn that fairly frichit them that saw her, an' they could hear
her teeth play dirl thegither in her chafts; but there was
naething for it but the ae way or the ither; an' Janet lifted up
her hand an' renounced the de'il before them a'.

'And now,' says Mr Soulis to the guidwives, 'home with ye,
one and all, and pray to God for His forgiveness.'

An' he gied Janet his arm, though she had little on her but
a sark, and took her up the clachan to her ain door like a
leddy o' the land; an' her screighin' an' laughin' as was a
scandal to be heard.

There were mony grave folk lang ower their prayers that
nicht; but when the morn cam' there was sic a fear fell upon
a' Ba'weary that the bairns hid theirsels, an' even the men-
folk stood an' keekit frae their doors. For there was Janet
comin' doun the clachan—her or her likeness, nane could tell
—wi' her neck thrawn, an' her heid on ae side, like a body
that has been hangit, an' a girn on her face like an unstreakit
corp. By an' by they got used wi' it, an' even speered at her to
ken what was wrang; but frae that day forth she couldna
speak like a Christian woman, but slavered an' played click
wi' her teeth like a pair o' shears; an' frae that day forth the
name o' God cam' never on her lips. Whiles she wad try to say
it, but it michtna be. Them that kenned best said least; but

they never gied that Thing the name o' Janet M'Clour; for
the auld Janet, by their way o't, was in muckle hell that day.
But the minister was neither to haud nor to bind; he preached
about naething but the folk's cruelty that had gi'en her a
stroke of the palsy; he skelpit the bairns that meddled her;
an' he had her up to the manse that same nicht, an' dwalled
there a' his lane wi' her under the Hangin' Shaw.

Weel, time gaed by: and the idler sort commenced to think
mair lichtly o' that black business. The minister was weel
thocht o'; he was aye late at the writing, folk wad see his
can'le doon by the Dule water after twal' at e'en; and he
seemed pleased wi' himsel' an' upsitten as at first, though a'
body could see that he was dwining. As for Janet she cam' an'
gaed; if she didna speak muckle afore, it was reason she should
speak less then; she meddled naebody; but she was an eldritch
thing to see, an' nane wad hae mistrysted wi' her for Ba'weary
glebe.

About the end o' July there cam' a spell o' weather, the
like o't never was in that country-side; it was lown an' het an'
heartless; the herds couldna win up the Black Hill, the bairns
were ower weariet to play; an' yet it was gousty too, wi' claps
o' het wund that rumm'led in the glens, and bits o' shouers
that slockened naething. We aye thocht it but to thun'er on
the morn; but the morn cam', an' the morn's morning, an' it
was aye the same uncanny weather, sair on folks and bestial.
O' a' that were the waur, nane suffered like Mr Soulis; he
could neither sleep nor eat, he tauld his elders; an' when he
wasna writin' at his weary book, he wad be stravaguin' ower
a' the country-side like a man possessed, when a' body else
was blithe to keep caller ben the house.

Abune Hangin' Shaw, in the bield o' the Black Hill, there's
a bit enclosed grund wi' an iron yett; an' it seems, in the auld
days, that was the kirkyaird o' Ba'weary, an' consecrated by
the Papists before the blessed licht shone upon the kingdom.
It was a great howff o' Mr Soulis's onyway; there he wad sit
an' consider his sermons; an' indeed it's a bieldy bit. Weel, as
he cam' ower the wast end o' the Black Hill, ae day, he saw
first twa, an' syne fower, an' syne seeven corbie craws fleein'
round an' round abune the auld kirkyaird. They flew laigh
an' heavy, an' squawked to ither as they gaed; an' it was clear
to Mr Soulis that something had put them frae their ordinar.

He wasna easy fleyed, an' gaed straucht up to the wa's; an'
what suld he find there but a man, or the appearance o' a
man, sittin' in the inside upon a grave. He was of a great
stature, an' black as hell, and his e'en were singular to see.[1]
Mr Soulis had heard tell o' black men, mony's the time; but
there was something unco about this black man that daunted
him. Het as he was, he took a kind o' cauld grue in the marrow
o' his banes; but up he spak for a' that; an' says he: 'My
friend, are you a stranger in this place?' The black man
answered never a word; he got upon his feet, an' begoud on
to hirsle to the wa' on the far side; but he aye lookit at the
minister; an' the minister stood an' lookit back; till a' in a
meenit the black man was ower the wa' an' rinnin' for the
bield o' the trees. Mr Soulis, he hardly kenned why, ran after
him; but he was fair forjeskit wi' his walk an' the het, unhale-
some weather; an' rin as he likit, he got nae mair than a
glisk o' the black man amang the birks, till he won doun to
the foot o' the hillside, an' there he saw him ance mair, gaun,
hap-step-an'-lowp, ower Dule water to the manse.

Mr Soulis wasna weel pleased that this fearsome gangrel
suld mak' sae free wi' Ba'weary manse; an' he ran the harder,
an', wet shoon, ower the burn, an' up the walk; but the de'il
a black man was there to see. He stepped out upon the road,
but there was naebody there; he gaed a' ower the gairden, but
na, nae black man. At the hinder end, an' a bit feared as was
but natural, he lifted the hasp an' into the manse; and there
was Janet M'Clour before his e'en, wi' her thrawn craig, an'
nane sae pleased to see him. An' he aye minded sinsyne, when
first he set his e'en upon her, he had the same cauld and deidly
grue.

'Janet,' says he, 'have you seen a black man?'

'A black man!' quo' she. 'Save us a'! Ye're no wise, minister.
There's nae black man in a' Ba'weary.'

But she didna speak plain, ye maun understand; but yam-
yammered, like a powney wi' the bit in its moo.

'Weel,' says he, 'Janet, if there was nae black man, I have
spoken with the Accuser of the Brethren.'

[1] It was a common belief in Scotland that the devil appeared as a black
man. This appears in several witch trials and I think in Law's *Memorials*,
that delightful storehouse of the quaint and grisly. R.L.S.

An' he sat doun like ane wi' a fever, an' his teeth chittered in his heid.

'Hoots,' says she, 'think shame to yoursel', minister'; an' gied him a drap brandy that she keept aye by her.

Syne Mr Soulis gaed into his study amang a' his books. It's a lang, laigh, mirk chalmer, perishin' cauld in winter, an' no' very dry even in the top o' the simmer, for the manse stands near the burn. Sae doun he sat, and thocht of a' that had come an' gane since he was in Ba'weary, an' his hame, an' the days when he was a bairn an' ran daffin' on the braes; an' that black man aye ran in his heid like the owercome of a sang. Aye the mair he thocht, the mair he thocht o' the black man. He tried the prayer, an' the words wouldna come to him; an' he tried, they say, to write at his book, but he couldna mak' nar mair o' that. There was whiles he thocht the black man was at his oxter, an' the swat stood upon him cauld as well-water; and there was ither whiles, when he cam' to himsel' like a christened bairn an' minded naething.

The upshot was that he gaed to the window an' stood glowrin' at Dule water. The trees are unco thick, an' the water lies deep an' black under the manse; an' there was Janet washin' the cla'es wi' her coats kilted. She had her back to the minister, an' he, for his pairt, hardly kenned what he was lookin' at. Syne she turned round, an' shawed her face; Mr Soulis had the same cauld grue as twice that day afore, an' it was borne in upon him what folk said, that Janet was deid lang syne, an' this was a bogle in her clay-cauld flesh. He drew back a pickle and he scanned her narrowly. She was tramp-trampin' in the cla'es croonin' to hersel'; and eh! Gude guide us, but it was a fearsome face. Whiles she sang louder, but there was nae man born o' woman that could tell the words o' her sang; an' whiles she lookit side-lang doun, but there was naething there for her to look at. There gaed a scunner through the flesh upon his banes; an' that was Heeven's advertisement. But Mr Soulis just blamed himsel', he said, to think sae ill o' a puir, auld afflicted wife that hadna a freend forbye himsel'; an' he put up a bit prayer for him an' her, an' drank a little caller water—for his heart rose again' the meat—an' gaed up to his naked bed in the gloamin'.

That was a nicht that has never been forgotten in Ba'weary, the nicht o' the seeventeenth o' August, seeventeen hun'er'

an' twal'. It had been het afore, as I hae said, but that nicht it
was hetter than ever. The sun gaed doun amang unco-lookin'
clouds; it fell as mirk as the pit; no' a star, no' a breath o'
wund; ye couldna see your han' afore your face, an' even the
auld folk cuist the covers frae their beds an lay pechin' for
their breath. Wi' a' that he had upon his mind, it was gey an'
unlikely Mr Soulis wad get muckle sleep. He lay an' he
tummled; the gude, caller bed that he got into brunt his very
banes; whiles he slept, an' whiles he waukened; whiles he
heard the time o' nicht, an' whiles a tyke yowlin' up the muir,
as if somebody was deid; whiles he thocht he heard bogles
claverin' in his lug, an' whiles he saw spunkies in the room.
He behoved, he judged, to be sick; an' sick he was—little he
jaloosed the sickness.

At the hinder end, he got a clearness in his mind, sat up in
his sark on the bed-side, an' fell thinkin' ance mair o' the
black man an' Janet. He couldna weel tell how—maybe it
was the cauld to his feet—but it cam' in upon him wi' a
spate that there was some connection between thir twa, an'
that either or baith o' them were bogles. An' just at that
moment, in Janet's room, which was neist to his, there cam'
a stramp o' feet as if men were wars'lin', an' then a loud bang;
an' then a wund gaed reishling round the fower quarters o'
the house; an' then a' was ance mair as seelent as the grave.

Mr Soulis was feared for neither man nor de'il. He got his
tinder-box, an' lit a can'le, an' made three steps o't ower to
Janet's door. It was on the hasp, an' he pushed it open, an'
keeked bauldly in. It was a big room, as big as the minister's
ain, an' plenished wi' grand, auld solid gear, for he had
naething else. There was a fower-posted bed wi' auld tapestry;
an' a braw cabinet o' aik, that was fu' o' the minister's divinity
books, an' put there to be out o' the gate; an' a wheen duds o'
Janet's lying here an' there about the floor. But nae Janet
could Mr Soulis see; nor ony sign o' a contention. In he gaed
(an' there's few that wad hae followed him) an' lookit a' round,
an' listened. But there was naething to be heard, neither
inside the manse nor in a' Ba'weary parish, an' naething to
be seen but the muckle shadows turnin' round the can'le.
An' then, a' at aince, the minister's heart played dunt an'
stood stock-still; an' a cauld wund blew amang the hairs o'
his heid. Whaten a weary sicht was that for the puir man's

e'en! For there was Janet hangin' frae a nail beside the auld aik cabinet: her heid aye lay on her shouther, her e'en were steekit, the tongue projected frae her mouth, an' her heels were twa feet clear abune the floor.

'God forgive us all!' thocht Mr Soulis, 'poor Janet's dead.'

He cam' a step nearer to the corp; an' then his heart fair whammled in his inside. For by what cantrip it wad ill beseem a man to judge, she was hangin', frae a single nail an' by a single wursted thread for darnin' hose.

It 's a awfu' thing to be your lane at nicht wi' siccan prodigies o' darkness; but Mr Soulis was strong in the Lord. He turned an' gaed his ways oot o' that room, an' lockit the door anint him; an' step by step, doun the stairs, as heavy as leed; and set doun the can'le on the table at the stairfoot. He couldna pray, he couldna think, he was dreepin' wi' caul' swat, an' naething could he hear but the dunt-dunt-duntin' o' his ain heart. He micht maybe hae stood there an hour, or maybe twa, he minded sae little; when a' o' a sudden, he heard a laigh, uncanny steer up-stairs; a foot gaed to an' fro in the chalmer whaur the corp was hangin'; syne the door was opened, though he minded weel that he had lockit it; an' syne there was a step upon the landin', an' it seemed to him as if the corp was lookin' ower the rail and doun upon him whaur he stood.

He took up the can'le again (for he couldna want the licht), an' as saftly as ever he could, gaed straucht out o' the manse an' to the far end o' the causeway. It was aye pit-mirk; the flame o' the can'le, when he set it on the grund, brunt steedy and clear as in a room; naething moved, but the Dule water seepin' and sabbin' doun the glen, an' yon unhaly footstep that cam' ploddin' doun the stairs inside the manse. He kenned the foot ower weel, for it was Janet's; an' at ilka step that cam' a wee thing nearer, the cauld got deeper in his vitals. He commended his soul to Him that made an' keepit him; 'and, O Lord,' said he, 'give me strength this night to war against the powers of evil.'

By this time the foot was comin' through the passage for the door; he could hear a hand skirt alang the wa', as if the fearsome thing was feelin' for its way. The saughs tossed an' maned thegither, a long sigh cam' ower the hills, the flame o' the can'le was blawn aboot; an' there stood the corp of

Thrawn Janet, wi' her grogram goun an' her black mutch, wi' the heid aye upon the shouther, an' the girn still upon the face o't—leevin', ye wad hae said—deid, as Mr Soulis weel kenned—upon the threshold o' the manse.

It 's a strange thing that the soul of man should be that thirled into his perishable body; but the minister saw that, an' his heart didna break.

She didna stand there lang; she began to move again an' cam' slowly towards Mr Soulis whaur he stood under the saughs. A' the life o' his body, a' the strength o' his speerit, were glowerin' frae his e'en. It seemed she was gaun to speak, but wanted words, an' made a sign wi' the left hand. There cam' a clap o' wund, like a cat's fuff; oot gaed the can'le, the saughs skreighed like folk; an' Mr Soulis kenned that, live or die, this was the end o't.

'Witch, beldame, devil!' he cried, 'I charge you, by the power of God, begone—if you be dead, to the grave—if you be damned, to hell.'

An' at that moment the Lord's ain hand out o' the Heevens struck the Horror whaur it stood; the auld, deid, desecrated corp o' the witch-wife, sae lang keepit frae the grave and hirsled round by de'ils, lowed up like a brunstane spunk an' fell in ashes to the grund; the thunder followed, peal on dirlin' peal, the rairin' rain upon the back o' that; and Mr Soulis lowped through the garden hedge, an' ran, wi' skelloch upon skelloch, for the clachan.

That same mornin', John Christie saw the Black Man pass the Muckle Cairn as it was chappin' six; before eicht, he gaed by the change-house at Knockdow; an' no' lang after, Sandy M'Lellan saw him gaun linkin' doun the braes frae Kilmackerlie. There 's little doubt but it was him that dwalled sae lang in Janet's body; but he was awa' at last; an' sinsyne the de'il has never fashed us in Ba'weary.

But it was a sair dispensation for the minister; lang, lang he lay ravin' in his bed; an' frae that hour to this, he was the man ye ken the day.

Essays

*

OLD MORTALITY
from
Moments and Portraits

THE LANTERN BEARERS
from
Across the Plains

OLD MORTALITY

I

THERE is a certain graveyard, looked upon on the one side by a prison, on the other by the windows of a quiet hotel; below, under a steep cliff, it beholds the traffic of many lines of rail, and the scream of the engine and the shock of meeting buffers mount to it all day long. The aisles are lined with the inclosed sepulchres of families, door beyond door, like houses in a street; and in the morning the shadow of the prison turrets, and of many tall memorials, fall upon the graves. There, in the hot fits of youth, I came to be unhappy. Pleasant incidents are woven with my memory of the place. I here made friends with a certain plain old gentleman, a visitor on sunny mornings, gravely cheerful, who, with one eye upon the place that awaited him, chirped about his youth like winter sparrows; a beautiful housemaid of the hotel once, for some days together, dumbly flirted with me from a window and kept my wild heart flying; and once—she possibly remembers—the wise Eugenia followed me to that austere inclosure. Her hair came down, and in the shelter of the tomb my trembling fingers helped her to repair the braid. But for the most part I went there solitary and, with irrevocable emotion, pored on the names of the forgotten. Name after name, and to each the conventional attributions and the idle dates: a regiment of the unknown that had been the joy of mothers, and had thrilled with the illusions of youth, and at last, in the dim sick-room, wrestled with the pangs of old mortality. In that whole crew of the silenced there was but one of whom my fancy had received a picture; and he, with his comely, florid countenance, bewigged and habited in scarlet, and in his day combining fame and popularity, stood forth, like a taunt, among that company of phantom appellations. It was then possible to leave behind us something more explicit than these severe, monotonous and lying epitaphs; and the thing left, the memory of a painted picture and what we call the immortality of a name, was hardly more desirable than mere oblivion. Even David Hume, as he lay composed beneath that 'circular idea', was fainter than a dream; and when the housemaid, broom in hand, smiled and beckoned from the open window, the fame of that bewigged philosopher melted like a raindrop in the sea.

And yet in soberness I cared as little for the housemaid as for David Hume. The interests of youth are rarely frank; his passions, like Noah's dove, come home to roost. The fire, sensibility, and volume of his own nature, that is all that he has learned to recognise. The tumultuary and gray tide of life, the empire of routine, the unrejoicing faces of his elders, fill him with contemptuous surprise; there also he seems to walk among the tombs of spirits; and it is only in the course of years, and after much rubbing with his fellow-men, that he begins by glimpses to see himself from without and his fellows from within: to know his own for one among the thousand unde-noted countenances of the city street, and to divine in others the throb of human agony and hope. In the meantime he will avoid the hospital doors, the pale faces, the cripple, the sweet whiff of chloroform—for there, on the most thoughtless, the pains of others are burned home; but he will continue to walk, in a divine self-pity, the aisles of the forgotten graveyard. The length of man's life, which is endless to the brave and busy, is scorned by his ambitious thought. He cannot bear to have come for so little, and to go again so wholly. He cannot bear, above all, in that brief scene, to be still idle, and by way of cure, neglects the little that he has to do. The parable of the talent is the brief epitome of youth. To believe in immortality is one thing, but it is first needful to believe in life. Denuncia-tory preachers seem not to suspect that they may be taken gravely and in evil part; that young men may come to think of time as of a moment, and with the pride of Satan wave back the inadequate gift. Yet here is a true peril; this it is that sets them to pace the graveyard alleys and to read, with strange extremes of pity and derision, the memorials of the dead.

Books were the proper remedy: books of vivid human import, forcing upon their minds the issues, pleasures, busy-ness, importance and immediacy of that life in which they stand; books of smiling or heroic temper, to excite or to console; books of a large design, shadowing the complexity of that game of consequences to which we all sit down, the hanger-back not least. But the average sermon flees the point, dis-porting itself in that eternity of which we know, and need to know, so little; avoiding the bright, crowded, and momentous fields of life where destiny awaits us. Upon the average book a writer may be silent; he may set it down to his ill-hap that when his own youth was in the acrid fermentation, he should have fallen and fed upon the cheerless fields of Obermann. Yet to Mr Arnold, who led him to these pastures, he still bears a grudge. The day is perhaps not far off when people will begin to count *Moll Flanders*, ay, or *The Country Wife*, more wholesome and more pious diet than these guide-books to consistent egoism.

But the most inhuman of boys soon wearies of the inhumanity of Obermann. And even while I still continued to be a haunter of the graveyard, I began insensibly to turn my attention to the grave-diggers, and was weaned out of myself to observe the conduct of visitors. This was dayspring, indeed, to a lad in such great darkness. Not that I began to see men, or to try to see them, from within, nor to learn charity and modesty and justice from the sight; but still stared at them externally from the prison windows of my affectation. Once I remember to have observed two working-women with a baby halting by a grave; there was something monumental in the grouping, one upright carrying the child, the other with bowed face crouching by her side. A wreath of immortelles under a glass dome had thus attracted them; and, drawing near, I overheard their judgment on that wonder. 'Eh! what extravagance!' To a youth afflicted with the callosity of sentiment, this quaint and pregnant saying appeared merely base.

My acquaintance with grave-diggers, considering its length, was unremarkable. One, indeed, whom I found plying his spade in the red evening, high above Allan Water and in the shadow of Dunblane Cathedral, told me of his acquaintance with the birds that still attended on his labours; how some would even perch about him, waiting for their prey; and in a true Sexton's Calendar, how the species varied with the season of the year. But this was the very poetry of the profession. The others whom I knew were somewhat dry. A faint flavour of the gardener hung about them, but sophisticated and disbloomed. They had engagements to keep, not alone with the deliberate series of the seasons, but with mankind's clocks and hour-long measurement of time. And thus there was no leisure for the relishing pinch, or the hour-long gossip, foot on

spade. They were men wrapped up in their grim business;
they liked well to open long-closed family vaults, blowing in
the key and throwing wide the grating; and they carried in
their minds a calendar of names and dates. It would be 'in
fifty-twa' that such a tomb was last opened for 'Miss Jemimy'.
It was thus they spoke of their past patients—familiarly but
not without respect, like old family servants. Here is indeed a
servant, whom we forget that we possess; who does not wait at
the bright table, or run at the bell's summons, but patiently
smokes his pipe beside the mortuary fire, and in his faithful
memory notches the burials of our race. To suspect Shakespeare in his maturity of a superficial touch savours of paradox;
yet he was surely in error when he attributed insensibility to
the digger of the grave. But perhaps it is on Hamlet that the
charge should lie; or perhaps the English sexton differs from
the Scotch. The 'goodman delver', reckoning up his years of
office, might have at least suggested other thoughts. It is a
pride common among sextons. A cabinet-maker does not
count his cabinets, nor even an author his volumes, save when
they stare upon him from the shelves; but the grave-digger
numbers his graves. He would indeed be something different
from human if his solitary open-air and tragic labours left not
a broad mark upon his mind. There, in his tranquil aisle,
apart from city clamour, among the cats and robins and the
ancient effigies and legends of the tomb, he waits the continual
passage of his contemporaries, falling like minute drops into
eternity. As they fall, he counts them; and this enumeration,
which was at first perhaps appalling to his soul, in the process
of years and by the kindly influence of habit grows to be his
pride and pleasure. There are many common stories telling
how he piques himself on crowded cemeteries. But I will
rather tell of the old grave-digger of Monkton, to whose un-
suffering bedside the minister was summoned. He dwelt in a
cottage built into the wall of the churchyard; and through a
bull's-eye pane above his bed he could see, as he lay dying,
the rank grasses and the upright and recumbent stones. Dr.
Laurie was, I think, a Moderate: 'tis certain, at least, that he
took a very Roman view of deathbed dispositions; for he told
the old man that he had lived beyond man's natural years,
that his life had been easy and reputable, that his family had
all grown up and been a credit to his care, and that it now

behoved him unregretfully to gird his loins and follow the majority. The grave-digger heard him out; then he raised himself upon one elbow, and with the other hand pointed through the window to the scene of his life-long labours. 'Doctor,' he said, 'I ha'e laid three hunner and fower-score in that kirkyaird; an it had been His wull,' indicating Heaven, 'I would ha'e likit weel to ha'e made out the fower hunner.' But it was not to be; this tragedian of the fifth act had now another part to play; and the time had come when others were to gird and carry him.

II

I would fain strike a note that should be more heroical; but the ground of all youth's suffering, solitude, hysteria, and haunting of the grave, is nothing else than naked, ignorant selfishness. It is himself that he sees dead; those are his virtues that are forgotten; his is the vague epitaph. Pity him but the more, if pity be your cue; for where a man is all pride, vanity, and personal aspiration, he goes through fire unshielded. In every part and corner of our life, to lose oneself is to be gainer; to forget oneself is to be happy; and this poor, laughable and tragic fool has not yet learned the rudiments; himself, giant Prometheus, is still ironed on the peaks of Caucasus. But by-and-by his truant interests will leave that tortured body, slip abroad and gather flowers. Then shall death appear before him in an altered guise; no longer as a doom peculiar to himself, whether fate's crowning injustice or his own last vengeance upon those who fail to value him; but now as a power that wounds him far more tenderly, not without solemn compensations, taking and giving, bereaving and yet storing up.

The first step for all is to learn to the dregs our own ignoble fallibility. When we have fallen through storey after storey of our vanity and aspiration, and sit rueful among the ruins, then it is that we begin to measure the stature of our friends: how they stand between us and our own contempt, believing in our best; how, linking us with others, and still spreading wide the influential circle, they weave us in and in with the fabric of contemporary life; and to what petty size they dwarf the virtues and the vices that appeared gigantic in our youth. So that at the last, when such a pin falls out—when there vanishes in the least breath of time one of those rich magazines of life on which we drew for our supply—when he who had first dawned upon us as a face among the faces of the city, and, still growing, came to bulk on our regard with those clear features of the loved and living man, falls in a breath to memory and shadow, there falls along with him a whole wing of the palace of our life.

III

One such face I now remember; one such blank some half-a-dozen of us labour to dissemble. In his youth he was most beautiful in person, most serene and genial by disposition; full of racy words and quaint thoughts. Laughter attended on his coming. He had the air of a great gentleman, jovial and royal with his equals, and to the poorest student gentle and attentive. Power seemed to reside in him exhaustless; we saw him stoop to play with us, but held him marked for higher destinies; we loved his notice; and I have rarely had my pride more gratified than when he sat at my father's table, my acknowledged friend. So he walked among us, both hands full of gifts, carrying with nonchalance the seeds of a most influential life.

The powers and the ground of friendship is a mystery; but, looking back, I can discern that, in part, we loved the thing he was, for some shadow of what he was to be. For with all his beauty, power, breeding, urbanity and mirth, there was in those days something soulless in our friend. He would astonish us by sallies, witty, innocent and inhumane; and by a mis-applied Johnsonian pleasantry, demolish honest sentiment. I can still see and hear him, as he went his way along the lamp-lit streets, *Là ci darem la mano* on his lips, a noble figure of a youth, but following vanity and incredulous of good; and sure enough, somewhere on the high seas of life, with his health, his hopes, his patrimony and his self-respect, miserably went down.

From this disaster, like a spent swimmer, he came desperately ashore, bankrupt of money and consideration; creeping to the family he had deserted; with broken wing, never more to rise. But in his face there was a light of knowledge that was new to it. Of the wounds of his body he was never healed;

died of them gradually, with clear-eyed resignation; of his wounded pride, we knew only from his silence. He returned to that city where he had lorded it in his ambitious youth; lived there alone, seeing few; striving to retrieve the irretrievable; at times still grappling with that mortal frailty that had brought him down; still joying in his friend's successes; his laugh still ready but with kindlier music; and over all his thoughts the shadow of that unalterable law which he had disavowed and which had brought him low. Lastly, when his bodily evils had quite disabled him, he lay a great while dying, still without complaint, still finding interests; to his last step gentle, urbane and with the will to smile.

The tale of this great failure is, to those who remained true to him, the tale of a success. In his youth he took thought for no one but himself; when he came ashore again, his whole armada lost, he seemed to think of none but others. Such was his tenderness for others, such his instinct of fine courtesy and pride, that of that impure passion of remorse he never breathed a syllable; even regret was rare with him, and pointed with a jest. You would not have dreamed, if you had known him then, that this was that great failure, that beacon to young men, over whose fall a whole society had hissed and pointed fingers. Often have we gone to him, red-hot with our own hopeful sorrows, railing on the roseleaves in our princely bed of life, and he would patiently give ear and wisely counsel; and it was only upon some return of our own thoughts that we were reminded what manner of man this was to whom we disembosomed: a man, by his own fault, ruined; shut out of the garden of his gifts; his whole city of hope both ploughed and salted; silently awaiting the deliverer. Then something took us by the throat; and to see him there, so gentle, patient, brave and pious, oppressed but not cast down, sorrow was so swallowed up in admiration that we could not dare to pity him. Even if the old fault flashed out again, it but awoke our wonder that, in that lost battle, he should have still the energy to fight. He had gone to ruin with a kind of kingly *abandon*, like one who condescended; but once ruined, with the lights all out, he fought as for a kingdom. Most men, finding themselves the authors of their own disgrace, rail the louder against God or destiny. Most men, when they repent, oblige their friends to share the bitterness of that repentance. But he had held an inquest and passed sentence: *mene, mene*; and condemned himself to smiling silence. He had given trouble enough; had earned misfortune amply, and foregone the right to murmur.

Thus was our old comrade, like Samson, careless in his days of strength; but on the coming of adversity, and when that strength was gone that had betrayed him—'for our strength is weakness'—he began to blossom and bring forth. Well, now, he is out of the fight: the burden that he bore thrown down before the great deliverer. We

> in the vast cathedral leave him;
> God accept him,
> Christ receive him!

IV

If we go now and look on these innumerable epitaphs, the pathos and the irony are strangely fled. They do not stand merely to the dead, these foolish monuments; they are pillars and legends set up to glorify the difficult but not desperate life of man. This ground is hallowed by the heroes of defeat.

I see the indifferent pass before my friend's last resting-place; pause, with a shrug of pity, marvelling that so rich an argosy had sunk. A pity, now that he is done with suffering, a pity most uncalled for, and an ignorant wonder. Before those who loved him, his memory shines like a reproach; they honour him for silent lessons; they cherish his example; and in what remains before them on their toil, fear to be unworthy of the dead. For this proud man was one of those who prospered in the valley of humiliation;—of whom Bunyan wrote that, 'Though Christian had the hard hap to meet in the valley with Apollyon, yet I must tell you, that in former times men have met with angels here; have found pearls here; and have in this place found the words of life.'

THE LANTERN BEARERS

I

THESE boys congregated every autumn about a certain easterly fisher-village, where they tasted in a high degree the glory of existence. The place was created seemingly on purpose for the diversion of young gentlemen. A street or two of houses, mostly red and many of them tiled; a number of fine trees clustered about the manse and the kirkyard, and turning the chief street into a shady alley; many little gardens more than usually bright with flowers; nets a-drying, and fisher-wives scolding in the backward parts; a smell of fish, a genial smell of seaweed; whiffs of blowing sand at the street-corners; shops with golf-balls and bottled lollipops; another shop with penny pickwicks (that remarkable cigar) and the *London Journal*, dear to me for its startling pictures, and a few novels, dear for their suggestive names: such, as well as memory serves me, were the ingredients of the town. These, you are to conceive posted on a spit between two sandy bays, and sparsely flanked with villas—enough for the boys to lodge in with their subsidiary parents, not enough (not yet enough) to cocknify the scene: a haven in the rocks in front: in front of that, a file of gray islets: to the left, endless links and sand wreaths, a wilderness of hiding-holes, alive with popping rabbits and soaring gulls: to the right, a range of seaward crags, one rugged brow beyond another; the ruins of a mighty and ancient fortress on the brink of one; coves between—now charmed into sunshine quiet, now whistling with wind and clamorous with bursting surges; the dens and sheltered hollows redolent of thyme and southernwood, the air at the cliff's edge brisk and clean and pungent of the sea—in front of all, the Bass Rock, tilted seaward like a doubtful bather, the surf ringing it with white, the solan-geese hanging round its summit like a great and glittering smoke. This choice piece of seaboard was sacred, besides, to the wrecker; and the Bass, in the eye of fancy, still flew the colours of King James; and in the ear of fancy the arches of Tantallon still rang with horse-shoe iron, and echoed to the commands of Bell-the-Cat.

There was nothing to mar your days, if you were a boy

summering in that part, but the embarrassment of pleasure. You might golf if you wanted; but I seem to have been better employed. You might secrete yourself in the Lady's Walk, a certain sunless dingle of elders, all mossed over by the damp as green as grass, and dotted here and there by the stream-side with roofless walls, the cold homes of anchorites. To fit themselves for life, and with a special eye to acquire the art of smoking, it was even common for the boys to harbour there; and you might have seen a single penny pickwick, honestly shared in lengths with a blunt knife, bestrew the glen with these apprentices. Again, you might join our fishing parties, where we sat perched as thick as solan-geese, a covey of little anglers, boy and girl, angling over each other's heads, to the much entanglement of lines and loss of podleys and consequent shrill recrimination—shrill as the geese themselves. Indeed, had that been all, you might have done this often; but though fishing be a fine pastime, the podley is scarce to be regarded as a dainty for the table; and it was a point of honour that a boy should eat all that he had taken. Or again, you might climb the Law, where the whale's jaw-bone stood landmark in the buzzing wind, and behold the face of many counties, and the smoke and spires of many towns, and the sails of distant ships. You might bathe, now in the flaws of fine weather, that we pathetically call our summer, now in a gale of wind, with the sand scourging your bare hide, your clothes thrashing abroad from underneath their guardian stone, the froth of the great breakers casting you headlong ere it had drowned your knees. Or you might explore the tidal rocks, above all in the ebb of springs, when the very roots of the hills were for the nonce discovered; following my leader from one group to another, groping in slippery tangle for the wreck of ships, wading in pools after the abominable creatures of the sea, and ever with an eye cast backward on the march of the tide and the menaced line of your retreat. And then you might go Crusoe-ing, a word that covers all extempore eating in the open air: digging perhaps a house under the margin of the links, kindling a fire of the sea-ware, and cooking apples there—if they were truly apples, for I sometimes suppose the merchant must have played us off with some inferior and quite local fruit, capable of resolving, in the neighbourhood of fire, into mere sand and smoke and iodine; or perhaps pushing to Tantallon, you might

lunch on sandwiches and visions in the grassy court, while the
wind hummed in the crumbling turrets; or clambering along
the coast, eat geans[1] (the worst, I must suppose, in Christendom) from an adventurous gean tree that had taken root under
a cliff, where it was shaken with an ague of east wind, and
silvered after gales with salt, and grew so foreign among its
bleak surroundings that to eat of its produce was an adventure
in itself.

There are mingled some dismal memories with so many that
were joyous. Of the fisher-wife, for instance, who had cut her
throat at Canty Bay; and of how I ran with the other children
to the top of the Quadrant, and beheld a posse of silent people
escorting a cart, and on the cart, bound in a chair, her throat
bandaged, and the bandage all bloody—horror!—the fisher-
wife herself, who continued thenceforth to hag-ride my
thoughts, and even to-day (as I recall the scene) darkens
daylight. She was lodged in the little old jail in the chief
street; but whether or no she died there, with a wise terror of
the worst, I never inquired. She had been tippling; it was but
a dingy tragedy; and it seems strange and hard that, after all
these years, the poor crazy sinner should be still pilloried on
her cart in the scrap-book of my memory. Nor shall I readily
forget a certain house in the Quadrant where a visitor died,
and a dark old woman continued to dwell alone with the dead
body; nor how this old woman conceived a hatred to myself
and one of my cousins, and in the dread hour of the dusk, as
we were clambering on the garden-walls, opened a window in
that house of mortality and cursed us in a shrill voice and with
a marrowy choice of language. It was a pair of very colourless
urchins that fled down the lane from this remarkable experience! But I recall with a more doubtful sentiment, compounded
out of fear and exultation, the coil of equinoctial tempests;
trumpeting squalls, scouring flaws of rain; the boats with their
reefed lugsails scudding for the harbour mouth, where danger
lay, for it was hard to make when the wind had any east in it;
the wives clustered with blowing shawls at the pier-head, where
(if fate was against them) they might see boat and husband
and sons—their whole wealth and their whole family—en-
gulfed under their eyes; and (what I saw but once) a troop of
neighbours forcing such an unfortunate homeward, and she

[1] Wild cherries.

squalling and battling in their midst, a figure scarcely human, a tragic Mænad.

These are things that I recall with interest; but what my memory dwells upon the most, I have been all this while with-holding. It was a sport peculiar to the place, and indeed to a week or so of our two months' holiday there. Maybe it still flourishes in its native spot; for boys and their pastimes are swayed by periodic forces inscrutable to man; so that tops and marbles reappear in their due season, regular like the sun and moon; and the harmless art of knucklebones has seen the fall of the Roman empire and the rise of the United States. It may still flourish in its native spot, but nowhere else, I am per-suaded; for I tried myself to introduce it on Tweedside, and was defeated lamentably; its charm being quite local, like a country wine that cannot be exported.

The idle manner of it was this:

Toward the end of September, when school-time was draw-ing near and the nights were already black, we would begin to sally from our respective villas, each equipped with a tin bull's-eye lantern. The thing was so well known that it had worn a rut in the commerce of Great Britain; and the grocers, about the due time, began to garnish their windows with our particular brand of luminary. We wore them buckled to the waist upon a cricket belt, and over them, such was the rigour of the game, a buttoned top-coat. They smelled noisomely of blistered tin; they never burned aright, though they would always burn our fingers; their use was naught; the pleasure of them merely fanciful; and yet a boy with a bull's-eye under his top-coat asked for nothing more. The fishermen used lanterns about their boats, and it was from them, I suppose, that we had got the hint; but theirs were not bull's-eyes, nor did we ever play at being fishermen. The police carried them at their belts, and we had plainly copied them in that; yet we did not pretend to be policemen. Burglars, indeed, we may have had some haunting thoughts of; and we had certainly an eye to past ages when lanterns were more common, and to certain story-books in which we had found them to figure very largely. But take it for all in all, the pleasure of the thing was substantive; and to be a boy with a bull's-eye under his top-coat was good enough for us.

When two of these asses met, there would be an anxious

'Have you got your lantern?' and a gratified 'Yes!' That was
the shibboleth, and very needful too; for, as it was the rule to
keep our glory contained, none could recognise a lantern-
bearer, unless (like the polecat) by the smell. Four or five
would sometimes climb into the belly of a ten-man lugger,
with nothing but the thwarts above them—for the cabin was
usually locked, or choose out some hollow of the links where the
wind might whistle overhead. There the coats would be un-
buttoned and the bull's-eyes discovered; and in the chequering
glimmer, under the huge windy hall of the night, and cheered
by a rich steam of toasting tinware, these fortunate young
gentlemen would crouch together in the cold sand of the links
or on the scaly bilges of the fishing-boat, and delight themselves with inappropriate talk. Woe is me that I may not give
some specimens—some of their foresights of life, or deep
inquiries into the rudiments of man and nature, these were so
fiery and so innocent, they were so richly silly, so romantically
young. But the talk, at any rate, was but a condiment; and
these gatherings themselves only accidents in the career of the
lantern-bearer. The essence of this bliss was to walk by yourself
in the black night; the slide shut, the top-coat buttoned; not a
ray escaping, whether to conduct your footsteps or to make
your glory public: a mere pillar of darkness in the dark; and
all the while, deep down in the privacy of your fool's heart, to
know you had a bull's-eye at your belt, and to exult and sing
over the knowledge.

II

It is said that a poet has died young in the breast of the most
stolid. It may be contended, rather, that this (somewhat
minor) bard in almost every case survives, and is the spice of
life to his possessor. Justice is not done to the versatility and
the unplumbed childishness of man's imagination. His life
from without may seem but a rude mound of mud; there will
be some golden chamber at the heart of it, in which he dwells
delighted; and for as dark as his pathway seems to the observer,
he will have some kind of a bull's-eye at his belt.

It would be hard to pick out a career more cheerless than
that of Dancer, the miser, as he figures in the 'Old Bailey
Reports', a prey to the most sordid persecutions, the butt of

his neighbourhood, betrayed by his hired man, his house beleaguered by the impish schoolboy, and he himself grinding and fuming and impotently fleeing to the law against these pin-pricks. You marvel at first that any one should willingly prolong a life so destitute of charm and dignity; and then you call to memory that had he chosen, had he ceased to be a miser, he could have been freed at once from these trials, and might have built himself a castle and gone escorted by a squadron. For the love of more recondite joys, which we cannot estimate, which, it may be, we should envy, the man had willingly forgone both comfort and consideration. 'His mind to him a kingdom was'; and sure enough, digging into that mind, which seems at first a dust-heap, we unearth some priceless jewels. For Dancer must have had the love of power and the disdain of using it, a noble character in itself; disdain of many pleasures, a chief part of what is commonly called wisdom; disdain of the inevitable end, that finest trait of mankind; scorn of men's opinions, another element of virtue; and at the back of all, a conscience just like yours and mine, whining like a cur, swindling like a thimble-rigger, but still pointing (there or thereabout) to some conventional standard. Here were a cabinet portrait to which Hawthorne perhaps had done justice; and yet not Hawthorne either, for he was mildly minded, and it lay not in him to create for us that throb of the miser's pulse, his fretful energy of gusto, his vast arms of ambition clutching in he knows not what: insatiable, insane, a god with a muck-rake. Thus, at least, looking in the bosom of the miser, consideration detects the poet in the full tide of life, with more, indeed, of the poetic fire than usually goes to epics; and tracing that mean man about his cold hearth, and to and fro in his discomfortable house, spies within him a blazing bonfire of delight. And so with others, who do not live by bread alone, but by some cherished and perhaps fantastic pleasure; who are meat salesmen to the external eye, and possibly to themselves are Shakespeares, Napoleons, or Beethovens; who have not one virtue to rub against another in the field of active life, and yet perhaps, in the life of contemplation, sit with the saints. We see them on the street, and we can count their buttons; but heaven knows in what they pride themselves! heaven knows where they have set their treasure!

There is one fable that touches very near the quick of life:

the fable of the monk who passed into the woods, heard a bird break into song, hearkened for a trill or two, and found himself on his return a stranger at his convent gates; for he had been absent fifty years, and of all his comrades there survived but one to recognise him. It is not only in the woods that this enchanter carols, though perhaps he is native there. He sings in the most doleful places. The miser hears him and chuckles, and the days are moments. With no more apparatus than an ill-smelling lantern I have evoked him on the naked links. All life that is not merely mechanical is spun out of two strands: seeking for that bird and hearing him. And it is just this that makes life so hard to value, and the delight of each so incommunicable. And just a knowledge of this, and a remembrance of those fortunate hours in which the bird has sung to us, that fills us with such wonder when we turn the pages of the realist. There, to be sure, we find a picture of life in so far as it consists of mud and of old iron, cheap desires and cheap fears, that which we are ashamed to remember and that which we are careless whether we forget; but of the note of that time-devouring nightingale we hear no news.

The case of these writers of romance is most obscure. They have been boys and youths; they have lingered outside the window of the beloved, who was then most probably writing to some one else; they have sat before a sheet of paper, and felt themselves mere continents of congested poetry, not one line of which would flow; they have walked alone in the woods, they have walked in cities under the countless lamps; they have been to sea, they have hated, they have feared, they have longed to knife a man, and maybe done it; the wild taste of life has stung their palate. Or, if you deny them all the rest, one pleasure at least they have tasted to the full—their books are there to prove it—the keen pleasure of successful literary composition. And yet they fill the globe with volumes, whose cleverness inspires me with despairing admiration, and whose consistent falsity to all I care to call existence, with despairing wrath. If I had no better hope than to continue to revolve among the dreary and petty businesses, and to be moved by the paltry hopes and fears with which they surround and animate their heroes, I declare I would die now. But there has never an hour of mine gone quite so dully yet; if it were spent waiting at a railway junction, I would have some scattering thoughts, I could count some grains of memory, compared to which the whole of one of these romances seems but dross.

These writers would retort (if I take them properly) that this was very true; that it was the same with themselves and other persons of (what they call) the artistic temperament; that in this we were exceptional, and should apparently be ashamed of ourselves; but that our works must deal exclusively with (what they call) the average man, who was a prodigious dull fellow, and quite dead to all but the paltriest considerations. I accept the issue. We can only know others by ourselves. The artistic temperament (a plague on the expression!) does not make us different from our fellowmen, or it would make us incapable of writing novels; and the average man (a murrain on the word!) is just like you and me, or he would not be average. It was Whitman who stamped a kind of Birmingham sacredness upon the latter phrase; but Whitman knew very well, and showed very nobly, that the average man was full of joys and full of a poetry of his own. And this harping on life's dulness and man's meanness is a loud profession of incompetence; it is one of two things: the cry of the blind eye, *I cannot see*, or the complaint of the dumb tongue, *I cannot utter*. To draw a life without delights is to prove I have not realised it. To picture a man without some sort of poetry—well, it goes near to prove my case, for it shows an author may have little enough. To see Dancer only as a dirty, old, small-minded, impotently fuming man, in a dirty house, besieged by Harrow boys, and probably beset by small attorneys, is to show myself as keen an observer as . . . the Harrow boys. But these young gentlemen (with a more becoming modesty) were content to pluck Dancer by the coat-tails; they did not suppose they had surprised his secret or could put him living in a book: and it is there my error would have lain. Or say that in the same romance—I continue to call these books romances, in the hope of giving pain—say that in the same romance, which now begins really to take shape, I should leave to speak of Dancer, and follow instead the Harrow boys; and say that I came on some such business as that of my lantern-bearers on the links; and described the boys as very cold, spat upon by flurries of rain, and drearily surrounded, all of which they were; and their talk as silly and indecent, which it certainly was. I might upon these lines, and had I Zola's genius, turn out, in a page

or so, a gem of literary art, render the lantern-light with the
touches of a master, and lay on the indecency with the
ungrudging hand of love; and when all was done, what a
triumph would my picture be of shallowness and dulness!
how it would have missed the point! how it would have
belied the boys! To the ear of the stenographer, the talk is
merely silly and indecent; but ask the boys themselves, and
they are discussing (as it is highly proper they should) the
possibilities of existence. To the eye of the observer they are
wet and cold and drearily surrounded; but ask themselves,
and they are in the heaven of a recondite pleasure, the ground
of which is an ill-smelling lantern. . . .

III

For, to repeat, the ground of a man's joy is often hard to hit.
It may hinge at times upon a mere accessory, like the lantern;
it may reside, like Dancer's, in the mysterious inwards of
psychology. It may consist with perpetual failure, and find
exercise in the continued chase. It has so little bond with
externals (such as the observer scribbles in his note-book) that
it may even touch them not; and the man's true life, for which
he consents to live, lie altogether in the field of fancy. The
clergyman, in his spare hours, may be winning battles, the
farmer sailing ships, the banker reaping triumph in the arts:
all leading another life, plying another trade from that they
chose; like the poet's housebuilder, who, after all, is cased in
stone,

'By his fireside, as impotent fancy prompts.
  Rebuilds it to his liking.'

In such a case the poetry runs underground. The observer
(poor soul, with his documents!) is all abroad. For to look at
the man is but to court deception. We shall see the trunk from
which he draws his nourishment; but he himself is above and
abroad in the green dome of foliage, hummed through by
winds and nested in by nightingales. And the true realism were
that of the poets, to climb up after him like a squirrel, and
catch some glimpse of the heaven for which he lives. And the

true realism, always and everywhere, is that of the poets: to find out where joy resides, and give it a voice far beyond singing.

For to miss the joy is to miss all. In the joy of the actors lies the sense of any action. That is the explanation, that the excuse. To one who has not the secret of the lanterns, the scene upon the links is meaningless. And hence the haunting and truly spectral unreality of realistic books. Hence, when we read the English realists, the incredulous wonder with which we observe the hero's constancy under the submerging tide of dulness, and how he bears up with his jibbing sweetheart, and endures the chatter of idiot girls, and stands by his whole unfeatured wilderness of an existence, instead of seeking relief in drink or foreign travel. Hence in the French, in that meat-market of middle-aged sensuality, the disgusted surprise with which we see the hero drift sidelong, and practically quite untempted, into every description of misconduct and dishonour. In each, we miss the personal poetry, the enchanted atmosphere, that rainbow work of fancy that clothes what is naked and seems to ennoble what is base; in each, life falls dead like dough, instead of soaring away like a balloon into the colours of the sunset; each is true, each inconceivable; for no man lives in the external truth, among salts and acids, but in the warm, phantasmagoric chamber of his brain, with the painted windows and the storied walls.

Of this falsity we have had a recent example from a man who knows far better—Tolstoi's *Powers of Darkness*. Here is a piece full of force and truth, yet quite untrue. For before Mikita was led into so dire a situation he was tempted, and temptations are beautiful at least in part; and a work which dwells on the ugliness of crime and gives no hint of any loveliness in the temptation, sins against the modesty of life, and even when a Tolstoi writes it, sinks to melodrama. The peasants are not understood; they saw their life in fairer colours; even the deaf girl was clothed in poetry for Mikita, or he had never fallen. And so, once again, even an Old Bailey melodrama, without some brightness of poetry and lustre of existence, falls into the inconceivable and ranks with fairy tales.

IV

In nobler books we are moved with something like the emotions of life; and this emotion is very variously provoked. We are so moved when Levine labours in the field, when André sinks beyond emotion, when Richard Feverel and Lucy Desborough meet beside the river, when Antony, 'not cowardly, puts off his helmet', when Kent has infinite pity on the dying Lear, when, in Dostoieffsky's *Despised and Rejected*, the uncomplaining hero drains his cup of suffering and virtue. These are notes that please the great heart of man. Not only love, and the fields, and the bright face of danger, but sacrifice and death and unmerited suffering humbly supported, touch in us the vein of the poetic. We love to think of them, we long to try them, we are humbly hopeful that we may prove heroes also.

We have heard, perhaps, too much of lesser matters. Here is the door, here is the open air. *Itur in antiquam silvam.*

D

Travel

*

A NIGHT AMONG THE PINES

FROM Bleymard after dinner, although it was already late, I set out to scale a portion of the Lozère. An ill-marked stony drove-road guided me forward; and I met nearly half-a-dozen bullock-carts descending from the woods, each laden with a whole pine-tree for the winter's firing. At the top of the woods, which do not climb very high upon this cold ridge, I struck leftward by a path among the pines, until I hit on a dell of green turf, where a streamlet made a little spout over some stones to serve me for a water-tap. 'In a more sacred or sequestered bower . . . nor nymph nor faunus haunted.' The trees were not old, but they grew thickly round the glade: there was no outlook, except north-eastward upon distant hill-tops, or straight upward to the sky; and the encampment felt secure and private like a room. By the time I had made my arrangements and fed Modestine, the day was already beginning to decline. I buckled myself to the knees into my sack and made a hearty meal; and as soon as the sun went down, I pulled my cap over my eyes and fell asleep.

Night is a dead monotonous period under a roof; but in the open world it passes lightly, with its stars and dews and perfumes, and the hours are marked by changes in the face of Nature. What seems a kind of temporal death to people choked between walls and curtains, is only a light and living slumber to the man who sleeps afield. All night long he can hear Nature breathing deeply and freely; even as she takes her rest, she turns and smiles; and there is one stirring hour unknown to those who dwell in houses, when a wakeful influence goes abroad over the sleeping hemisphere, and all the outdoor world are on their feet. It is then that the cock first crows, not this time to announce the dawn, but like a cheerful watchman speeding the course of night. Cattle awake on the meadows; sheep break their fast on dewy hill-sides, and change to a new lair among the ferns; and houseless men, who have lain down with the fowls, open their dim eyes and behold the beauty of the night.

At what inaudible summons, at what gentle touch of Nature, are all these sleepers thus recalled in the same hour to life? Do the stars rain down an influence, or do we share some thrill of mother earth below our resting bodies? Even shepherds and old country-folk, who are the deepest read in these arcana, have not a guess as to the means or purpose of this nightly resurrection. Towards two in the morning they declare the thing takes place; and neither know nor inquire further. And at least it is a pleasant incident. We are disturbed in our slumber only, like the luxurious Montaigne, 'that we may the better and more sensibly relish it'. We have a moment to look upon the stars. And there is a special pleasure for some minds in the reflection that we share the impulse with all out-door creatures in our neighbourhood, that we have escaped out of the Bastille of civilization, and are become, for the time being, a mere kindly animal and a sheep of Nature's flock.

When that hour came to me among the pines, I wakened thirsty. My tin was standing by me half full of water. I emptied it at a draught; and feeling broad awake after this internal cold aspersion, sat upright to make a cigarette. The stars were clear, coloured, and jewel-like, but not frosty. A faint silvery vapour stood for the Milky Way. All around me the black fir-points stood upright and stock-still. By the whiteness of the pack-saddle, I could see Modestine walking round and round at the length of her tether; I could hear her steadily munching at the sward; but there was not another sound, save the indescribable quiet talk of the runnel over the stones. I lay lazily smoking and studying the colour of the sky, as we call the void of space, from where it showed a reddish grey behind the pines to where it showed a glossy blue-black between the stars. As if to be more like a pedlar, I wear a silver ring. This I could see faintly shining as I raised or lowered the cigarette; and at each whiff the inside of my hand was illuminated, and became for a second the highest light in the landscape.

A faint wind, more like a moving coolness than a stream of air, passed down the glade from time to time; so that even in my great chamber the air was being renewed all night long. I thought with horror of the inn at Chasseradès and the con-gregated nightcaps; with horror of the nocturnal prowesses of clerks and students, of hot theatres and pass-keys and close rooms. I have not often enjoyed a more serene possession of

myself, nor felt more independent of material aids. The outer
world, from which we cower into our houses, seemed after all
a gentle habitable place; and night after night a man's bed,
it seemed, was laid and waiting for him in the fields, where
God keeps an open house. I thought I had rediscovered one
of those truths which are revealed to savages and hid from
political economists: at the least, I had discovered a new
pleasure for myself. And yet even while I was exulting in my
solitude I became aware of a strange lack. I wished a companion to lie near me in the starlight, silent and not moving,
but ever within touch. For there is a fellowship more quiet
even than solitude, and which, rightly understood, is solitude
made perfect. And to live out of doors with the woman a man
loves is of all lives the most complete and free.

As I thus lay, between content and longing, a faint noise
stole towards me through the pines. I thought, at first, it was
the crowing of cocks or the barking of dogs at some very
distant farm; but steadily and gradually it took articulate
shape in my ears, until I became aware that a passenger was
going by upon the high-road in the valley, and singing loudly
as he went. There was more of good-will than grace in his
performance; but he trolled with ample lungs; and the sound
of his voice took hold upon the hillside and set the air shaking
in the leafy glens. I have heard people passing by night in
sleeping cities; some of them sang; one, I remember, played
loudly on the bagpipes. I have heard the rattle of a cart or
carriage spring up suddenly after hours of stillness, and pass,
for some minutes, within the range of my hearing as I lay
abed. There is a romance about all who are abroad in the
black hours, and with something of a thrill we try to guess
their business. But here the romance was double: first, this
glad passenger, lit internally with wine, who sent up his voice
in music through the night; and then I, on the other hand,
buckled into my sack, and smoking alone in the pine-woods
between four and five thousand feet towards the stars.

When I awoke again (Sunday, 29th September), many of
the stars had disappeared; only the stronger companions of
the night still burned visibly overhead; and away towards the
east I saw a faint haze of light upon the horizon, such as had
been the Milky Way when I was last awake. Day was at hand.
I lit my lantern, and by its glow-worm light put on my boots

and gaiters; then I broke up some bread for Modestine, filled my can at the water-tap, and lit my spirit-lamp to boil myself some chocolate. The blue darkness lay long in the glade where I had so sweetly slumbered; but soon there was a broad streak of orange melting into gold along the mountain-tops of Vivarais. A solemn glee possessed my mind at this gradual and lovely coming in of day. I heard the runnel with delight; I looked round me for something beautiful and unexpected; but the still black pine-trees, the hollow glade, the munching ass, remained unchanged in figure. Nothing had altered but the light, and that, indeed, shed over all a spirit of life and of breathing peace, and moved me to a strange exhilaration.

I drank my water-chocolate, which was hot if it was not rich, and strolled here and there, and up and down about the glade. While I was thus delaying, a gush of steady wind, as long as a heavy sigh, poured direct out of the quarter of the morning. It was cold, and set me sneezing. The trees near at hand tossed their black plumes in its passage; and I could see the thin distant spires of pine along the edge of the hill rock slightly to and fro against the golden east. Ten minutes after, the sunlight spread at a gallop along the hillside, scattering shadows and sparkles, and the day had come completely.

I hastened to prepare my pack, and tackle the steep ascent that lay before me; but I had something on my mind. It was only a fancy; yet a fancy will sometimes be importunate. I had been most hospitably received and punctually served in my green caravanserai. The room was airy, the water excellent, and the dawn had called me to a moment. I say nothing of the tapestries or the inimitable ceiling, nor yet of the view which I commanded from the windows; but I felt I was in some one's debt for all this liberal entertainment. And so it pleased me, in a half-laughing way, to leave pieces of money on the turf as I went along, until I had left enough for my night's lodging. I trust they did not fall to some rich and churlish drover.

THE ACT OF SQUATTING

THERE were four of us squatters—myself and my wife, the King and Queen of Silverado; Sam, the Crown Prince; and Chuchu, the Grand Duke. Chuchu, a setter crossed with spaniel, was the most unsuited for a rough life. He had been nurtured tenderly in the society of ladies; his heart was large and soft; he regarded the sofa-cushion as a bed-rock necessary of existence. Though about the size of a sheep, he loved to sit in ladies' laps; he never said a bad word in all his blameless days; and if he had seen a flute, I am sure he could have played upon it by nature. It may seem hard to say it of a dog, but Chuchu was a tame cat.

The king and queen, the grand duke, and a basket of cold provender for immediate use, set forth from Calistoga in a double buggy; the crown prince, on horseback, led the way like an outrider. Bags and boxes and a second-hand stove were to follow close upon our heels by Hanson's team.

It was a beautiful still day; the sky was one field of azure. Not a leaf moved, not a speck appeared in heaven. Only from the summit of the mountain one little snowy wisp of cloud after another kept detaching itself, like smoke from a volcano, and blowing southward in some high stream of air: Mount Saint Helena still at her interminable task, making the weather, like a Lapland witch.

By noon we had come in sight of the mill: a great brown building, half-way up the hill, big as a factory, two storeys high, and with tanks and ladders along the roof; which, as a pendicle of Silverado mine, we held to be an outlying province of our own. Thither, then, we went, crossing the valley by a grassy trail; and there lunched out of the basket, sitting in a kind of portico, and wondering, while we ate, at this great bulk of useless building. Through a chink we could look far down in the interior, and see sunbeams floating in the dust and striking on tier after tier of silent, rusty machinery. It cost six thousand dollars, twelve hundred English sovereigns; and now, here it stands deserted like the temple of a forgotten

religion, the busy millers toiling somewhere else. All the time
we were there, mill and mill town showed no sign of life; that
part of the mountain-side, which is very open and green, was
tenanted by no living creature but ourselves and the insects;
and nothing stirred but the cloud manufactory upon the mountain summit. It was odd to compare this with the former days,
when the engine was in full blast, the mill palpitating to its
strokes, and the carts came rattling down from Silverado,
charged with ore.

By two we had been landed at the mine, the buggy was gone
again, and we were left to our own reflections and the basket
of cold provender, until Hanson should arrive. Hot as it was
by the sun, there was something chill in such a home-coming,
in that world of wreck and rust, splinter and rolling gravel,
where for so many years no fire had smoked.

Silverado platform filled the whole width of the canyon.
Above, as I have said, this was a wild, red, stony gully in the
mountains; but below it was a wooded dingle. And through
this, I was told, there had gone a path between the mine and
the Toll House—our natural north-west passage to civilization.
I found and followed it, clearing my way as I went through
fallen branches and dead trees. It went straight down that
steep canyon, till it brought you out abruptly over the roofs of
the hotel. There was nowhere any break in the descent. It
almost seemed as if, were you to drop a stone down the old iron
chute at our platform, it would never rest until it hopped upon
the Toll House shingles. Signs were not wanting of the ancient
greatness of Silverado. The footpath was well marked, and
had been well trodden in the old days by thirsty miners. And
far down, buried in foliage, deep out of sight of Silverado, I
came on a last outpost of the mine—a mound of gravel, some
wreck of wooden aqueduct, and the mouth of a tunnel, like
a treasure grotto in a fairy story. A stream of water, fed by the
invisible leakage from our shaft, and dyed red with cinnabar
or iron, ran trippingly forth out of the bowels of the cave; and,
looking far under the arch, I could see something like an iron
lantern fastened on the rocky wall. It was a promising spot
for the imagination. No boy could have left it unexplored.

The stream thenceforward stole along the bottom of the
dingle, and made, for that dry land, a pleasant warbling in
the leaves. Once, I suppose, it ran splashing down the whole

length of the canyon, but now its head waters had been tapped
by the shaft at Silverado, and for a great part of its course it
wandered sunless among the joints of the mountain. No
wonder that it should better its pace when it sees, far before it,
daylight whitening in the arch, or that it should come trotting
forth into the sunlight with a song.

The two stages had gone by when I got down, and the Toll
House stood, dozing in sun and dust and silence, like a place
enchanted. My mission was after hay for bedding, and that I
was readily promised. But when I mentioned that we were
waiting for Rufe, the people shook their heads. Rufe was not a
regular man any way, it seemed; and if he got playing poker—
Well, poker was too many for Rufe. I had not yet heard them
bracketted together; but it seemed a natural conjunction, and
commended itself swiftly to my fears; and as soon as I returned
to Silverado and had told my story, we practically gave
Hanson up, and set ourselves to do what we could find do-able
in our desert-island state.

The lower room had been the assayer's office. The floor was
thick with _débris_—part human, from the former occupants;
part natural, sifted in by mountain winds. In a sea of red
dust there swam or floated sticks, boards, hay, straw, stones,
and paper; ancient newspapers, above all—for the newspaper,
especially when torn, soon becomes an antiquity—and bills of
the Silverado boarding-house, some dated Silverado, some
Calistoga Mine. Here is one, verbatim; and if any one can
calculate the scale of charges, he has my envious admiration.

Calistoga Mine, May 3rd, 1875.

JOHN STANLEY

To S. CHAPMAN, Cr.

To board from April 1st to April 30	$25	75
,, ,, ,, May 1st to 3rd	2	00
	27	75

Where is John Stanley mining now? Where is S. Chapman,
within whose hospitable walls we were to lodge? The date was
but five years old, but in that time the world had changed for
Silverado; like Palmyra in the desert, it had outlived its people
and its purpose; we camped, like Layard, amid ruins, and

these names spoke to us of prehistoric time. A bootjack, a pair of boots, a dog-hutch, and these bills of Mr Chapman's were the only speaking relics that we disinterred from all that vast Silverado rubbish-heap; but what would I not have given to unearth a letter, a pocket-book, a diary, only a ledger, or a roll of names, to take me back, in a more personal manner, to the past? It pleases me, besides, to fancy that Stanley or Chapman, or one of their companions, may light upon this chronicle, and be struck by the name, and read some news of their anterior home, coming, as it were, out of a subsequent epoch of history in that quarter of the world.

As we were tumbling the mingled rubbish on the floor, kicking it with our feet, and groping for these written evidences of the past, Sam, with a somewhat whitened face, produced a paper bag. 'What's this?' said he. It contained a granulated powder, something the colour of Gregory's Mixture, but rosier; and as there were several of the bags, and each more or less broken, the powder was spread widely on the floor. Had any of us ever seen giant powder? No, nobody had; and instantly there grew up in my mind a shadowy belief, verging with every moment nearer to certitude, that I had somewhere heard somebody describe it as just such a powder as the one around us. I have learnt since that it is a substance not unlike tallow, and is made up in rolls for all the world like tallow candles.

Fanny, to add to our happiness, told us a story of a gentleman who had camped one night, like ourselves, by a deserted mine. He was a handy, thrifty fellow, and looked right and left for plunder, but all he could lay his hands on was a can of oil. After dark he had to see to the horses with a lantern; and not to miss an opportunity, filled up his lamp from the oil can. Thus equipped, he set forth into the forest. A little while after, his friends heard a loud explosion; the mountain echoes bellowed, and then all was still. On examination, the can proved to contain oil, with the trifling addition of nitro-glycerine; but no research disclosed a trace of either man or lantern.

It was a pretty sight, after this anecdote, to see us sweeping out the giant powder. It seemed never to be far enough away. And, after all, it was only some rock pounded for assay.

So much for the lower room. We scraped some of the rougher dirt off the floor, and left it. That was our sitting-room and kitchen, though there was nothing to sit upon but the table, and no provision for a fire except a hole in the roof of the room above, which had once contained the chimney of a stove.

To that upper room we now proceeded. There were the eighteen bunks in a double tier, nine on either hand, where from eighteen to thirty-six miners had once snored together all night long, John Stanley, perhaps, snoring loudest. There was the roof, with a hole in it through which the sun now shot an arrow. There was the floor, in much the same state as the one below, though, perhaps, there was more hay, and certainly there was the added ingredient of broken glass, the man who stole the window-frames having apparently made a miscarriage with this one. Without a broom, without hay or bedding, we could but look about us with a beginning of despair. The one bright arrow of day, in that gaunt and shattered barrack, made the rest look dirtier and darker, and the sight drove us at last into the open.

Here, also, the handiwork of man lay ruined: but the plants were all alive and thriving; the view below was fresh with the colours of nature; and we had exchanged a dim, human garret for a corner, even although it were untidy, of the blue hall of heaven. Not a bird, not a beast, not a reptile. There was no noise in that part of the world, save when we passed beside the staging, and heard the water musically falling in the shaft.

We wandered to and fro. We searched among that drift of lumber—wood and iron, nails and rails, and sleepers and the wheels of trucks. We gazed up the cleft into the bosom of the mountain. We sat by the margin of the dump and saw, far below us, the green treetops standing still in the clear air. Beautiful perfumes, breaths of bay, resin, and nutmeg, came to us more often and grew sweeter and sharper as the afternoon declined. But still there was no word of Hanson.

I set to with pick and shovel, and deepened the pool behind the shaft, till we were sure of sufficient water for the morning; and by the time I had finished, the sun had begun to go down behind the mountain shoulder, the platform was plunged in quiet shadow, and a chill descended from the sky. Night began early in our cleft. Before us, over the margin of the dump, we could see the sun still striking aslant into the wooded nick below, and on the battlemented, pine-bescattered ridges on the farther side.

There was no stove, of course, and no hearth in our lodging, so we betook ourselves to the blacksmith's forge across the platform. If the platform be taken as a stage, and the out-curving margin of the dump to represent the line of the foot-lights, then our house would be the first wing on the actor's left, and this blacksmith's forge, although no match for it in size, the foremost on the right. It was a low, brown cottage, planted close against the hill, and overhung by the foliage and peeling boughs of a madrona thicket. Within it was full of dead leaves and mountain dust, and rubbish from the mine. But we soon had a good fire brightly blazing, and sat close about it on impromptu seats. Chuchu, the slave of sofa-cushions, whimpered for a softer bed; but the rest of us were greatly revived and comforted by that good creature—fire, which gives us warmth and light and companionable sounds, and colours up the emptiest building with better than frescoes. For a while it was even pleasant in the forge, with the blaze in the midst, and a look over our shoulders on the woods and mountains where the day was dying like a dolphin.

It was between seven and eight before Hanson arrived, with a waggonful of our effects and two of his wife's relatives to lend him a hand. The elder showed surprising strength. He would pick up a huge packing-case, full of books of all things, swing it on his shoulder, and away up the two crazy ladders and the breakneck spout of rolling mineral, familiarly termed a path, that led from the cart-track to our house. Even for a man unburthened, the ascent was toilsome and precarious; but Irvine scaled it with a light foot, carrying box after box, as the hero whisks the stage child up the practicable footway beside the waterfall of the fifth act. With so strong a helper, the business was speedily transacted. Soon the assayer's office was thronged with our belongings, piled higgledy-piggledy, and upside down, about the floor. There were our boxes, indeed, but my wife had left her keys in Calistoga. There was the stove, but, alas! our carriers had forgot the chimney, and lost one of the plates along the road. The Silverado problem was scarce solved.

Rufe himself was grave and good-natured over his share of blame; he even, if I remember right, expressed regret. But his crew, to my astonishment and anger, grinned from ear to ear, and laughed aloud at our distress. They thought it 'real funny' about the stove-pipe they had forgotten; 'real funny'

that they should have lost a plate. As for hay, the whole party
refused to bring us any till they should have supped. See how
late they were! Never had there been such a job as coming up
that grade! Nor often, I suspect, such a game of poker as that
before they started. But about nine, as a particular favour, we
should have some hay.

So they took their departure, leaving me still staring, and
we resigned ourselves to wait for their return. The fire in the
forge had been suffered to go out, and we were one and all too
weary to kindle another. We dined, or, not to take the word in
vain, we ate after a fashion, in the nightmare disorder of the
assayer's office, perched among boxes. A single candle lighted
us. It could scarce be called a house-warming; for there was,
of course, no fire, and with the two open doors and the open
window gaping on the night, like breaches in a fortress, it
began to grow rapidly chill. Talk ceased; nobody moved but
the unhappy Chuchu, still in quest of sofa-cushions, who
tumbled complainingly among the trunks. It required a certain
happiness of disposition to look forward hopefully, from so
dismal a beginning, across the brief hours of night, to the warm
shining of to-morrow's sun.

But the hay arrived at last, and we turned, with our last
spark of courage, to the bedroom. We had improved the
entrance, but it was still a kind of rope-walking; and it would
have been droll to see us mounting, one after another, by
candle-light, under the open stars.

The western door—that which looked up the canyon, and
through which we entered by our bridge of flying plank—was
still entire, a handsome, panelled door, the most finished piece
of carpentry in Silverado. And the two lowest bunks next to
this we roughly filled with hay for that night's use. Through
the opposite, or eastern-looking gable, with its open door and
window, a faint, diffused starshine came into the room like
mist; and when we were once in bed, we lay, awaiting sleep,
in a haunted incomplete obscurity. At first the silence of the
night was utter. Then a high wind began in the distance
among the treetops, and for hours continued to grow higher.
It seemed to me much such a wind as we had found on our
visit; yet here in our open chamber we were fanned only by
gentle and refreshing draughts, so deep was the canyon, so
close our house was planted under the overhanging rock.

THE KING OF APEMAMA

THERE is one great personage in the Gilberts: Tembinok' of Apemama: solely conspicuous, the hero of song, the butt of gossip. Through the rest of the group the kings are slain or fallen in tutelage: Tembinok' alone remains, the last tyrant, the last erect vestige of a dead society. The white man is everywhere else, building his houses, drinking his gin, getting in and out of trouble with the weak native governments. There is only one white on Apemama, and he on sufferance, living far from court, and hearkening and watching his conduct like a mouse in a cat's ear. Through all the other islands a stream of native visitors comes and goes, travelling by families, spending years on the grand tour. Apemama alone is left upon one side, the tourist dreading to risk himself within the clutch of Tembinok'. And fear of the same Gorgon follows and troubles them at home. Maiana once paid him tribute; he once fell upon and seized Nonuti: first steps to the empire of the archipelago. A British warship coming on the scene, the conqueror was driven to disgorge, his career checked in the outset, his dear-bought armoury sunk in his own lagoon. But the impression had been made; periodical fear of him still shakes the islands: rumour depicts him mustering his canoes for a fresh onfall; rumour can name his destination; and Tembinok' figures in the patriotic war-songs of the Gilberts like Napoleon in those of our grandfathers.

We were at sea, bound from Mariki to Nonuti and Tapituea, when the wind came suddenly fair for Apemama. The course was at once changed; all hands were turned-to to clean ship, the decks holystoned, the cabin washed, the trade-room overhauled. In all our cruising we never saw the *Equator* so smart as she was made for Tembinok'. Nor was Captain Reid alone in these coquetries; for, another schooner chancing to arrive during my stay in Apemama, I found that she also was dandified for the occasion. And the two cases stand alone in my experience of South Sea traders.

We had on board a family of native tourists, from the

grandsire to the babe in arms, trying (against an extraordinary series of ill-luck) to regain their native island of Peru.[1]
Five times already they had paid their fare and taken ship;
five times they had been disappointed, dropped penniless
upon strange islands, or carried back to Butaritari, whence they
sailed. This last attempt had been no better starred; their
provisions were exhausted. Peru was beyond hope, and they
had cheerfully made up their minds to a fresh stage of exile
in Tapituea or Nonuti. With this slant of wind their random
destination became once more changed; and like the Calendar's pilot, when the 'black mountains' hove in view, they
changed colour and beat upon their breasts. Their camp,
which was on deck in the ship's waist, resounded with
complaint. They would be set to work, they must become
slaves, escape was hopeless, they must live and toil and die in
Apemama, in the tyrant's den. With this sort of talk they so
greatly terrified their children, that one (a big hulking boy)
must at last be torn screaming from the schooner's side. And
their fears were wholly groundless. I have little doubt they
were not suffered to be idle; but I can vouch for it that they
were kindly and generously used. For, the matter of a year
later, I was once more shipmate with these inconsistent wanderers on board the *Janet Nicoll*. Their fare was paid by
Tembinok'; they who had gone ashore from the *Equator*
destitute, reappeared upon the *Janet* with new clothes, laden
with mats and presents, and bringing with them a magazine
of food, on which they lived like fighting cocks throughout
the voyage; I saw them at length repatriated, and I must say
they showed more concern on quitting Apemama than
delight at reaching home.

We entered by the north passage (Sunday, September 1st),
dodging among shoals. It was a day of fierce equatorial sunshine; but the breeze was strong and chill; and the mate, who
conned the schooner from the cross-trees, returned shivering
to the deck. The lagoon was thick with many-tinted wavelets;
a continuous roaring of the outer sea overhung the anchorage;
and the long, hollow crescent of palm ruffled and sparkled in
the wind. Opposite our berth the beach was seen to be surmounted for some distance by a terrace of white coral, seven
or eight feet high and crowned in turn by the scattered and

[1] In the Gilbert Group.

incongruous buildings of the palace. The village adjoins on the south, a cluster of high-roofed maniap's. And village and palace seemed deserted.

We were scarce yet moored, however, before distant and busy figures appeared upon the beach, a boat was launched, and a crew pulled out to us bringing the king's ladder. Tembinok' had once an accident; has feared ever since to intrust his person to the rotten chandlery of South Sea traders; and devised in consequence a frame of wood, which is brought on board a ship as soon as she appears, and remains lashed to her side until she leave. The boat's crew, having applied this engine, returned at once to shore. They might not come on board; neither might we land, or not without danger of offence; the king giving pratique in person. An interval followed, during which dinner was delayed for the great man; the prelude of the ladder, giving us some notion of his weighty body and sensible, ingenious character, had highly whetted our curiosity; and it was with something like excitement that we saw the beach and terrace suddenly blacken with attendant vassals, the king and party embark, the boat (a man-of-war gig) come flying towards us dead before the wind, and the royal coxswain lay us cleverly aboard, mount the ladder with a jealous diffidence, and descend heavily on deck.

Not long ago he was overgrown with fat, obscured to view, and a burthen to himself. Captains visiting the island advised him to walk; and though it broke the habits of a life and the traditions of his rank, he practised the remedy with benefit. His corpulence is now portable; you would call him lusty rather than fat; but his gait is still dull, stumbling, and elephantine. He neither stops nor hastens, but goes about his business with an implacable deliberation. We could never see him and not be struck with his extraordinary natural means for the theatre: a beaked profile like Dante's in the mask, a mane of long black hair, the eye brilliant, imperious, and inquiring: for certain parts, and to one who could have used it, the face was a fortune. His voice matched it well, being shrill, powerful, and uncanny, with a note like a sea-bird's. Where there are no fashions, none to set them, few to follow them it they were set, and none to criticize, he dresses—as Sir Charles Grandison lived—'to his own heart.' Now he wears a woman's frock, now a naval uniform; now (and more usually) figures in a masquerade costume of his own design: trousers and a singular jacket with shirt tails, the cut and fit wonderful for island workmanship, the material always handsome, sometimes green velvet, sometimes cardinal red silk. This masquerade becomes him admirably. In the woman's frock he looks ominous and weird beyond belief. I see him now come pacing towards me in the cruel sun, solitary, a figure out of Hoffmann.

A visit on board ship, such as that at which we now assisted, makes a chief part and by far the chief diversion of the life of Tembinok'. He is not only the sole ruler, he is the sole merchant of his triple kingdom, Apemama, Aranuka, and Kuria, well-planted islands. The taro goes to the chiefs, who divide as they please among their immediate adherents; but certain fish, turtles—which abound in Kuria—and the whole produce of the cocoa-palm, belong exclusively to Tembinok'. 'A' cobra[1] berong me,' observed his majesty with a wave of his hand; and he counts and sells it by the houseful. 'You got copra, king?' I have heard a trader ask. 'I got two, three outches,'[2] his majesty replied: 'I think three.' Hence the commercial importance of Apemama, the trade of three islands being centred there in a single hand; hence it is that so many whites have tried in vain to gain or to preserve a footing; hence ships are adorned, cooks have special orders, and captains array themselves in smiles, to greet the king. If he be pleased with his welcome and the fare he may pass days on board, and every day, and sometimes every hour, will be of profit to the ship. He oscillates between the cabin, where he is entertained with strange meats, and the trade-room, where he enjoys the pleasures of shopping on a scale to match his person. A few obsequious attendants squat by the house door, awaiting his least signal. In the boat, which has been suffered to drop astern, one or two of his wives lie covered from the sun under mats, tossed by the short sea of the lagoon, and enduring agonies of heat and tedium. This severity is now and then relaxed and the wives allowed on board. Three or four were thus favoured on the day of our arrival: substantial ladies airily attired in *ridis*. Each had a share of copra,

[1] Copra: the dried kernel of the cocoa-nut, the chief article of commerce throughout the Pacific Islands.
[2] Houses.

her *peculium*, to dispose of for herself. The display in the trade-room—hats, ribbons, dresses, scents, tins of salmon—the pride of the eye and the lust of the flesh—tempted them in vain. They had but the one idea—tobacco, the island currency, tantamount to minted gold; returned to shore with it, burthened but rejoicing; and late into the night, on the royal terrace, were to be seen counting the sticks by lamplight in the open air.

The king is no such economist. He is greedy of things new and foreign. House after house, chest after chest, in the palace precinct, is already crammed with clocks, musical boxes, blue spectacles, umbrellas, knitted waist-coats, bolts of stuff, tools, rifles, fowling-pieces, medicines, European foods, sewing-machines, and, what is more extraordinary, stoves: all that ever caught his eye, tickled his appetite, pleased him for its use, or puzzled him with its apparent inutility. And still his lust is unabated. He is possessed by the seven devils of the collector. He hears a thing spoken of, and a shadow comes on his face. 'I think I no got him,' he will say; and the treasures he has seem worthless in comparison. If a ship be bound for Apemama, the merchant racks his brain to hit upon some novelty. This he leaves carelessly in the main cabin or partly conceals in his own berth, so that the king shall spy it for himself. 'How much you want?' inquires Tembinok', passing and pointing. 'No, king; that too dear,' returns the trader. 'I think I like him,' says the king. This was a bowl of gold-fish. On another occasion it was scented soap. 'No, king; that cost too much,' said the trader; 'too good for a Kanaka.' 'How much you got? I take him all,' replied his majesty, and became the lord of seventeen boxes at two dollars a cake. Or again, the merchant feigns the article is not for sale, is private property, an heirloom or a gift; and the trick infallibly succeeds. Thwart the king and you hold him. His autocratic nature rears at the affront of opposition. He accepts it for a challenge; sets his teeth like a hunter going at a fence; and with no mark of emotion, scarce even of interest, stolidly piles up the price. Thus, for our sins, he took a fancy to my wife's dressing-bag, a thing entirely useless to the man, and sadly battered by years of service. Early one forenoon he came to our house, sat down, and abruptly offered to purchase it. I told him I sold nothing, and the bag at any rate was a present from a friend; but he was acquainted with these pretexts from of old, and knew what they were worth and how to meet them. Adopting what I believe is called 'the object method', he drew out a bag of English gold, sovereigns and half-sovereigns, and began to lay them one by one in silence on the table; at each fresh piece reading our faces with a look. In vain I continued to protest I was no trader; he deigned not to reply. There must have been twenty pounds on the table, he was still going on, and irritation had begun to mingle with our embarrassment, when a happy idea came to our delivery. Since his majesty thought so much of the bag, we said, we must beg him to accept it as a present. It was the most surprising turn in Tembinok's experience. He perceived too late that his persistence was unmannerly; hung his head a while in silence: then, lifting up a sheepish countenance, 'I 'shamed,' said the tyrant. It was the first and the last time we heard him own to a flaw in his behaviour. Half an hour after he sent us a camphor-wood chest, worth only a few dollars—but then heaven knows what Tembinok' had paid for it.

Cunning by nature, and versed for forty years in the government of men, it must not be supposed that he is cheated blindly, or has resigned himself without resistance to be the milch-cow of the passing trader. His efforts have been even heroic. Like Nakaeia of Makin, he has owned schooners. More fortunate than Nakaeia, he has found captains. Ships of his have sailed as far as to the colonies. He has trafficked direct, in his own bottoms, with New Zealand. And even so, even there, the world-enveloping dishonesty of the white man prevented him; his profit melted, his ship returned in debt, the money for the insurance was embezzled, and when the *Coronet* came to be lost, he was astonished to find he had lost all. At this he dropped his weapons; owned he might as hopefully wrestle with the winds of heaven; and like an experienced sheep, submitted his fleece thenceforward to the shearers. He is the last man in the world to waste anger on the incurable; accepts it with cynical composure; asks no more in those he deals with than a certain decency of moderation: drives as good a bargain as he can; and when he considers he is more than usually swindled, writes it in his memory against the merchant's name. He once ran over to me a list of captains and supercargoes with whom he had done business, classing them under three heads: 'He cheat a litty'—'He cheat plenty'—and 'I think he cheat too much.' For the first two classes he expressed perfect toleration; sometimes, but not always, for the third. I was present when a certain merchant was turned about his business, and was the means (having a considerable influence ever since the bag) of patching up the dispute. Even on the day of our arrival there was like to have been a hitch with Captain Reid: the ground of which is perhaps worth recital. Among goods exported specially for Tembinok' there is a beverage known (and labelled) as Hennessy's brandy. It is neither Hennessy, nor even brandy; is about the colour of sherry, but is not sherry; tastes of kirsch, and yet neither is it kirsch. The king, at least, has grown used to this amazing brand, and rather prides himself upon the taste; and any substitution is a double offence, being at once to cheat him and to cast a doubt upon his palate. A similar weakness is to be observed in all connoisseurs. Now, the last case sold by the *Equator* was found to contain a different and I would fondly fancy a superior distillation; and the conversation opened very black for Captain Reid. But Tembinok' is a moderate man. He was reminded and admitted that all men were liable to error, even himself; accepted the principle that a fault handsomely acknowledged should be condoned; and wound the matter up with this proposal: 'Tuppoti[1] I mi'take you 'peakee me. Tuppoti you mi'take, I 'peakee you. Mo' betta.'

After dinner and supper in the cabin, a glass or two of 'Hennetti'—the genuine article this time, with the kirsch bouquet—and five hours' lounging on the trade-room counter, royalty embarked for home. Three tacks grounded the boat before the palace; the wives were carried ashore on the backs of vassals; Tembinok' stepped on a railed platform like a steamer's gangway, and was borne shoulder-high through the shallows, up the beach, and by an inclined plane, paved with pebbles, to the glaring terrace where he dwells.

* Suppose.

Poems

*

Poems

TO H. F. BROWN

BRAVE lads in olden musical centuries
Sang, night by night, adorable choruses,
   Sat late by alehouse doors in April
   Chaunting in song as the moon was rising:

Moon-seen and merry, under the trellises,
Flush-faced they played with old polysyllables;
   Spring scents inspired, old wine diluted,
   Love and Apollo were there to chorus.

Now these, the songs, remain to eternity,
Those, only those, the bountiful choristers
   Gone—those are gone, those unremembered
   Sleep and are silent in earth for ever.

So man himself appears and evanishes,
So smiles and goes; as wanderers halting at
   Some green-embowered house, play their music,
   Play and are gone on the windy highway;

Yet dwells the strain enshrined in the memory
Long after they departed eternally,
   Forth-fairing tow'rd far mountain summits,
   Cities of men on the sounding Ocean.

Youth sang the song in years immemorial;
Brave chanticleer, he sang and was beautiful;
   Bird-haunted, green tree-tops in spring-time
   Heard and were pleased by the voice of singing;

Youth goes, and leaves behind him a prodigy—
Songs sent from thee afar from Venetian
   Sea-grey lagunes, sea-paven highways,
   Dear to me here in my Alpine exile.

THE HOUSE BEAUTIFUL

A NAKED house, a naked moor,
A shivering pool before the door,
A garden bare of flowers and fruit
And poplars at the garden foot:
Such is the place that I live in,
Bleak without and bare within.

Yet shall your ragged moor receive
The incomparable pomp of eve,
And the cold glories of the dawn
Behind your shivering trees be drawn;
And when the wind from place to place
Doth the unmoored cloud-galleons chase,
Your garden gloom and gleam again,
With leaping sun, with glancing rain.
Here shall the wizard moon ascend
The heavens, in the crimson end
Of day's declining spendour; here
The army of the stars appear.
The neighbour hollows dry or wet,
Spring shall with tender flowers beset;
And oft the morning muser see
Larks rising from the broomy lea,
And every fairy wheel and thread
Of cobweb dew-bediamonded.
When daisies go, shall winter time
Silver the simple grass with rime;
Autumnal frosts enchant the pool
And make the cart-ruts beautiful;
And when snow-bright the moor expands,
How shall your children clap their hands!
To make this earth our hermitage,
A cheerful and a changeful page,
God's bright and intricate device
Of days and seasons doth suffice.

TO WILL. H. LOW

YOUTH now flees on feathered foot,
Faint and fainter sounds the flute,
Rarer songs of gods; and still
Somewhere on the sunny hill,
Or along the winding stream,
Through the willows, flits a dream;
Flits but shows a smiling face,
Flees but with so quaint a grace,
None can choose to stay at home,
All must follow, all must roam.

This is unborn beauty: she
Now in air floats high and free,
Takes the sun and breaks the blue;—
Late with stooping pinion flew
Raking hedgerow trees, and wet
Her wing in silver streams, and set
Shining foot on temple roof:
Now again she flies aloof,
Coasting mountain clouds and kiss't
By the evening's amethyst.

In wet wood and miry lane,
Still we pant and pound in vain;
Still with leaden foot we chase
Waning pinion, fainting face;
Still with gray hair we stumble on,
Till, behold, the vision gone!
Where hath fleeting beauty led?
To the doorway of the dead.
Life is over, life was gay:
We have come the primrose way.

ET TU IN ARCADIA VIXISTI

TO R. A. M. STEVENSON

In ancient tales, O friend, thy spirit dwelt;
There, from of old, thy childhood passed; and there
High expectation, high delights and deeds,
Thy fluttering heart with hope and terror moved.
And thou hast heard of yore the Blatant Beast,
And Roland's horn, and that war-scattering shout
Of all-unarmed Achilles, ægis-crowned.
And perilous lands thou sawest, sounding shores
And seas and forests drear, island and dale
And mountain dark. For thou with Tristam rod'st
Or Bedevere, in farthest Lyonesse.

Thou hadst a booth in Samarcand, whereat
Side-looking Magians trafficked; thence, by night,
An Afreet snatched thee, and with wings upbore
Beyond the Aral mount; or, hoping gain,
Thou, with a jar of money, didst embark,
For Balsorah, by sea. But chiefly thou
In that clear air took'st life; in Arcady
The haunted, land of song; and by the wells
Where most the gods frequent. There Chiron old,
In the Pelethronian antre, taught thee lore:
The plants, he taught, and by the shining stars
In forests dim to steer. There hast thou seen
Immortal Pan dance secret in a glade,
And, dancing, roll his eyes; these, where they fell,
Shed glee, and through the congregated oaks
A flying horror winged; while all the earth
To the god's pregnant footing thrilled within.
Or whiles, beside the sobbing stream, he breathed,
In his clutched pipe unformed and wizard strains
Divine yet brutal; which the forest heard,
And thou, with awe; and far upon the plain
The unthinking ploughman started and gave ear.

Now things there are that, upon him who sees,
A strong vocation lay; and strains there are
That whoso hears shall hear for evermore.

For evermore thou hear'st immortal Pan
And those melodious godheads, ever young
And ever quiring, on the mountains old.

What was this earth, child of the gods, to thee?
Forth from thy dreamland thou, a dreamer, cam'st
And in thine ears the olden music rang,
And in thy mind the doings of the dead,
And those heroic ages long forgot.
To a so fallen earth, alas! too late,
Alas! in evil days, thy steps return,
To list at noon for nightingales, to grow
A dweller on the beach till Argo come
That came long since, a lingerer by the pool
Where that desirèd angel bathes no more.

As when the Indian to Dakota comes,
Or farthest Idaho, and where he dwelt,
He with his clan, a humming city finds;
Thereon awhile, amazed, he stares, and then
To right and leftward, like a questing dog,
Seeks first the ancestral altars, then the hearth
Long cold with rains, and where old terror lodged,
And where the dead. So thee undying Hope,
With all her pack, hunts screaming through the years:
Here, there, thou fleëst; but nor here nor there
The pleasant gods abide, the glory dwells.

That, that was not Apollo, not the god.
This was not Venus, though she Venus seemed
A moment. And though fair yon river move,
She, all the way, from disenchanted fount
To seas unhallowed runs; the gods forsook
Long since her trembling rushes; from her plains
Disconsolate, long since adventure fled;

And now although the inviting river flows,
And every poplared cape, and every bend
Or willowy islet, win upon thy soul
And to thy hopeful shallop whisper speed;
Yet hope not thou at all; hope is no more;
And O, long since the golden groves are dead
The faery cities vanished from the land!

THE CELESTIAL SURGEON

If I have faltered more or less
In my great task of happiness;
If I have moved among my race
And shown no glorious morning face;
If beams from happy human eyes
Have moved me not; if morning skies,
Books, and my food, and summer rain
Knocked on my sullen heart in vain;—
Lord, thy most pointed pleasure take
And stab my spirit broad awake;
Or, Lord, if too obdurate I,
Choose thou, before that spirit die,
A piercing pain, a killing sin,
And to my dead heart run them in!

IN MEMORIAM F. A. SITWELL

Yet, O stricken heart, remember, O remember
   How of human days he lived the better part.
April came to bloom and never dim December
   Breathed its killing chills upon the head or heart.

Doomed to know not Winter, only Spring, a being
   Trod the flowery April blithely for a while,
Took his fill of music, joy of thought and seeing,
   Came and stayed and went, nor ever ceased to smile.

Came and stayed and went, and now when all is finished,
   You alone have crossed the melancholy stream,
Yours the pang, but his, O his, the undiminished
   Undecaying gladness, undeparted dream.

All that life contains of torture, toil, and treason,
   Shame, dishonour, death, to him were but a name.
Here, a boy, he dwelt through all the singing season
   And ere the day of sorrow departed as he came.

THE SPAEWIFE

O, I wad like to ken—to the beggar-wife says I—
Why chops are guid to brander and nane sae guid to fry.
An' siller, that's sae braw to keep, is brawer still to gi'e.
—*It's gey an' easy spierin'*, says the beggar-wife to me.

O, I wad like to ken—to the beggar-wife says I—
Hoo a' things come to be whaur we find them when we try,
The lasses in their claes an' the fishes in the sea.
—*It's gey an' easy spierin'*, says the beggar-wife to me.

O, I wad like to ken—to the beggar-wife says I—
Why lads are a' to sell an' lasses a' to buy;
An' naebody for dacency but barely twa or three
—*It's gey an' easy spierin'*, says the beggar-wife to me.

O, I wad like to ken—to the beggar-wife says I—
Gin death's as shüre to men as killin' is to kye,
Why God has filled the yearth sae fu' o' tasty things to pree.
—*It's gey an' easy spierin'*, says the beggar-wife to me.

O, I wad like to ken—to the beggar-wife says I—
The reason o' the cause an' the wherefore o' the why,
Wi' mony anither riddle brings the tear into my e'e.
—*It's gey an' easy spierin'*, says the beggar-wife to me.

* *Spaewife*, fortune-teller; *siller*, silver; *gey an' easy spierin'*, very easy to ask;
kye, cattle; *pree*, taste.

I WILL MAKE YOU BROOCHES

I WILL make you brooches and toys for your delight
Of bird-song at morning and star-shine at night.
I will make a palace fit for you and me
Of green days in forests and blue days at sea.

I will make my kitchen, and you shall keep your room,
Where white flows the river and bright blows the broom,
And you shall wash your linen and keep your body white
In rainfall at morning and dewfall at night.

And this shall be for music when no one else is near,
The fine song for singing, the rare song to hear!
That only I remember, that only you admire,
Of the broad road that stretches and the roadside fire.

IN THE HIGHLANDS

In the highlands, in the country places,
Where the old plain men have rosy faces,
And the young fair maidens
Quiet eyes;
Where essential silence cheers and blesses,
And for ever in the hill-recesses
Her more lovely music
Broods and dies.

O to mount again where erst I haunted;
Where the old red hills are bird-enchanted,
And the low green meadows
Bright with sward;
And when even dies, the million-tinted,
And the night has come, and planets glinted,
Lo, the valley hollow
Lamp-bestarred!

O to dream, O to awake and wander
There, and with delight to take and render,
Through the trance of silence,
Quiet breath;
Lo! for there, among the flowers and grasses,
Only the mightier movement sounds and passes;
Only winds and rivers,
Life and death.

I HAVE TROD . . .

I have trod the upward and the downward slope;
I have endured and done in days before;
I have longed for all, and bid farewell to hope;
And I have lived and loved, and closed the door.

TO MY OLD FAMILIARS

Do you remember—can we e'er forget?—
How, in the coiled perplexities of youth,
In our wild climate, in our scowling town,
We gloomed and shivered, sorrowed, sobbed and feared?
The belching winter wind, the missile rain,
The rare and welcome silence of the snows,
The laggard morn, the haggard day, the night,
The grimy spell of the nocturnal town,
Do you remember?—Ah, could one forget!
As when the fevered sick that all night long
Listed the wind intone, and hear at last
The ever-welcome voice of chanticleer
Sing in the bitter hour before the dawn,—
With sudden ardour, these desire the day:
So sang in the gloom of youth the bird of hope;
So we, exulting, hearkened and desired.
For lo! as in the palace porch of life
We huddled with chimeras, from within—
How sweet to hear!—the music swelled and fell,
And through the breach of the revolving doors
What dreams of splendour blinded us and fled!

I have since then contended and rejoiced;
Amid the glories of the house of life
Profoundly entered, and the shrine beheld:
Yet when the lamp from my expiring eyes
Shall dwindle and recede, the voice of love
Fall insignificant on my closing ears,
What sound shall come but the old cry of the wind
In our inclement city? what return
But the image of the emptiness of youth,
Filled with the sound of footsteps and that voice
Of discontent and rapture and despair?
So, as in darkness, from the magic lamp,
The momentary pictures gleam and fade
And perish, and the night resurges—these
Shall I remember, and then all forget.

E

TO SIDNEY COLVIN

I HEARD the pulse of the besieging sea
Throb far away all night. I heard the wind
Fly crying and convulse tumultuous palms.
I rose and strolled. The isle was all bright sand,
And flailing fans and shadows of the palm;
The heaven all moon and wind and the blind vault;
The keenest planet slain, for Venus slept.

The king, my neighbour, with his host of wives,
Slept in the precinct of the palisade;
Where single, in the wind, under the moon,
Among the slumbering cabins, blazed a fire,
Sole street-lamp and the only sentinel.

To other lands and nights my fancy turned—
To London first, and chiefly to your house,
The many-pillared and the well-beloved.
There yearning fancy lighted; there again
In the upper room I lay, and heard far off
The unsleeping city murmur like a shell;
The muffled tramp of the Museum guard
Once more went by me; I beheld again
Lamps vainly brighten the dispeopled street;
Again I longed for the returning morn,
The awaking traffic, the bestirring birds,
The consentaneous trill of tiny song
That weaves round monumental cornices
A passing charm of beauty. Most of all,
For your light foot I wearied, and your knock
That was the glad réveillé of my day.

Lo, now, when to your task in the great house
At morning through the portico you pass,
One moment glance, where by the pillared wall
Far-voyaging island gods, begrimed with smoke,
Sit now unworshipped, the rude monument
Of faiths forgot and races undivined:
Sit now disconsolate, remembering well
The priest, the victim, and the songful crowd,
The blaze of the blue noon, and that huge voice,

Incessant, of the breakers on the shore.
As far as these from their ancestral shrine,
So far, so foreign, your divided friends
Wander, estranged in body, not in mind.

OVER THE SEA TO SKYE

SING me a song of a lad that is gone,
  Say, could that lad be I?
Merry of soul he sailed on a day
  Over the sea to Skye.

Mull was astern, Rum on the port,
  Eigg on the starboard bow:
Glory of youth glowed in his soul:
  Where is that glory now?

Sing me a song of a lad that is gone,
  Say, could that lad be I?
Merry of soul he sailed on a day
  Over the sea to Skye.

Give me again all that was there,
  Give me the sun that shone!
Give me the eyes, give me the soul,
  Give me the lad that's gone!

Sing me a song of a lad that is gone,
  Say, could that lad be I?
Merry of soul he sailed on a day
  Over the sea to Skye.

Billow and breeze, islands and seas,
  Mountains of rain and sun,
All that was good, all that was fair,
  All that was me is gone.

TO S. R. CROCKETT

Blows the wind to-day, and the sun and the rain are flying,
  Blows the wind on the moors to-day and now,
Where about the graves of the martyrs the whaups are crying,
  My heart remembers how!

Grey recumbent tombs of the dead in desert places,
  Standing stones on the vacant wine-red moor,
Hills of sheep, and the howes of the silent vanished races,
  And winds, austere and pure:

Be it granted me to behold you again in dying,
  Hills of home! and to hear again the call;
Hear about the graves of the martyrs the peewees crying,
  And hear no more at all.

Letters

*

TO HIS MOTHER MRS THOMAS STEVENSON

13 *Rosengasse, Frankfurt,*
Tuesday Morning, August 1872

. . .[1] LAST night I was at the theatre and heard *Die Judin*
(*La Juive*), and was thereby terribly excited. At last, in the
middle of the fifth act, which was perfectly beastly, I had to
slope. I could stand even seeing the cauldron with the sham
fire beneath, and the two hateful executioners in red; but
when at last the girl's courage breaks down, and, grasping
her father's arm, she cries out—O so shudderfully!—I thought
it high time to be out of that *galère*, and so I do not know yet
whether it ends well or ill; but if I ever afterwards find that
they do carry things to the extremity, I shall think more meanly
of my species. It was raining and cold outside, so I went into
a *Bierhalle*, and sat and brooded over a *Schnitt* (half-glass) for
nearly an hour. An opera is far more *real* than real life to me.
It seems as if stage illusion, and particularly this hardest to
swallow and most conventional illusion of them all—an opera
—would never stale upon me. I wish that life was an opera.
I should like to *live* in one; but I don't know in what quarter
of the globe I shall find a society so constituted. Besides, it
would soon pall: imagine asking for three-kreuzer cigars in
recitative, or giving the washerwoman the inventory of your
dirty clothes in a sustained and *flourishous* aria.

I am in a right good mood this morning to sit here and write
to you; but not to give you news. There is a great stir of life, in
a quiet, almost country fashion, all about us here. Some one is
hammering a beef-steak in the *rez-de-chaussée*: there is a great
clink of pitchers and noise of the pump-handle at the public
well in the little square-kin round the corner. The children,
all seemingly within a month, and certainly none above five,
that always go halting and stumbling up and down the road-
way, are ordinarily very quiet, and sit sedately puddling in the
gutter, trying, I suppose, poor little devils! to understand
their *Muttersprache*; but they, too, make themselves heard from
time to time in little incomprehensible antiphonies, about the
drift that comes down to them by their rivers from the strange

[1] Omissions from these letters are indicated by stops (. . .).

127

lands higher up the Gasse. Above all, there is here such a twittering of canaries (I can see twelve out of our window), and such continual visitation of grey doves and big-nosed sparrows, as make our little bye-street into a perfect aviary.

I look across the Gasse at our opposite neighbour, as he dandles his baby about, and occasionally takes a spoonful or two of some pale slimy nastiness that looks like *dead porridge*, if you can take the conception. These two are his only occupations. All day long you can hear him singing over the brat when he is not eating; or see him eating when he is not keeping baby. Besides which, there comes into his house a continual round of visitors that puts me in mind of the luncheon hour at home. As he has thus no ostensible avocation, we have named him 'the W.S.' to give a flavour of respectability to the street.—Adieu, my dear mother, and believe me, ever your affectionate son,

ROBERT LOUIS STEVENSON
(*Rentier*)

TO MRS SITWELL

Edinburgh, Tuesday, September 16, 1873

. . . I MUST be very strong to have all this vexation and still to be well. I was weighed the other day, and the gross weight of my large person was eight stone six! Does it not seem surprizing that I can keep the lamp alight, through all this gusty weather, in so frail a lantern? And yet it burns cheerily. . . .

7.20 *p.m.*—I must tell you a thing I saw to-day. I was going down to Portobello in the train, when there came into the next compartment (third class) an artisan, strongly marked with smallpox, and with sunken, heavy eyes—a face hard and unkind, and without anything lovely. There was a woman on the platform seeing him off. At first sight, with her one eye blind and the whole cast of her features strongly plebeian, and even vicious, she seemed as unpleasant as the man; but there was something beautifully soft, a sort of light of tenderness, as on some Dutch Madonna, that came over her face when she looked at the man. They talked for a while together through the window; the man seemed to have been asking money. 'Ye ken the last time,' she said, 'I gave ye two shillin's for your ludgin', and ye said——' it died off into whisper. Plainly Falstaff and Dame Quickly over again. The man laughed unpleasantly, even cruelly, and said something; and the woman turned her back on the carriage and stood a long while so, and, do what I might, I could catch no glimpse of her expression, although I thought I saw the heave of a sob in her shoulders. At last, after the train was already in motion, she turned round and put two shillings into his hand. I saw her stand and look after us with a perfect heaven of love on her face—this poor one-eyed Madonna—until the train was out of sight; but the man, sordidly happy with his gains, did not put himself to the inconvenience of one glance to thank her for her ill-deserved kindness.

I have been up at the Spec. and looked out a reference I wanted. The whole town is drowned in white, wet vapour off the sea. Everything drips and soaks. The very statues seem wet to the skin. I cannot pretend to be very cheerful; I did not see one contented face in the streets; and the poor did look so helplessly chill and dripping, without a stitch to change, or so much as a fire to dry themselves at, or perhaps money to buy a meal, or perhaps even a bed. My heart shivers for them.

Saturday. [Dumfries]—And to-day it came—warmth, sunlight and a strong, hearty living wind among the trees. I found myself a new being. My father and I went off a long walk, through a country most beautifully wooded and various, under a range of hills. You should have seen one place where the wood suddenly fell away in front of us down a long, steep hill between a double row of trees, with one small fair-haired child framed in shadow in the foreground; and when we got to the foot there was the little kirk and kirkyard of Irongray, among broken fields and woods by the side of the bright, rapid river. In the kirkyard there was a wonderful congregation of tombstones, upright and recumbent on four legs (after our Scotch fashion), and of flat-armed fir-trees. One gravestone was erected by Scott (at a cost, I learn, of £70) to the poor woman who served him as heroine in the *Heart of Midlothian*, and the inscription in its stiff, Jedediah Cleishbotham fashion is not without something touching. We went up the stream a little further to where two Covenanters lie buried in an oakwood; the tombstone (as the custom is) containing the details of their grim little tragedy in funnily bad rhyme, one verse of which sticks in my memory:

> 'We died, their furious rage to stay,
> Near to the kirk of Iron-grey.'

We then fetched a long compass round about through Holywood Kirk and Lincluden ruins to Dumfries. But the walk came sadly to grief as a pleasure excursion before our return . . . R. L. S.

TO SIDNEY COLVIN

608 *Bush Street, San Francisco*
[*January* 10, 1880]

MY DEAR COLVIN,—This is a circular letter to tell my estate fully. You have no right to it, being the worst of correspondents; but I wish to efface the impression of my last, so to you it goes.

Any time between eight and half-past nine in the morning, a slender gentleman in an ulster, with a volume buttoned into the breast of it, may be observed leaving No. 608 Bush and descending Powell with an active step. The gentleman is R. L. S.; the volume relates to Benjamin Franklin, on whom he meditates one of his charming essays. He descends Powell, crosses Market, and descends in Sixth on a branch of the original Pine Street Coffee House, no less; I believe he would be capable of going to the original itself, if he could only find it. In the branch he seats himself at a table covered with waxcloth, and a pampered menial, of High-Dutch extraction and, indeed, as yet only partially extracted, lays before him a cup of coffee, a roll and a pat of butter, all, to quote the deity, very good. A while ago and R. L. S. used to find the supply of butter insufficient; but he has now learned the art to exactitude, and butter and roll expire at the same moment. For this refection he pays ten cents, or five pence sterling (£0. 0s. 5d.).

Half an hour later, the inhabitants of Bush Street observe the same slender gentleman armed, like George Washington, with his little hatchet, splitting, kindling, and breaking coal for his fire. He does this quasipublicly upon the window-sill; but this is not to be attributed to any love of notoriety, though he is indeed vain of his prowess with the hatchet (which he persists in calling an axe), and daily surprised at the perpetuation of his fingers. The reason is this: that the sill is a strong, supporting beam, and that blows of the same emphasis in other parts of his room might knock the entire shanty into hell. Thenceforth, for from three to four hours, he is engaged darkly with an ink bottle. Yet he is not blacking his boots, for the only pair that he possesses are innocent of lustre and wear the natural hue of the material turned up with caked and venerable slush. The youngest child of his landlady remarks several times a day, as this strange occupant enters or quits the house, 'Dere's de author'. Can it be that this bright-haired innocent has found the true clue to the mystery? The being in question is, at least, poor enough to belong to that honourable craft.

His next appearance is at the restaurant of one Donadieu, in Bush Street, between Dupont and Kearney, where a copious meal, half a bottle of wine, coffee and brandy may be procured for the sum of four bits, *alias* fifty cents, £0, 2s. 2d. sterling. The wine is put down in a whole bottleful, and it is strange and painful to observe the greed with which the gentleman in question seeks to secure the last drop of his allotted half, and the scrupulousness with which he seeks to avoid taking the first drop of the other. This is partly explained by the fact that if he were to go over the mark—bang would go a tenpence. He is again armed with a book, but his best friends will learn with pain that he seems at this hour to have deserted the more serious studies of the morning. When last observed, he was studying with apparent zest the exploits of one Rocambole by the late Viscomte Ponson du Terrail. This work, originally of prodigious dimensions, he had cut into liths or thicknesses apparently for convenience of carriage.

Then the being walks, where is not certain. But by about half-past four, a light beams from the windows of 608 Bush, and he may be observed sometimes engaged in correspondence, sometimes once again plunged in the mysterious rites of the forenoon. About six he returns to the Branch Original, where he once more imbrues himself to the worth of fivepence in coffee and roll. The evening is devoted to writing and reading, and by eleven or half-past darkness closes over this weird and truculent existence.

As for coin, you see I don't spend much, only you and Henley both seem to think my work rather bosh nowadays, and I do want to make as much as I was making, that is £200; if I can do that, I can swim: last year with my ill health I touched only £109; that would not do, I could not fight it through on that; but on £200, as I say, I am good for the world, and can even in this quiet way save a little, and that I must do. The worst is my health; it is suspected I had an ague chill yesterday; I shall know by to-morrow, and you know if I am to be laid down with ague the game is pretty well lost. But I don't know; I managed to write a good deal down in Monterey, when I was pretty sickly most of the time, and, by God, I'll try, ague and all. I have to ask you frankly, when you write, to give me any good news you can, and chat a little, but *just in the meantime*, give me no bad. If I could get *Thoreau*, *Emigrant* and *Vendetta* all finished and out of my hand, I should feel like a man who had made half a year's income in a half year; but until the two last are *finished*, you see, they don't fairly count.

I am afraid I bore you sadly with this perpetual talk about my affairs; I will try and stow it; but you see, it touches me nearly. I'm the miser in earnest now: last night, when I felt so ill, the supposed ague chill, it seemed strange not to be able to afford a drink. I would have walked half a mile, tired as I felt, for a brandy and soda.—Ever yours,   R. L. S.

TO COSMO MONKHOUSE

La Solitude, Hyères, March 16, 1884

MY DEAR MONKHOUSE,—You see with what promptitude I plunge into correspondence; but the truth is, I am condemned to a complete inaction, stagnate dismally, and love a letter. Yours, which would have been welcome at any time, was thus doubly precious.

Dover sounds somewhat shiveringly in my ears. You should see the weather *I* have—cloudless, clear as crystal, with just a punkah-draft of the most aromatic air, all pine and gum tree. You would be ashamed of Dover; you would scruple to refer, sir, to a spot so paltry. To be idle at Dover is a strange pretension; pray, how do you warm yourself? If I were there I should grind knives or write blank verse, or—— But at least you do not bathe? It is idle to deny it: I have—I may say I nourish— a growing jealousy of the robust, large-legged, healthy Britain-dwellers, patient of grog, scorners of the timid umbrella, innocuously breathing fog: all which I once was, and I am ashamed to say liked it. How ignorant is youth! grossly rolling among unselected pleasures; and how nobler, purer, sweeter, and lighter, to sip the choice tonic, to recline in the luxurious invalid chair, and to tread, well-shawled, the little round of the constitutional. Seriously, do you like to repose? Ye gods, I hate it. I never rest with any acceptation; I do not know what people mean who say they like sleep and that damned bedtime which, since long ere I was breeched, has rung a knell to all my day's doings and beings. And when a man, seemingly sane, tells me he has 'fallen in love with stagnation', I can only say to him, 'You will never be a Pirate!' This may not cause any regret to Mrs Monkhouse; but in your own soul it will clang hollow—think of it! Never! After all boyhood's aspirations and youth's immoral day-dreams, you are condemned to sit down, grossly draw in your chair to the fat board, and be a beastly Burgess till you die. Can it be? Is there not some escape, some furlough from the Moral Law, some holiday jaunt contrivable into a Better Land? Shall we never shed blood? This prospect is too grey.

> Here lies a man who never did
> Anything but what he was bid;
> Who lived his life in paltry ease.
> And died of commonplace disease.

To confess plainly, I had intended to spend my life (or any leisure I might have from Piracy upon the high seas) as the leader of a great horde of irregular cavalry, devastating whole valleys. I can still, looking back, see myself in many favourite attitudes; signalling for a boat from my pirate ship with a pocket-handkerchief, I at the jetty end, and one or two of my bold blades keeping the crowd at bay; or else turning in the saddle to look back at my whole command (some five thousand strong) following me at the hand-gallop up the road out of the burning valley: this last by moonlight. . . .

This astonishing gush of nonsense I now hasten to close, envelope, and expedite to Shakespeare's Cliff. Remember me to Shakespeare, and believe me, yours very sincerely,

ROBERT LOUIS STEVENSON

TO SIDNEY COLVIN

Vailima, Friday, March 19th [1891]

MY DEAR S. C.,—You probably expect that now I am back at Vailima I shall resume the practice of the diary letter. . . .

I will give you to-day. I sleep now in one of the lower rooms of the new house, where my wife has recently joined me. We have two beds, an empty case for a table, a chair, a tin basin, a bucket and a jug; next door in the dining-room, the carpenters camp on the floor, which is covered with their mosquito nets. Before the sun rises, at 5.45 or 5.50, Paul brings me tea, bread, and a couple of eggs; and by about six I am at work. I work in bed—my bed is of mats, no mattress, sheets, or filth—mats, a pillow, and a blanket—and put in some three hours. It was 9.5 this morning when I set off to the stream-side to my weeding; where I toiled, manuring the ground with the best enricher, human sweat, till the conch-shell was blown from our verandah at 10.30. At eleven we dine; about half-past twelve I tried (by exception) to work again, could make nothing on't, and by one was on my way to the weeding, where I wrought till three. Half-past five is our next meal, and I read Flaubert's Letters till the hour came round; dined, and then, Fanny having a cold, and I being tired, came over to my den in the unfinished house, where I now write to you, to the tune of the carpenters' voices, and by the light—I crave your pardon—by the twilight of three vile candles filtered through the medium of my mosquito bar. Bad ink being of the party, I write quite blindfold, and can only hope you may be granted to read that which I am unable to see while writing.

I said I was tired; it is a mild phrase; my back aches like toothache; when I shut my eyes to sleep, I know I shall see before them—a phenomenon to which both Fanny and I are quite accustomed—endless vivid deeps of grass and weed, each plant particular and distinct, so that I shall lie inert in body, and transact for hours the mental part of my day business, choosing the noxious from the useful. And in my dreams I shall be hauling on recalcitrants, and suffering stings from nettles, stabs from citron thorns, fiery bites from ants, sickening resistances of mud and slime, evasions of slimy roots, dead weight of heat, sudden puffs of air, sudden starts from bird-calls in the contiguous forest—some mimicking my name, some laughter, some the signal of a whistle, and living over again at large the business of my day.

Though I write so little, I pass all my hours of field-work in continual converse and imaginary correspondence. I scarce pull up a weed, but I invent a sentence on the matter to yourself; it does not get written; *autant en emportent les vents*; but the intent is there, and for me (in some sort) the companionship. To-day, for instance, we had a great talk. I was toiling, the sweat dripping from my nose, in the hot fit after a squall of rain: methought you asked me—frankly, was I happy. Happy (said I); I was only happy once; that was at Hyères; it came to an end from a variety of reasons, decline of health, change of place, increase of money, age with his stealing steps; since then, as before then, I know not what it means. But I know pleasure still; pleasure with a thousand faces, and none perfect, a thousand tongues all broken, a thousand hands, and all of them with scratching nails. High among these I place this delight of weeding out here alone by the garrulous water, under the silence of the high wood, broken by incongruous sound of birds.

And take my life all through, look at it fore and back, and upside down—though I would very fain change myself—I would not change my circumstances, unless it were to bring you here. And yet God knows perhaps this intercourse of writing serves as well; and I wonder, were you here indeed, would I commune so continually with the thought of you. I say 'I wonder' for a form; I know, and I know I should not.

So far, and much further, the conversation went, while I groped in slime after viscous roots, nursing and sparing little spears of grass, and retreating (even with outcry) from the prod of the wild lime. I wonder if any one had ever the same attitude to Nature as I hold, and have held for so long? This business fascinates me like a tune or a passion; yet all the while I thrill with a strong distaste. The horror of the thing, objective and subjective, is always present to my mind; the horror of creeping things, a superstitious horror of the void and the powers about me, the horror of my own devastation and continual murders. The life of the plants comes through my finger-tips, their struggles go to my heart like supplications. I feel myself blood-boltered; then I look back on my cleared grass, and count myself an ally in a fair quarrel, and make stout my heart.

It is but a little while since I lay sick in Sydney, beating the fields about the navy and Dean Swift and Dryden's Latin hymns; judge if I love this reinvigorating climate, where I can already toil till my head swims and every string in the poor jumping Jack (as he now lies in bed) aches with a kind of yearning strain, difficult to suffer in quiescence.

As for my damned literature,[1] God knows what a business it is, grinding along without a scrap of inspiration or a note of style. But it has to be ground, and the mill grinds exceeding slowly though not particularly small. The last two chapters have taken me considerably over a month, and they are still beneath pity. This I cannot continue, time not sufficing; and the next will just have to be worse. All the good I can express is just this; some day, when style revisits me, they will be excellent matter to rewrite. Of course, my old cure of a change of work would probably answer, but I cannot take it now. The treadmill turns; and, with a kind of desperate cheerfulness, I mount the idle stair. . . .   [R. L. S.]

[1] The South Sea Letters.

Friday 12th Sept. 1873

I must write you a line or two, my dear friend, although I shall not send it away ~~until I hear from you at least~~. I was ~~out~~ last night contrary to my own wish, in Leven, Fife; and this morning I had a conversation of which, I think, some account might interest you. I was up with a cousin who was fishing in a mill-lade; and a shower of rain drove me for shelter into a tumble-down steading attached to the mill. There, I found an old man cleaning a byre; with whom I fell into talk. The man was to all appearance as heavy, as hebétè, as any typical clod-hopper; but I knew I was in Scotland and launched out forthright into Education & Politics & the aims of one's life. I told him how I had found the peasantry in Suffolk and added that their state had made me feel quite pained and down-hearted. "It but to do that," he said, "to anybody that thinks at a' (all)!

Part of a letter to Mrs Sitwell;
from the original in the National Library of Scotland

Then again, he said that he could not conceive how anything could daunt or cast down a man who had an aim in life. "They that have had a guid schoolin' and do nae mair, whatever they do, they have done; but him that has aye something ayont (before) need never be weary". I have had to mutilate the dialect much, so that it might be comprehensible to you; but I think the sentiment will keep, even through a change of words, something of the heartsome ring of encouragement that it had for me. And that from a man cleaning a byre! You see what John Knox & his schools have done ....

ever your faithful friend
Robert Louis Stevenson.

TO SIDNEY COLVIN

[Vailima,] Sept. 28, 1891

MY DEAR COLVIN,—Since I last laid down my pen, I have written and rewritten *The Beach of Falesá*; something like sixty thousand words of sterling domestic fiction (the story, you will understand, is only half that length); and now I don't want to write any more again for ever, or feel so; and I've got to overhaul it once again to my sorrow. I was all yesterday revising, and found a lot of slackness and (what is worse in this kind of thing) some literaryisms. One of the puzzles is this: It is a first person story—a trader telling his own adventure in an island. When I began I allowed myself a few liberties, because I was afraid of the end; now the end proved quite easy, and could be done in the pace; so the beginning remains about a quarter tone out (in places); but I have rather decided to let it stay so. The problem is always delicate; it is the only thing that worries me in first person tales, which otherwise (quo' Alan) 'set better wi' my genius'. There is a vast deal of fact in the story, and some pretty good comedy. It is the first realistic South Sea story; I mean with real South Sea character and details of life. Everybody else who has tried, that I have seen, got carried away by the romance, and ended in a kind of sugar candy sham epic, and the whole effect was lost— there was no etching, no human grin, consequently no conviction. Now I have got the smell and look of the thing a good deal. You will know more about the South Seas after you have read my little tale than if you had read a library. As to whether any one else will read it, I have no guess. I am in an off time, but there is just the possibility it might make a hit; for the yarn is good and melodramatic, and there is quite a love affair—for me; and Mr Wiltshire (the narrator) is a huge lark, though I say it. But there is always the exotic question, and everything, the life, the place, the dialects—trader's talk, which is a strange conglomerate of literary expressions and English and American slang, and Beach de Mar, or native English—the very trades and hopes and fears of the characters, are all novel, and may be found unwelcome to that great, hulking, bullering whale, the public. . . .   [R. L. S.]

TO HENRY JAMES

[*Vailima, October* 1891]

MY DEAR HENRY JAMES,—From this perturbed and hunted being expect but a line, and that line shall be but a whoop for Adela.[1] O she's delicious, delicious; I could live and die with Adela—die, rather the better of the two; you never did a straighter thing, and never will.

David Balfour, second part of *Kidnapped*, is on the stocks at last; and is not bad, I think. As for *The Wrecker*, it's a machine, you know—don't expect aught else—a machine, and a police machine; but I believe the end is one of the most genuine butcheries in literature; and we point to our machine with a modest pride, as the only police machine without a villain. Our criminals are a most pleasing crew, and leave the dock with scarce a stain upon their character.

What a different line of country to be trying to draw Adela, and trying to write the last four chapters of *The Wrecker*! Heavens, it's like two centuries; and ours is such rude, tran-spontine business, aiming only at a certain fervour of conviction and sense of energy and violence in the men; and yours is so neat and bright and of so exquisite a surface! Seems dreadful to send such a book to such an author; but your name is on the list. And we do modestly ask you to consider the chapters on the *Norah Creina* with the study of Captain Nares, and the forementioned last four, with their brutality of substance and the curious (and perhaps unsound) technical manœuvre of running the story together to a point as we go along, the narra-tive becoming more succinct and the details fining off with every page.—Sworn affidavit of   R. L. S.

No person now alive has beaten Adela: I adore Adela and her maker.
Sic subscrib.

ROBERT LOUIS STEVENSON

[1] Adela Chart, the heroine of Henry James's story, *The Marriages*.

TO SIDNEY COLVIN

[Vailima, May 1892]

I HAVE celebrated my holiday from *Samoa* by a plunge at the beginning of *The Young Chevalier*.[1] I am afraid my touch is a little broad in a love story; I can't mean one thing and write another. As for women, I am no more in any fear of them; I can do a sort all right; age makes me less afraid of a petticoat, but I am a little in fear of grossness. However, this David Balfour's love affair, that's all right—might be read out to a mothers' meeting—or a daughters' meeting. The difficulty in a love yarn, which dwells at all on love, is the dwelling on one string; it is manifold, I grant, but the root fact is there unchanged, and the sentiment being very intense, and already very much handled in letters, positively calls for a little pawing and gracing. With a writer of my prosaic literalness and pertinency of point of view, this all shoves toward grossness—positively even toward the far more damnable *closeness*. This has kept me off the sentiment hitherto, and now I am to try: Lord! Of course Meredith can do it, and so could Shakespeare; but with all my romance, I am a realist and a prosaist, and a most fanatical lover of plain physical sensations plainly and expressly rendered; hence my perils. To do love in the same spirit as I did (for instance) D. Balfour's fatigue in the heather; my dear sir, there were grossness—ready made! And hence, how to sugar? . . .

I have had my little holiday outing in my kick at *The Young Chevalier*, and I guess I can settle to *David Balfour* to-morrow or Friday like a little man. I wonder if any one had ever more energy upon so little strength?—I know there is a frost; the Samoa book can only increase that—I can't help it, that book is not written for me but for Miss Manners; but I mean to break that frost inside two years, and pull off a big success, and Vanity whispers in my ear that I have the strength. If I haven't, whistle ower the lave o't! I can do without glory and perhaps the time is not far off when I can do without coin. It is a time coming soon enough, anyway; and I have endured some two and forty years without public shame, and had a good

[1] This story was never finished.

time as I did it. If only I could secure a violent death, what a
fine success! I wish to die in my boots; no more Land of
Counterpane for me. To be drowned, to be shot, to be thrown
from a horse—ay, to be hanged, rather than pass again through
that slow dissolution.

I fancy this gloomy ramble is caused by a twinge of age; I
put on an under-shirt yesterday (it was the only one I could
find) that barely came under my trousers; and just below it,
a fine healthy rheumatism has now settled like a fire in my
hip. From such small causes do these valuable considerations
flow!

I shall now say adieu, dear Sir, having ten rugged miles
before me and the horrors of a native feast and parliament
without an interpreter, for to-day I go alone.—Yours ever,

R. L. S.

TO HIS COUSIN R. A. M. STEVENSON

[Vailima, September 1894]

DEAR BOB,—You are in error about the Picts. They were a
Gaelic race, spoke a Celtic tongue, and we have no evidence
that I know of that they were blacker than other Celts. The
Balfours, I take it, were plainly Celts; their name shows it—
the 'cold croft', it means; so does their country. Where the
black Scotch come from nobody knows; but I recognize with
you the fact that the whole of Britain is rapidly and progressively becoming more pigmented; already in one man's life
I can decidedly trace a difference in the children about a
school door. But colour is not an essential part of a man or a
race. Take my Polynesians, an Asiatic people probably from
the neighbourhood of the Persian Gulf. They range through
any amount of shades, from the burnt hue of the Low Archipelago islander, which seems half negro, to the 'bleached'
pretty women of the Marquesas (close by on the map), who
come out for a festival no darker than an Italian; their colour
seems to vary directly with the degree of exposure to the sun.

And, as with negroes, the babes are born white; only it should
seem a *little sack* of pigment at the lower part of the spine,
which presently spreads over the whole field. Very puzzling.
But to return. . . . What a singular thing is this undistinguished perpetuation of a family throughout the centuries,
and the sudden bursting forth of character and capacity that
began with our grandfather! But as I go on in life, day by day,
I become more of a bewildered child; I cannot get used to this
world, to procreation, to heredity, to sight, to hearing; the
commonest things are a burthen. The prim obliterated polite
face of life, and the broad, bawdy, and orgiastic—or mænadic
—foundations, form a spectacle to which no habit reconciles
me; and 'I could wish my days to be bound each to each' by
the same open-mouthed wonder. They *are* anyway, and
whether I wish it or not.

I remember very well your attitude to life, this conventional
surface of it. You had none of that curiosity for the social stage
directions, the trivial *ficelles* of the business; it is simian, but
that is how the wild youth of man is captured; you wouldn't
imitate, hence you kept free—a wild dog, outside the kennel—
and came dam near starving for your pains. The key to the
business is of course the belly; difficult as it is to keep that in
view in the zone of three miraculous meals a day in which we
were brought up. Civilization has become reflex with us; you
might think that hunger was the name of the best sauce; but
hunger to the cold solitary under a bush of a rainy night is the
name of something quite different. I defend civilization for the
thing it is, for the thing it has *come* to be, the standpoint of a
real old Tory. My ideal would be the Female Clan. But how
can you turn these crowding dumb multitudes *back*? They don't
do anything *because*; they do things, write able articles, stitch
shoes, dig, from the purely simian impulse. Go and reason
with monkeys! . . .

Enough of this sham antiquarianism. Yes, it is in the matter
of the book, [*The Wrecker*] of course, that collaboration shows;
as for the manner, it is superficially all mine, in the sense that
the last copy is all in my hand. Lloyd did not even put pen to
paper in the Paris scenes or the Barbizon scene; it was no good;
he wrote and often rewrote all the rest; I had the best service
from him on the character of Nares. You see, we had been just
meeting the man, and his memory was full of the man's words

and ways. And Lloyd is an impressionist, pure and simple. The great difficulty of collaboration is that you can't explain what you mean. I know what kind of effect I mean a character to give—what kind of *tache* he is to make; but how am I to tell my collaborator in words? Hence it was necessary to say, 'Make him So-and-so'; and this was all right for Nares and Pinkerton and Loudon Dodd, whom we both knew, but for Bellairs, for instance—a man with whom I passed ten minutes fifteen years ago—what was I to say? and what could Lloyd do? I, as a personal artist, can begin a character with only a haze in my head, but how if I have to translate the haze into words before I begin? In our manner of collaboration (which I think the only possible—I mean that of one person being responsible, and giving the *coup de pouce* to every part of the work) I was spared the obviously hopeless business of trying to explain to my collaborator what *style* I wished a passage to be treated in. These are the times that illustrate to a man the inadequacy of spoken language. Now—to be just to written language—I can (or could) find a language for my every mood, but how could I *tell* any one beforehand what this effect was to be, which it would take every art that I possessed, and hours and hours of deliberate labour and selection and rejection, to produce? These are the impossibilities of collaboration. Its immediate advantage is to focus two minds together on the stuff, and to produce in consequence an extraordinarily greater richness of purview, consideration, and invention. The hardest chapter of all was 'Cross Questions and Crooked Answers'. You would not believe what that cost us before it assumed the least unity and colour. Lloyd wrote it at least thrice, and I at least five times—this is from memory. And was that last chapter worth the trouble it cost? Alas, that I should ask the question! Two classes of men—the artist and the educationalist—are sworn, on soul and conscience, not to ask it. You get an ordinary, grinning, red-headed boy, and you have to educate him. Faith supports you; you give your valuable hours, the boy does not seem to profit, but that way your duty lies, for which you are paid, and you must persevere. Education has always seemed to me one of the few possible and dignified ways of life. A sailor, a shepherd, a schoolmaster— to a less degree, a soldier—and (I don't know why, upon my soul, except as a sort of schoolmaster's unofficial assistant, and a kind of acrobat in tights) an artist, almost exhaust the category.

If I had to begin again—I know not—*si jeunesse savait, si vieillesse pouvait* . . . I know not at all—I believe I should try to honour Sex more religiously. The worst of our education is that Christianity does not recognize and hallow Sex. It looks askance at it, over its shoulder, oppressed as it is by reminiscences of hermits and Asiatic self-tortures. It is a terrible hiatus in our modern religions that they cannot see and make venerable that which they ought to see first and hallow most. Well, it is so; I cannot be wiser than my generation.

But no doubt there is something great in the half-success that has attended the effort of turning into an emotional religion, Bald Conduct, without any appeal, or almost none, to the figurative, mysterious, and constitutive facts of life. Not that conduct is not constitutive, but dear! it's dreary! On the whole, conduct is better dealt with on the cast-iron 'gentleman' and duty formula, with as little fervour and poetry as possible; stoical and short. . . . There is a new something or other in the wind, which exercises me hugely: anarchy—I mean, anarchism. People who (for pity's sake) commit dastardly murders very basely, die like saints, and leave beautiful letters behind 'em (did you see Vaillant to his daughter? it was the New Testament over again); people whose conduct is inexplicable to me, and yet their spiritual life higher than that of most. This is just what the early Christians must have seemed to the Romans. Is this, then, a new *drive*[1] among the monkeys? Mind you, Bob, if they go on being martyred a few years more, the gross, dull, not unkindly bourgeois may get tired or ashamed or afraid of going on martyring; and the anarchists come out at the top just like the early Christians. That is, of course, they will step into power as a *personnel*, but God knows what they may believe when they come to do so; it can't be stranger or more improbable than what Christianity had come to be by the same time.

Your letter was easily read, the pagination presented no difficulty, and I read it with much edification and gusto. To look back, and to stereotype one bygone humour—what hopeless thing! The mind runs ever in a thousand eddies like a river between cliffs. You (the ego) are always spinning round in it,

---

[1] *Trieb*, impulse.

east, west, north, and south. You are twenty years old, and forty, and five, and the next moment you are freezing at an imaginary eighty; you are never the plain forty-four that you should be by dates. (The most philosophical language is the Gaelic, which has *no present tense*—and the most useless.) How, then, to choose some former age, and stick there?   R. L. S.

Novels

*

THE BEACH OF FALESÁ
from
Island Nights Entertainments

WEIR OF HERMISTON
(*unfinished*)

THE BEACH OF FALESÁ

Chapter I

A SOUTH SEA BRIDAL

I SAW that island first when it was neither night nor morning. The moon was to the west, setting, but still broad and bright. To the east, and right amidships of the dawn, which was all pink, the day-star sparkled like a diamond. The land breeze blew in our faces, and smelt strong of wild lime and vanilla: other things besides, but these were the most plain; and the chill of it set me sneezing. I should say I had been for years on a low island near the line, living for the most part solitary among natives. Here was a fresh experience: even the tongue would be quite strange to me; and the look of these woods and mountains, and the rare smell of them, renewed my blood.

The captain blew out the binnacle lamp.

'There!' said he, 'there goes a bit of smoke, Mr Wiltshire, behind the break of the reef. That's Falesá, where your station is, the last village to the east; nobody lives to windward—I don't know why. Take my glass, and you can make the houses out.'

I took the glass; and the shores leaped nearer, and I saw the tangle of the woods and the breach of the surf, and the brown roofs and the black insides of houses peeped among the trees.

'Do you catch a bit of white there to the east'ard?' the captain continued. 'That's your house. Coral built, stands high, verandah you could walk on three abreast; best station in the South Pacific. When old Adams saw it, he took and shook me by the hand. "I've dropped into a soft thing here," says he. "So you have," says I, "and time too!" Poor Johnny! I never saw him again but the once, and then he had changed his tune—couldn't get on with the natives, or the whites, or something; and the next time we came round there he was dead and buried. I took and put up a bit of a stick to him: "John Adams, *obit* eighteen and sixty eight. Go thou and do likewise." I missed that man. I never could see much harm in Johnny.'

'What did he die of?' I inquired.

'Some kind of sickness,' says the captain. 'It appears it took him sudden. Seems he got up in the night, and filled up on Pain-Killer and Kennedy's Discovery. No go: he was booked beyond Kennedy. Then he tried to open a case of gin. No go again: not strong enough. Then he must have turned to and run out on the verandah, and capsized over the rail. When they found him, the next day, he was clean crazy—carried on all the time about somebody watering his copra. Poor John!'

'Was it thought to be the island?' I asked.

'Well, it was thought to be the island, or the trouble, or something,' he replied. 'I never could hear but what it was a healthy place. Our last man, Vigours, never turned a hair. He left because of the beach—said he was afraid of Black Jack and Case and Whistling Jimmie, who was still alive at the time, but got drowned soon afterward when drunk. As for old Captain Randall, he's been here any time since eighteen-forty, forty-five. I never could see much harm in Billy, nor much change. Seems as if he might live to be Old Kafoozleum. No, I guess it's healthy.'

'There's a boat coming now,' said I. 'She's right in the pass; looks to be a sixteen-foot whaler; two white men in the stern sheets.'

'That's the boat that drowned Whistling Jimmie!' cried the Captain; 'let's see the glass. Yes, that's Case, sure enough, and the darkie. They've got a gallows bad reputation, but you know what a place the beach is for talking. My belief, that Whistling Jimmie was the worst of the trouble; and he's gone to glory, you see. What'll you bet they ain't after gin? Lay you five to two they take six cases.'

When these two traders came aboard I was pleased with the looks of them at once, or, rather, with the looks of both, and the speech of one. I was sick for white neighbours after my four years at the line, which I always counted years of prison; getting tabooed, and going down to the Speak House to see and get it taken off; buying gin and going on a break, and then repenting; sitting in the house at night with the lamp for company; or walking on the beach and wondering what kind of a fool to call myself for being where I was. There were no other whites upon my island, and when I sailed to the next, rough customers made the most of the society. Now to see these two when they came aboard was a pleasure. One was a negro, to be sure; but they were both rigged out smart in striped pyjamas and straw hats, and Case would have passed muster in a city. He was yellow and smallish, had a hawk's nose to his face, pale eyes, and his beard trimmed with scissors. No man knew his country, beyond he was of English speech; and it was clear he came of a good family and was splendidly educated. He was accomplished too; played the accordion first-rate; and give him a piece of string or a cork or a pack of cards, and he could show you tricks equal to any professional. He could speak, when he chose, fit for a drawing-room; and when he chose he could blaspheme worse than a Yankee boatswain, and talk smart to sicken a Kanaka. The way he thought would pay best at the moment, that was Case's way, and it always seemed to come natural, and like as if he was born to it. He had the courage of a lion and the cunning of a rat; and if he's not in hell to-day, there's no such place. I know but one good point to the man: that he was fond of his wife, and kind to her. She was a Samoa woman, and dyed her hair red, Samoa style; and when he came to die (as I have to tell of) they found one strange thing—that he had made a will, like a Christian, and the widow got the lot: all this, they said, and all Black Jack's, and the most of Billy Randall's in the bargain, for it was Case that kept the books. So she went off home in the schooner *Manu'a*, and does the lady to this day in her own place.

But of all this on that first morning I knew no more than a fly. Case used me like a gentleman and like a friend, made me welcome to Falesá, and put his services at my disposal, which was the more helpful from my ignorance of the native. All the better part of the day we sat drinking better acquaintance in the cabin, and I never heard a man talk more to the point. There was no smarter trader, and none dodgier, in the islands. I thought Falesá seemed to be the right kind of a place; and the more I drank the lighter my heart. Our last trader had fled the place at half an hour's notice, taking a chance passage in a labour ship from up west. The captain, when he came, had found the station closed, the keys left with the native pastor, and a letter from the runaway, confessing he was fairly frightened of his life. Since then the firm had not been represented, and of course there was no cargo. The wind, besides, was fair, the captain hoped he could make his next island by dawn, with a good tide, and the business of landing my trade was gone about lively. There was no call for me to fool with it, Case said: nobody would touch my things, everyone was honest in Falesá, only about chickens or an odd knife or an odd stick of tobacco; and the best I could do was to sit quiet till the vessel left, then come straight to his house, see old Captain Randall, the father of the beach, take pot-luck, and go home to sleep when it got dark. So it was nigh noon, and the schooner was under way before I set my foot on shore at Falesá.

I had a glass or two on board; I was just off a long cruise, and the ground heaved under me like a ship's deck. The world was like all new painted; my foot went along to music; Falesá might have been Fiddler's Green, if there is such a place, and more's the pity if there isn't! It was good to foot the grass, to look aloft at the green mountains, to see the men with their green wreaths and the women in their bright dresses, red and blue. On we went, in the strong sun and the cool shadow, liking both; and all the children in the town came trotting after with their shaven heads and their brown bodies, and raising a thin kind of a cheer in our wake, like crowing poultry.

'By-the-bye,' says Case, 'we must get you a wife.'

'That's so,' said I; 'I had forgotten.'

There was a crowd of girls about us, and I pulled myself up and looked among them like a Bashaw. They were all dressed out for the sake of the ship being in; and the women of Falesá are a handsome lot to see. If they have a fault, they are a trifle broad in the beam; and I was just thinking so when Case touched me.

'That's pretty,' says he.

I saw one coming on the other side alone. She had been fishing; all she wore was a chemise, and it was wetted through. She was young and very slender for an island maid, with a long face, a high forehead, and a shy, strange, blindish look, between a cat's and a baby's.

'Who's she?' said I. 'She'll do.'

'That's Uma,' said Case, and he called her up and spoke to her in the native. I didn't know what he said; but when he was in the midst she looked up at me quick and timid, like a child dodging a blow, then down again, and presently smiled.

She had a wide mouth, the lips and chin cut like any statue's; and the smile came out for a moment and was gone. Then she stood with her head bent, and heard Case to an end, spoke back in the pretty Polynesian voice, looking him full in the face, heard him again in answer, and then with an obeisance started off. I had just a share of the bow, but never another shot of her eye, and there was no more word of smiling.

'I guess it's all right,' said Case. 'I guess you can have her. I'll make it square with the old lady. You can have your pick of the lot for a plug of tobacco,' he added, sneering.

I suppose it was the smile stuck in my memory, for I spoke back sharp. 'She doesn't look that sort,' I cried.

'I don't know that she is,' said Case. 'I believe she's as right as the mail. Keeps to herself, don't go round with the gang, and that. O no, don't you misunderstand me—Uma's on the square.' He spoke eager, I thought, and that surprised and pleased me. 'Indeed,' he went on, 'I shouldn't make so sure of getting her, only she cottoned to the cut of your jib. All you have to do is to keep dark and let me work the mother my own way; and I'll bring the girl round to the captain's for the marriage.'

I didn't care for the word marriage, and I said so.

'Oh, there's nothing to hurt in the marriage,' says he. 'Black Jack's the chaplain.'

By this time we had come in view of the house of these three white men; for a negro is counted a white man, and so is Chinese! a strange idea, but common in the islands. It was a board house with a strip of rickety verandah. The store was to the front, with a counter, scales, and the poorest possible display of trade: a case or two of tinned meats, a barrel of hard bread, a few bolts of cotton stuff, not to be compared with mine; the only thing well represented being the contraband, fire-arms and liquor. 'If these are my only rivals,' thinks I, 'I should do well in Falesá.' Indeed, there was only the one way they could touch me, and that was with the guns and drink.

In the back room was old Captain Randall, squatting on the floor native fashion, fat and pale, naked to the waist, grey as a badger, and his eyes set with drink. His body was covered with grey hair and crawled over by flies; one was in the corner of his eye—he never heeded; and the mosquitoes hummed about the man like bees. Any clean-minded man would have had the creature out at once and buried him; and to see him, and think he was seventy, and remember he had once commanded a ship, and come ashore in his smart togs, and talked big in bars and consulates, and sat in club verandahs, turned me sick and sober.

He tried to get up when I came in, but that was hopeless; so he reached me a hand instead, and stumbled out some salutation.

'Papa's[1] pretty full this morning,' observed Case. 'We've had an epidemic here, and Captain Randall takes gin for a prophylactic—don't you, Papa?'

'Never took such a thing in my life!' cried the captain indignantly. 'Take gin for my health's sake, Mr Wha's-ever-your-name— 's a precautionary measure.'

'That's all right, Papa,' said Case. 'But you'll have to brace up. There's going to be a marriage—Mr Wiltshire here is going to get spliced.'

The old man asked to whom.

'To Uma,' said Case.

'Uma!' cried the captain. 'Wha's he want Uma for? 's he come here for his health, anyway? Wha' 'n hell 's he want Uma for?'

'Dry up, Papa,' said Case. ' 'Tain't you that's to marry her. I guess you're not her godfather and godmother. I guess Mr Wiltshire's going to please himself.'

With that he made an excuse to me that he must move about the marriage, and left me alone with the poor wretch that was his partner and (to speak the truth) his gull. Trade and station belonged both to Randall; Case and the negro were parasites; they crawled and fed upon him like the flies, he none the wiser. Indeed, I have no harm to say of Billy Randall beyond the fact that my gorge rose at him, and the time I now passed in his company was like a nightmare.

The room was stifling hot, and full of flies; for the house was dirty and low and small, and stood in a bad place, behind the village, in the borders of the bush, and sheltered from the trade. The three men's beds were on the floor, and a litter of pans and dishes. There was no standing furniture; Randall, when he was violent, tearing it to laths. There I sat and had

[1] Please pronounce *pappa* throughout.

a meal which was served us by Case's wife; and there I was
entertained all day by that remains of man, his tongue
stumbling among low old jokes and long old stories, and his
own wheezy laughter always ready, so that he had no sense
of my depression. He was nipping gin all the while. Sometimes
he fell asleep, and awoke again, whimpering and shivering,
and every now and again he would ask me why I wanted to
marry Uma. 'My friend,' I was telling myself all day, 'you
must not come to be an old gentleman like this.'

It might be four in the afternoon, perhaps, when the back
door was thrust slowly open and a strange old native woman
crawled into the house almost on her belly. She was swathed
in black stuff to her heels; her hair was grey in swatches: her
face was tattooed, which was not the practice in that island;
her eyes big and bright and crazy. These she fixed upon
me with a rapt expression that I saw to be part acting. She
said no plain word, but smacked and mumbled with her lips,
and hummed aloud, like a child over its Christmas pudding.
She came straight across the house, heading for me, and, as
soon as she was alongside, caught up my hand and purred
and crooned over it like a great cat. From this she slipped into
a kind of song.

'Who the devil's this?' cried I, for the thing startled me.

'It's Fa'avao,' says Randall; and I saw he had hitched along
the floor into the farthest corner.

'You ain't afraid of her?' I cried.

'Me 'fraid?' cried the captain. 'My dear friend, I defy her!
I don't let her put her foot in here, only I suppose 's different
to-day, for the marriage. 's Uma's mother.'

'Well, suppose it is: what's she carrying on about?' I asked,
more irritated, perhaps more frightened, than I cared to show;
and the captain told me she was making up a quantity of
poetry in my praise because I was to marry Uma. 'All right,
old lady,' says I, with a rather a failure of a laugh, 'anything
to oblige. But when you're done with my hand, you might let
me know.'

She did as though she understood; the song rose into a cry,
and stopped; the woman crouched out of the house the same way
that she came in, and must have plunged straight into the bush,
for when I followed her to the door she had already vanished.

'These are rum manners,' said I.

F

' 's a rum crowd,' said the captain, and, to my surprise, he made the sign of the cross on his bare bosom.

'Hillo!' says I, 'are you a Papist?'

He repudiated the idea with contempt. 'Hard-shell Baptis',' said he. 'But, my dear friend, the Papist got some good ideas too; and tha' 's one of 'em. You take my advice, and whenever you come across Uma Fa'avao or Vigours, or any of that crowd, you take a leaf out o' the priests, and do what I do. Savvy?' says he, repeated the sign, and winked his dim eye at me. 'No, *sir*!' he broke out again, 'no Papist here!' and for a long time entertained me with his religious opinions.

I must have been taken with Uma from the first, or I should certainly have fled from that house, and got into the clean air, and the clean sea, or some convenient river—though, it's true, I was committed to Case; and, besides, I could never have held my head up in that island if I had run from a girl upon my wedding-night.

The sun was down, the sky all on fire, and the lamp had been some time lighted, when Case came back with Uma and the negro. She was dressed and scented; her kilt was of fine tapa, looking richer in the folds than any silk; her bust, which was of the colour of dark honey, she wore bare only for some half a dozen necklaces of seeds and flowers; and behind her ears and in her hair she had the scarlet flowers of the hibiscus. She showed the best bearing for a bride conceivable, serious and still; and I thought shame to stand up with her in that mean house and before that grinning negro. I thought shame, I say; for the mountebank was dressed with a big paper collar, the book he made believe to read from was on odd volume of a novel, and the words of his service not fit to be set down. My conscience smote me when we joined hands; and when she got her certificate I was tempted to throw up the bargain and confess. Here is the document. It was Case that wrote it, signatures and all, in a leaf out of the ledger:

This is to certify that Uma, daughter of Fa'avao of Falesá, Island of——, is illegally married to Mr John Wiltshire for one week, and Mr John Wiltshire is at liberty to send her to hell when he pleases.

JOHN BLACKAMOAR.
Chaplain to the Hulks.

Extracted from the Register by William T. Randall,
Master Mariner.

A nice paper to put in a girl's hand and see her hide away like gold. A man might easily feel cheap for less. But it was the practice in these parts, and (as I told myself) not the least the fault of us white men, but of the missionaries. If they had let the natives be, I had never needed this deception, but taken all the wives I wished, and left them when I pleased, with a clear conscience.

The more ashamed I was, the more hurry I was in to be gone; and our desires thus jumping together, I made the less remark of a change in the traders. Case had been all eagerness to keep me; now, as though he had attained a purpose, he seemed all eagerness to have me go. Uma, he said, could show me to my house, and the three bade us farewell indoors.

The night was nearly come; the village smelt of trees and flowers and the sea and bread-fruit-cooking; there came a fine roll of sea from the reef, and from a distance, among the woods and houses, many pretty sounds of men and children. It did me good to breathe free air; it did me good to be done with the captain and see, instead, the creature at my side. I felt for all the world as though she were some girl at home in the Old Country, and, forgetting myself for the minute, took her hand to walk with. Her fingers nestled into mine, I heard her breathe deep and quick and all at once she caught my hand to her face and pressed it there. 'You good!' she cried, and ran ahead of me, and stopped and looked back and smiled, and ran ahead of me again, thus guiding me through the edge of the bush, and by a quiet way to my own house.

The truth is, Case had done the courting for me in style— told her I was mad to have her, and cared nothing for the consequence; and the poor soul, knowing that which I was still ignorant of, believed it, every word, and had her head nigh turned with vanity and gratitude. Now, of all this I had no guess; I was one of those most opposed to any nonsense about native women, having seen so many whites eaten up by their wives' relatives, and made fools of in the bargain; and I told myself I must make a stand at once, and bring her to her bearings. But she looked so quaint and pretty as she ran away and then awaited me, and the thing was done so like a child or a kind dog, that the best I could do was just to follow her whenever she went on, to listen for the fall of her bare feet, and to watch in the dusk for the shining of her body. And there was another thought came in my head. She played kitten with me now when we were alone; but in the house she had carried it the way a countess might, so proud and humble. And what with her dress—for all there was so little of it, and that native enough—what with her fine tapa and fine scents, and her red flowers and seeds, that were quite as bright as jewels, only larger—it came over me she was a kind of countess really, dressed to hear great singers at a concert, and no even mate for a poor trader like myself.

She was the first in the house; and while I was still without I saw a match flash and the lamplight kindle in the windows. The station was a wonderful fine place, coral built, with quite a wide verandah, and the main room high and wide. My chests and cases had been piled in, and made rather of a mess; and there, in the thick of the confusion, stood Uma by the table, awaiting me. Her shadow went all the way up behind her into the hollow of the iron roof; she stood against it bright, the lamplight shining on her skin. I stopped in the door, and she looked at me, not speaking, with eyes that were eager and yet daunted; then she touched herself on the bosom.

'Me—your wifie,' she said. It had never taken me like that before; but the want of her took and shook all through me, like the wind in the luff of a sail.

I could not speak if I had wanted; and if I could, I would not. I was ashamed to be so much moved about a native, ashamed of the marriage too, and the certificate she had treasured in her kilt; and I turned aside and made believe to rummage among my cases. The first thing I lighted on was a case of gin, the only one that I had brought; and, partly for the girl's sake, and partly for horror of the recollections of old Randall, took a sudden resolve. I prized the lid off. One by one I drew the bottles with a pocket corkscrew, and sent Uma out to pour the stuff from the verandah.

She came back after the last, and looked at me puzzled like.

'No good,' said I, for I was now a little better master of my tongue. 'Man he drink, he no good.'

She agreed with this, but kept considering. 'Why you bring him?' she asked presently. 'Suppose you no want drink, you no bring him, I think.'

'That's all right,' said I. 'One time I want drink too much;

now no want. You see, I no savvy I get one little wifie. Suppose I drink gin, my little wifie he 'fraid.'

To speak to her kindly was about more than I was fit for; I had made my vow I would never let on to weakness with a native, and I had nothing for it but to stop.

She stood looking gravely down at me where I sat by the open case. 'I think you good man,' she said. And suddenly she had fallen before me on the floor. 'I belong to you all-e-same pig!' she cried.

Chapter II

THE BAN

I came on the verandah just before the sun rose on the morrow. My house was the last on the east; there was a cape of woods and cliffs behind that hid the sunrise. To the west, a swift cold river ran down, and beyond was the green of the village, dotted with cocoa-palms and breadfruits and houses. The shutters were some of them down and some open; I saw the mosquito bars still stretched, with shadows of people new-awakened sitting up inside; and all over the green others were stalking silent, wrapped in their many-coloured sleeping clothes like Bedouins in Bible pictures. It was mortal still and solemn and chilly, and the light of the dawn on the lagoon was like the shining of a fire.

But the thing that troubled me was nearer hand. Some dozen young men and children made a piece of a half-circle, flanking my house: the river divided them, some were on the near side, some on the far, and one on a boulder in the midst; and they all sat silent, wrapped in their sheets, and stared at me and my house as straight as pointer dogs. I thought it strange as I went out. When I had bathed and come back again, and found them all there, and two or three more along with them, I thought it stranger still. What could they see to gaze at in my house, I wondered, and went in.

But the thought of these starers stuck in my mind, and presently I came out again. The sun was now up, but it was still behind the cape of woods. Say a quarter of an hour had come and gone. The crowd was greatly increased, the far bank of the river was lined for quite a way—perhaps thirty grown folk, and of children twice as many, some standing, some squatted on the ground, and all staring at my house. I have seen a house in a South Sea village thus surrounded, but then a trader was thrashing his wife inside, and she singing out. Here was nothing: the stove was alight, the smoke going up in a Christian manner; all was shipshape and Bristol fashion. To be sure, there was a stranger come, but they had a chance to see that stranger yesterday, and took it quiet enough. What ailed them now? I leaned my arms on the rail and stared back. Devil a wink they had in them! Now and then I could see the children chatter, but they spoke so low not even the hum of their speaking came my length. The rest were like graven images: they stared at me, dumb and sorrowful, with their bright eyes; and it came upon me things would look not much different if I were on the platform of the gallows, and these good folk had come to see me hanged.

I felt I was getting daunted, and began to be afraid I looked it, which would never do. Up I stood, made believe to stretch myself, came down the verandah stair, and strolled towards the river. There went a short buzz from one to the other, like what you hear in theatres when the curtain goes up; and some of the nearest gave back the matter of a pace. I saw a girl lay one hand on a young man and make a gesture upward with the other; at the same time she said something in native with a gasping voice. Three little boys sat beside my path, where I must pass within three feet of them. Wrapped in their sheets, with their shaved heads and bits of top-knots, and queer faces, they looked like figures on a chimney-piece. Awhile they sat their ground, solemn as judges. I came up hand over fist, doing my five knots, like a man that meant business; and I thought I saw a sort of a wink and gulp in the three faces. Then one jumped up (he was the farthest off) and ran for his mammy. The other two, trying to follow suit, got foul, came to the ground together bawling, wriggled right out of their sheets mother-naked, and in a moment there were all three of them scampering for their lives and singing out like pigs.

The natives, who would never let a joke slip, even at a burial, laughed and let up, as short as a dog's bark.

They say it scares a man to be alone. No such thing. What scares him in the dark or the high bush is that he can't make sure, and there might be an army at his elbow. What scares him worst is to be right in the midst of a crowd, and have no guess of what they're driving at. When that laugh stopped, I stopped too. The boys had not yet made their offing, they were still on the full stretch going the other way, when I had already gone about ship and was sheering off the other. Like a fool I had come out, doing my five knots; like a fool I went back again. It must have been the funniest thing to see, and what knocked me silly, this time no one laughed; only one old woman gave a kind of pious moan, the way you have heard Dissenters in their chapels at the sermon.

'I never saw such fools of Kanakas as your people here,' I said once to Uma, glancing out of the window at the starers.

'Savvy nothing,' says Uma, with a kind of disgusted air that she was good at.

And that was all the talk we had upon the matter, for I was put out, and Uma took the thing so much as a matter of course that I was fairly ashamed.

All day, off and on, now fewer and now more, the fools sat about the west end of my house and across the river, waiting for the show, whatever that was—fire to come down from heaven, I suppose, and consume me, bones and baggage. But by evening, like real islanders, they had wearied of the business, and got away, and had a dance instead in the big house of the village, where I heard them singing and clapping hands till, may be, ten at night, and the next day it seemed they had forgotten I existed. If fire had come down from heaven or the earth opened and swallowed me, there would have been nobody to see the sport or take the lesson, or whatever you like to call it. But I was to find that they hadn't forgot either, and kept an eye lifting for phenomena over my way.

I was hard at it both these days getting my trade in order and taking stock of what Vigours had left. This was a job that made me pretty sick, and kept me from thinking on much else. Ben had taken stock the trip before—I knew I could trust Ben—but it was plain somebody had been making free in the meantime. I found I was out by what might easily cover six months' salary and profit, and I could have kicked myself all round the village to have been such a blamed ass, sitting boozing with that Case instead of attending to my own affairs and taking stock.

However, there's no use crying over spilt milk. It was done now, and couldn't be undone. All I could do was to get what was left of it, and my new stuff (my own choice) in order, to go round and get after the rats and cockroaches, and to fix up that store regular Sydney style. A fine show I made of it; and the third morning when I had lit my pipe and stood in the doorway and looked in, and turned and looked far up the mountain and saw the cocoanuts waving and posted up the tons of copra, and over the village green and saw the island dandies and reckoned up the yards of print they wanted for their kilts and dresses, I felt as if I was in the right place to make a fortune, and go home again and start a public-house. There was I, sitting in that verandah, in as handsome a piece of scenery as you could find, a splendid sun, and a fine fresh healthy trade that stirred up a man's blood like sea-bathing; and the whole thing was clean gone from me, and I was dreaming England, which is, after all, a nasty, cold, muddy hole, with not enough light to see to read by; and dreaming the looks of my public, by a cant of a broad high-road like an avenue, and with the sign on a green tree.

So much for the morning, but the day passed and the devil anyone looked near me, and from all I knew of natives in other islands I thought this strange. People laughed a little at our firm and their fine stations, and at this station of Falesá in particular; all the copra in the district wouldn't pay for it (I had heard them say) in fifty years, which I supposed was an exaggeration. But when the day went, and no business came at all, I began to get downhearted; and, about three in the afternoon, I went for a stroll to cheer me up. On the green I saw a white man coming with a cassock on, by which and by the face of him I knew he was a priest. He was a good-natured old soul to look at, gone a little grizzled, and so dirty you could have written with him on a piece of paper.

'Good day, sir,' said I.

He answered me eagerly in native.

'Don't you speak any English?' said I.

'French,' says he.

'Well,' said I, 'I'm sorry, but I can't do anything there.'

He tried me awhile in the French, and then again in native, which he seemed to think was the best chance. I made out he was after more than passing the time of day with me, but had something to communicate, and I listened harder. I heard the names of Adams and Case and of Randall—Randall the oftenest—and the word 'poison', or something like it, and a native word that he said very often. I went home, repeating it to myself.

'What does fussy-ocky mean?' I asked of Uma, for that was as near as I could come to it.

'Make dead,' said she.

'The devil it does!' says I. 'Did ever you hear that Case had poisoned Johnnie Adams?'

'Every man he savvy that,' says Uma, scornful-like. 'Give him white sand—bad sand. He got the bottle still. Suppose he give you gin, you no take him.'

Now I had heard much the same sort of story in other islands, and the same white powder always to the front, which made me think the less of it. For all that, I went over to Randall's place to see what I could pick up, and found Case on the doorstep, cleaning a gun.

'Good shooting here?' says I.

'A 1,' says he. 'The bush is full of all kinds of birds. I wish copra was as plenty,' say he—I thought, slyly—'but there don't seem anything doing.'

I could see Black Jack in the store, serving a customer.

'That looks like business, though,' said I.

'That's the first sale we've made in three weeks,' said he.

'You don't tell me?' says I. 'Three weeks? Well, well.'

'If you don't believe me,' he cries, a little hot, 'you can go and look at the copra-house. It's half empty to this blessed hour.'

'I shouldn't be much the better for that, you see,' says I. 'For all I can tell, it might have been whole empty yesterday.'

'That's so,' says he, with a bit of a laugh.

'By-the-bye,' I said, 'what sort of a party is that priest? Seems rather a friendly sort.'

At this Case laughed right out loud. 'Ah!' says he, 'I see what ails you now. Galuchet's been at you.' *Father Galoshes* was the name he went by most, but Case always gave it the

French quirk, which was another reason we had for thinking him above the common.

'Yes, I have seen him,' I says. 'I made out he didn't think much of your Captain Randall.'

'That he don't!' says Case. 'It was the trouble about poor Adams. The last day, when he lay dying, there was young Buncombe round. Ever met Buncombe?'

I told him no.

'He's a cure, is Buncombe!' laughs Case. 'Well, Buncombe took it in his head that, as there was no other clergyman about, bar Kanaka pastors, we ought to call in Father Galuchet, and have the old man administered and take the sacrament. It was all the same to me, you may suppose; but I said I thought Adams was the fellow to consult. He was jawing away about watered copra and a sight of foolery. "Look here," I said, "you're pretty sick. Would you like to see Galoshes?" He sat right up on his elbow. "Get the priest," says he, "get the priest; don't let me die here like a dog!" He spoke kind of fierce and eager, but sensible enough. There was nothing to say against that, so we sent and asked Galuchet if he would come. You bet he would. He jumped in his dirty linen at the thought of it. But we had reckoned without Papa. He's a hard-shell Baptist, is Papa; no Papists need apply. And he took and locked the door. Buncombe told him he was bigoted, and I thought he would have had a fit. "Bigoted!" he says. "Me bigoted? Have I lived to hear it from a jackanapes like you?" And he made for Buncombe, and I had to hold them apart; and there was Adams in the middle, gone luny again, and carrying on about copra like a born fool. It was good as the play, and I was about knocked out of time with laughing, when all of a sudden Adams sat up, clapped his hands to his chest, and went into the horrors. He died hard, did John Adams,' says Case, with a kind of a sudden sternness.

'And what became of the priest?' I asked.

'The priest?' says Case. 'O! he was hammering on the door outside, and crying on the natives to come and beat it in, and singing out it was a soul he wished to save, and that. He was in a rare taking, was the priest. But what would you have? Johnny had slipped his cable; no more Johnny in the market; and the administration racket clean played out. Next thing, word came to Randall the priest was praying upon Johnny's grave. Papa was pretty full, and got a club, and lit out straight for the place, and there was Galoshes on his knees, and a lot of natives looking on. You wouldn't think Papa cared that much about anything, unless it was liquor; but he and the priest stuck to it two hours, slanging each other in native, and every time Galoshes tried to kneel down Papa went for him with the club. There never were such larks in Falesá. The end of it was that Captain Randall knocked over with some kind of a fit or stroke, and the priest got in his goods after all. But he was the angriest priest you ever heard of, and complained to the chiefs about the outrage, as he called it. That was no account, for our chiefs are Protestant here; and, anyway, he had been making trouble about the drum for morning school, and they were glad to give him a wipe. Now he swears old Randall gave Adams poison or something, and when the two meet they grin at each other like baboons.'

He told this story as natural as could be, and like a man that enjoyed the fun; though, now I come to think of it after so long, it seems rather a sickening yarn. However, Case never set up to be soft, only to be square and hearty, and a man all round; and, to tell the truth, he puzzled me entirely.

I went home and asked Uma if she were a Popey, which I had made out to be the native word for Catholics.

'*E le ai!*' says she. She always used the native when she meant 'no' more than usually strong, and, indeed, there's more of it. 'No good Popey,' she added.

Then I asked her about Adams and the priest, and she told me much the same yarn in her own way. So that I was left not much farther on, but inclined, upon the whole, to think the bottom of the matter was the row about the sacrament, and the poisoning only talk.

The next day was a Sunday, when there was no business to be looked for. Uma asked me in the morning if I was going to 'pray'; I told her she bet not, and she stopped home herself with no more words. I thought this seemed unlike a native, and a native woman, and a woman that had new clothes to show off; however, it suited me to the ground, and I made the less of it. The queer thing was that I came next door to going to church after all, a thing I'm little likely to forget. I had turned out for a stroll, and heard the hymn tune up. You know how it is. If you hear folk singing, it seems to draw you:

and pretty soon I found myself alongside the church. It was a little long low place, coral built, rounded off at both ends like a whale-boat, a big native roof on the top of it, windows without sashes and doorways without doors. I stuck my head into one of the windows, and the sight was so new to me—for things went quite different in the islands I was acquainted with—that I stayed and looked on. The congregation sat on the floor on mats, the women on one side, the men on the other, all rigged out to kill—the women with dresses and trade hats, the men in white jackets and shirts. The hymn was over; the pastor, a big buck Kanaka, was in the pulpit, preaching for his life; and by the way he wagged his hand, and worked his voice, and made his points, and seemed to argue with the folk, I made out he was a gun at the business. Well, he looked up suddenly and caught my eye, and I give you my word he staggered in the pulpit; his eyes bulged out of his head, his hand rose and pointed at me like as if against his will, and the sermon stopped right there.

It isn't a fine thing to say for yourself, but I ran away; and if the same kind of a shock was given me, I should run away again to-morrow. To see that palavering Kanaka struck all of a heap at the mere sight of me gave me a feeling as if the bottom had dropped out of the world. I went right home, and stayed there, and said nothing. You might think I would tell Uma, but that was against my system. You might have thought I would have gone over and consulted Case; but the truth was I was ashamed to speak of such a thing, I thought every-one would blurt out laughing in my face. So I held my tongue, and thought all the more; and the more I thought, the less I liked the business.

By Monday night I got it clearly in my head I must be tabooed. A new store to stand open two days in a village and not a man or woman come to see the trade was past believing.

'Uma,' said I, 'I think I'm tabooed.'

'I think so,' said she.

I thought awhile whether I should ask her more, but it's a bad idea to set natives up with any notion of consulting them, so I went to Case. It was dark and he was sitting alone, as he did mostly, smoking on the stairs.

'Case,' said I, 'here's a queer thing. I'm tabooed.'

'O, fudge!' says he; 'tain't the practice in these islands.'

'That may be, or it mayn't,' said I. 'It's the practice where I was before. You can bet I know what it's like; and I tell it you for a fact, I'm tabooed.'

'Well,' said he, 'what have you been doing?'

'That's what I want to find out,' said I.

'O, you can't be,' said he; 'it ain't possible. However, I'll tell you what I'll do. Just to put your mind at rest, I'll go round and find out for sure. Just you waltz in and talk to Papa.' 'Thank you,' I said, 'I'd rather stay right out here on the verandah. Your house is so close.'

'I'll call Papa out here, then,' says he.

'My dear fellow,' I says, 'I wish you wouldn't. The fact is, I don't take to Mr Randall.'

Case laughed, took a lantern from the store, and set out into the village. He was gone perhaps a quarter of an hour, and he looked mighty serious when he came back.

'Well,' said he, clapping down the lantern on the verandah steps, 'I would never have believed it. I don't know where the impudence of these Kanakas 'll go next; they seem to have lost all idea of respect for whites. What we want is a man-of-war—a German, if we could—they know how to manage Kanakas.'

'I *am* tabooed, then?' I cried.

'Something of the sort,' said he. 'It's the worst thing of the kind I've heard of yet. But I'll stand by you, Wiltshire, man to man. You come round here to-morrow about nine, and we'll have it out with the chiefs. They're afraid of me, or they used to be; but their heads are so big by now, I don't know what to think. Understand me, Wiltshire; I don't count this your quarrel,' he went on, with a great deal of resolution, 'I count it all of our quarrel, I count it the White Man's Quarrel, and I'll stand to it through thick and thin, and there's my hand on it.'

'Have you found out what's the reason?' I asked.

'Not yet,' said Case. 'But we'll fix them down to-morrow.'

Altogether I was pretty well pleased with his attitude, and almost more the next day, when we met to go before the chiefs, to see him so stern and resolved. The chiefs awaited us in one of their big oval houses, which was marked out to us from a long way off by the crowd about the eaves, a hundred strong if there was one—men, women, and children. Many of the men were on their way to work and wore green wreaths, and it put me in thoughts of the 1st of May at home. This crowd opened and buzzed about the pair of us as we went in, with a sudden angry animation. Five chiefs were there; four mighty stately men, the fifth old and puckered. They sat on mats in their white kilts and jackets; they had fans in their hands, like fine ladies; and two of the younger ones wore Catholic medals, which gave me matter of reflection. Our place was set, and the mats laid for us over against these grandees, on the near side of the house; the midst was empty; the crowd, close at our backs, murmured and craned and jostled to look on, and the shadows of them tossed in front of us on the clean pebbles of the floor. I was just a hair put out by the excitement of the commons, but the quiet civil appearance of the chiefs reassured me, all the more when their spokesman began and made a long speech in a low tone of voice, sometimes waving his hand towards Case, sometimes towards me, and sometimes knocking with his knuckles on the mat. One thing was clear: there was no sign of anger in the chiefs.

'What's he been saying?' I asked, when he had done.

'O, just that they're glad to see you, and they understand by me you wish to make some kind of complaint, and you're to fire away, and they'll do the square thing.'

'It took a precious long time to say that,' said I.

'O, the rest was sawder and *bonjour* and that,' said Case. 'You know what Kanakas are.'

'Well, they don't get much *bonjour* out of me,' said I. 'You tell them who I am. I'm a white man, and a British subject, and no end of a big chief at home; and I've come here to do them good, and bring them civilization; and no sooner have I got my trade sorted out than they go and taboo me, and no one dare come near my place! Tell them I don't mean to fly in the face of anything legal; and if what they want's a present, I'll do what's fair. I don't blame any man looking out for himself, tell them, for that's human nature; but if they think they're going to come any of their native ideas over me, they'll find themselves mistaken. And tell them plain that I demand the reason of this treatment as a white man and a British subject.'

That was my speech. I know how to deal with Kanakas: give them plain sense and fair dealing, and—I'll do them

that much justice—they knuckle under every time. They
haven't any real government or any real law, that's what
you've got to knock into their heads; and even if they had, it
would be a good joke if it was to apply to a white man. It
would be a strange thing if we came all this way and couldn't
do what we pleased. The mere idea has always put my monkey
up, and I rapped my speech out pretty big. Then Case translated it—or made believe to, rather—and the first chief
replied, and then a second, and a third, all in the same style,
easy and genteel, but solemn underneath. Once a question
was put to Case, and he answered it, and all hands (both
chiefs and commons) laughed out aloud, and looked at me.
Last of all, the puckered old fellow and the big young chief
that spoke first started in to put Case through a kind of cate-
chism. Sometimes I made out that Case was trying to fence,
and they stuck to him like hounds, and the sweat ran down his
face, which was no very pleasant sight to me, and at some of his
answers the crowd moaned and murmured, which was a worse
hearing. It's a cruel shame I knew no native, for (as I now
believe) they were asking Case about my marriage, and he must
have had a tough job of it to clear his feet. But leave Case
alone; he had the brains to run a parliament.

'Well, is that all?' I asked, when a pause came.

'Come along,' says he, mopping his face; 'I'll tell you outside.'

'Do you mean they won't take the taboo off?' I cried.

'It's something queer,' said he. 'I'll tell you outside. Better
come away.'

'I won't take it at their hands,' cried I. 'I ain't that kind of a
man. You don't find me turn my back on a parcel of Kanakas.'

'You'd better,' said Case.

He looked at me with a signal in his eye; and the five chiefs
looked at me civilly enough, but kind of pointed; and the
people looked at me and craned and jostled. I remembered
the folks that watched my house, and how the pastor had
jumped in his pulpit at the bare sight of me; and the whole
business seemed so out of the way that I rose and followed Case.
The crowd opened again to let us through, but wider than
before, the children on the skirts running and singing out, and
as we two white men walked away they all stood and watched us.

'And now,' said I, 'what is all this about?'

'The truth is I can't rightly make it out myself. They have a down on you,' says Case.

'Taboo a man because they have a down on him!' I cried. 'I never heard the like.'

'It's worse than that, you see,' said Case. 'You ain't tabooed —I told you that couldn't be. The people won't go near you, Wiltshire, and there's where it is.'

'They won't go near me? What do you mean by that? Why won't they go near me?' I cried.

Case hesitated. 'Seems they're frightened,' says he, in a low voice.

I stopped dead short. 'Frightened?' I repeated. 'Are you gone crazy, Case? What are they frightened of?'

'I wish I could make out,' Case answered, shaking his head. 'Appears like one of their tom-fool superstitions. That's what I don't cotton to,' he said. 'It's like the business about Vigours.'

'I'd like to know what you mean by that, and I'll trouble you to tell me,' says I.

'Well, you know, Vigours lit out and left all standing,' said he. 'It was some superstition business—I never got the hang of it, but it began to look bad before the end.'

'I've heard a different story about that,' said I, 'and I had better tell you so. I heard he ran away because of you.'

'O! well, I suppose he was ashamed to tell the truth,' says Case; 'I guess he thought it silly. And that it's a fact that I packed him off. "What would you do, old man?" says he. "Get," says I, "and not think twice about it." I was the gladdest kind of man to see him clear away. It ain't my notion to turn my back on a mate when he's in a tight place, but there was that much trouble in the village that I couldn't see where it might likely end. I was a fool to be so much about with Vigours. They cast it up to me to-day. Didn't you hear Maea—that's the young chief, the big one—ripping out about "Vika"? That was him they were after. They don't seem to forget it, somehow.'

'This is all very well,' said I, 'but it don't tell me what's wrong; it don't tell me what they're afraid of—what their idea is.'

'Well, I wish I knew,' said Case. 'I can't say fairer than that.'

'You might have asked, I think,' says I.

'And so I did,' says he. 'But you must have seen for yourself, unless you're blind, that the asking got the other way. I'll go as far as I dare for another white man; but when I find I'm in the scrape myself, I think first of my own bacon. The loss of me is I'm too good-natured. And I'll take the freedom of telling you you show a queer kind of gratitude to a man who's got into all this mess along of your affairs.'

'There's a thing I am thinking of,' said I. 'You were a fool to be so much about with Vigours. One comfort, you haven't been much about with me. I notice you've never been inside my house. Own up now; you had word of this before?'

'It's a fact I haven't been,' said he. 'It was an oversight, and I am sorry for it, Wiltshire. But about coming now, I'll be quite plain.'

'You mean you won't?' I asked.

'Awfully sorry, old man, but that's the size of it,' says Case.

'In short, you're afraid?' says I.

'In short, I'm afraid,' says he.

'And I'm still to be tabooed for nothing?' I asked.

'I tell you you're not tabooed,' said he. 'The Kanakas won't go near you, that's all. And who's to make 'em? We traders have a lot of gall, I must say; we make these poor Kanakas take back their laws, and take up their taboos, and that, whenever it happens to suit us. But you don't mean to say you expect a law obliging people to deal in your store whether they want to or not? You don't mean to tell me you've got the gall for that? And if you had, it would be a queer thing to propose to me. I would just like to point out to you, Wiltshire, that I'm a trader myself.'

'I don't think I would talk of gall if I was you,' said I. 'Here's about what it comes to, as well as I can make out: None of the people are to trade with me, and they're all to trade with you. You're to have the copra, and I'm to go to the devil and shake myself. And I don't know any native, and you're the only man here worth mention that speaks English, and you have the gall to up and hint to me my life's in danger, and all you've got to tell me is you don't know why!'

'Well, it *is* all I have to tell you,' said he. 'I don't know—I wish I did.'

'And so you turn your back and leave me to myself! Is that the position?' says I.

'If you like to put it nasty,' says he. 'I don't put it so. I say merely, "I'm going to keep clear of you; or, if I don't, I'll get in danger for myself".'

'Well,' says I, 'you're a nice kind of a white man!'

'O, I understand; you're riled,' said he. 'I would be myself. I can make excuses.'

'All right,' I said, 'go and make excuses somewhere else. Here's my way, there's yours!'

With that we parted, and I went straight home, in a hot temper, and found Uma trying on a lot of trade goods like a baby.

'Here,' I said, 'you quit that foolery! Here's a pretty mess to have made, as if I wasn't bothered enough anyway! And I thought I told you to get dinner!'

And then I believe I gave her a bit of the rough side of my tongue, as she deserved. She stood up at once, like a sentry to his officer; for I must say she was always well brought up, and had a great respect for whites.

'And now,' says I, 'you belong round here, you're bound to understand this. What am I tabooed for, anyway? Or, if I ain't tabooed, what makes the folks afraid of me?'

She stood and looked at me with eyes like saucers.

'You no savvy?' she gasps at last.

'No,' said I. 'How would you expect me to? We don't have any such craziness where I come from.'

'Ese no tell you?' she asked again.

(*Ese* was the name the natives had for Case; it may mean foreign, or extraordinary; or it might mean a mummy apple; but most like it was only his own name misheard and put in a Kanaka spelling.)

'Not much,' said I.

'D—n Ese!' she cried.

You might think it funny to hear this Kanaka girl come out with a big swear. No such thing. There was no swearing in her—no, nor anger; she was beyond anger, and meant the word simple and serious. She stood there straight as she said it. I cannot justly say that I ever saw a woman look like that before or after, and it struck me mum. Then she made a kind of an obeisance, but it was the proudest kind, and threw her hands out open.

'I 'shamed,' she said. 'I think you savvy. Ese tell me you

savvy, he tell me you no mind, tell me you love me too much. Taboo belong to me,' she said, touching herself on the bosom as she had done upon our wedding-night. 'Now I go 'way, taboo he go 'way too. Then you get too much copra. You like more better, I think. *Tofá, alii,*' says she in the native— 'Farewell, chief!'

'Hold on!' I cried. 'Don't be in such a hurry.'

She looked at me sidelong with a smile. 'You see, you get copra,' she said, the same as you might offer candies to a child.

'Uma,' said I, 'hear reason. I didn't know, and that's a fact; and Case seems to have played it pretty mean upon the pair of us. But I do know now, and I don't mind; I love you too much. You no go 'way, you no leave me, I too much sorry.'

'You no love me,' she cried, 'you talk me bad words!' And she threw herself in a corner of the floor, and began to cry.

Well, I'm no scholar, but I wasn't born yesterday, and I thought the worst of that trouble was over. However, there she lay—her back turned, her face to the wall—and shook with sobbing like a little child, so that her feet jumped with it. It's strange how it hits a man when he's in love; for there's no use mincing things—Kanaka and all, I was in love with her, or just as good. I tried to take her hand, but she would none of that. 'Uma,' I said, 'there's no sense in carrying on like this. I want you stop here, I want my little wifie, I tell you true.'

'No tell me true,' she sobbed.

'All right,' says I, 'I'll wait till you're through with this.' And I sat right down beside her on the floor, and set to smooth her hair with my hand. At first she wriggled away when I touched her; then she seemed to notice me no more; then her sobs grew gradually less, and presently stopped; and the next thing I knew she raised her face to mine.

'You tell me true? You like me stop?' she asked.

'Uma,' said I, 'I would rather have you than all the copra in the South Seas,' which was a very big expression, and the strangest thing was that I meant it.

She threw her arms about me, sprang close up, and pressed her face to mine in the island way of kissing, so that I was all wetted with her tears, and my heart went out to her wholly. I never had anything so near me as this little brown bit of a girl. Many things went together, and all helped to turn my head. She was pretty enough to eat; it seemed she was my only friend in that queer place; I was ashamed that I had spoken rough to her: and she was a woman, and my wife, and a kind of a baby besides that I was sorry for; and the salt of her tears was in my mouth. And I forgot Case and the natives; and I forgot that I knew nothing of the story, or only remembered it to banish the remembrance; and I forgot that I was to get no copra, and so could make no livelihood; and I forgot my employers, and the strange kind of service I was doing them, when I preferred my fancy to their business; and I forgot even that Uma was no true wife of mine, but just a maid beguiled, and that in a pretty shabby style. But that is to look too far on. I will come to that part of it next.

It was late before we thought of getting dinner. The stove was out, and gone stone-cold; but we fired up after a while, and cooked each a dish, helping and hindering each other, and making a play of it like children. I was so greedy of her nearness that I sat down to dinner with my lass upon my knee, made sure of her with one hand, and ate with the other. Ay, and more than that. She made the worst cook I suppose God made; the things she set her hand to it would have sickened an honest horse to eat of; yet I made my meal that day on Uma's cookery, and can never call to mind to have been better pleased.

I didn't pretend to myself, and I didn't pretend to her. I saw I was clean gone; and if she was to make a fool of me, she must. And I suppose it was this that set her talking, for now she made sure that we were friends. A lot she told me, sitting in my lap and eating my dish, as I ate hers, from foolery—a lot about herself and her mother and Case, all which would be very tedious, and fill sheets if I set it down in Beach de Mar, but which I must give a hint of in plain English, and one thing about myself, which had a very big effect on my concerns, as you are soon to hear.

It seems she was born in one of the Line Islands; had been only two or three years in these parts, where she had come with a white man, who was married to her mother and then died; and only the one year in Falesá. Before that they had been a good deal on the move, trekking about after the white man, who was one of those rolling stones that keep going round after a soft job. They talk about looking for gold at the end of a rainbow; but if a man wants an employment that'll last him till he dies, let him start out on the soft-job hunt. There's meat and drink in it too, and beer and skittles, for you never hear of them starving, and rarely see them sober; and as for steady sport, cock-fighting isn't in the same county with it. Anyway, this beachcomber carried the woman and her daughter all over the shop but mostly to out-of-the-way islands, where there were no police, and he thought, perhaps, the soft job hung out. I've my own view of this old party; but I was just as glad he had kept Uma clear of Apia and Papeete and these flash towns. At last he struck Fale-alii on this island, got some trade—the Lord knows how!—muddled it all away in the usual style, and died worth next to nothing, bar a bit of land at Falesá that he had got for a bad debt, which was what put it in the minds of the mother and daughter to come there and live. It seems Case encouraged them all he could, and helped to get their house built. He was very kind those days, and gave Uma trade, and there is no doubt he had his eye on her from the beginning. However, they had scarce settled, when up turned a young man, a native, and wanted to marry her. He was a small chief, and had some fine mats and old songs in his family, and was 'very pretty', Uma said; and, altogether, it was an extraordinary match for a penniless girl and an out-islander.

At the first word of this I got downright sick with jealousy.

'And you mean to say you would have married him?' I cried.

'*Ioe*, yes,' said she. 'I like too much!'

'Well!' I said. 'And suppose I had come round after?'

'I like you more better now,' said she. 'But, suppose, I marry Ioane, I one good wife. I no common Kanaka. Good girl!' says she.

Well, I had to be pleased with that; but I promise you I didn't care about the business one little bit. And I liked the end of that yarn no better than the beginning. For it seems this proposal of marriage was the start of all the trouble. It seems, before that, Uma and her mother had been looked down upon, of course, for kinless folk and out-islanders, but nothing to hurt; and, even when Ioane came forward, there was less trouble at first than might have been looked for. And then, all of a sudden, about six months before my coming, Ioane backed out and left that part of the island, and from that day to this Uma and her mother had found themselves alone. None called at their house, none spoke to them on the roads. If they went to church, the other women drew their mats away and left them in a clear place by themselves. It was a regular excommunication, like what you read of in the Middle Ages; and the cause or sense of it beyond guessing. It was some *tala pepelo*, Uma said, some lie, some calumny; and all she knew of it was that the girls who had been jealous of her luck with Ioane used to twit her with his desertion, and cry out when they met her alone in the woods, that she would never be married. 'They tell me no man he marry me. He too much 'fraid,' she said.

The only soul that came about them after this desertion was Master Case. Even he was chary of showing himself, and turned up mostly by night; and pretty soon he began to table his cards and make up to Uma. I was still sore about Ioane, and when Case turned up in the same line of business I cut up downright rough.

'Well,' I said, sneering, 'and I suppose you thought Case "very pretty"' and "liked too much"?'

'Now you talk silly,' said she. 'White man, he come here, I marry him all-e-same Kanaka; very well, then, he marry me all-e-same white woman. Suppose he no marry, he go 'way, woman he post. All-e-same thief, empty hand, Tonga-heart— no can love! Now you come marry me. You big heart—you no 'shamed island-girl. That thing I love you for too much. I proud.'

I don't know that ever I felt sicker all the days of my life. I laid down my fork, and I put away 'the island-girl'; I didn't seem somehow to have any use for either, and I went and walked up and down the house, and Uma followed me with her eyes, for she was troubled, and small wonder! But troubled, was no word for it with me. I so wanted, and so feared, to make a clean breast of the sweep that I had been.

And just then there came a sound of singing out of the sea; it sprang up suddenly clear and near, as the boat turned the headland, and Uma, running to the window, cried out it was 'Misi' come upon his rounds.

I thought it was a strange thing I should be glad to have a missionary; but, if it was strange, it was still true.

'Uma,' said I, 'you stop here in this room, and don't budge a foot out of it till I come back.'

Chapter III

THE MISSIONARY

As I came out of the verandah, the mission-boat was shooting for the mouth of the river. She was a long whaleboat painted white; a bit of an awning astern; a native pastor crouched on the wedge of the poop, steering; some four-and-twenty paddles flashing and dipping, true to the boat-song; and the missionary under the awning, in his white clothes, reading in a book, and set him up! It was pretty to see and hear; there's no smarter sight in the islands than a missionary boat with a good crew and a good pipe to them; and I considered it for half a minute, with a bit of envy perhaps, and then strolled down towards the river.

From the opposite side there was another man aiming for the same place, but he ran and got there first. It was Case; doubtless his idea was to keep me apart from the missionary, who might serve me as interpreter; but my mind was upon other things. I was thinking how he had jockeyed us about the marriage, and tried his hand on Uma before; and at the sight of him rage flew into my nostrils.

'Get out of that, you low swindling thief!' I cried.

'What's that you say?' says he.

I gave him the word again, and rammed it down with a good oath. 'And if ever I catch you within six fathoms of my house,' I cried, 'I'll clap a bullet in your measly carcase.'

'You must do as you like about your house,' said he, 'where I told you I have no thought of going; but this is a public place.'

'It's a place where I have private business,' said I. 'I have no idea of a hound like you eaves-dropping, and I give you notice to clear out.'

'I don't take it, though,' says Case.

'I'll show you, then,' said I.

'We'll have to see about that,' said he.

He was quick with his hands, but he had neither the height nor the weight, being a flimsy creature alongside a man like me, and besides, I was blazing to that height of wrath that I could have bit into a chisel. I gave him first the one and then the other, so that I could hear his head rattle and crack, and he went down straight.

'Have you had enough?' cried I. But he only looked up white and blank, and the blood spread upon his face like wine upon a napkin. 'Have you had enough?' I cried again. 'Speak up, and don't lie malingering there, or I'll take my feet to you.'

He sat up at that, and held his head—by the look of him you could see it was spinning—and the blood poured on his pyjamas.

'I've had enough for this time,' says he, and he got up staggering, and went off by the way that he had come.

The boat was close in; I saw the missionary had laid his book to one side, and I smiled to myself. 'He'll know I'm a man, anyway,' thinks I.

This was the first time, in all my years in the Pacific, I had ever exchanged two words with any missionary, let alone asked one for a favour. I didn't like the lot, no trader does; they look down upon us, and make no concealment; and, besides, they're partly Kanakaized, and suck up with natives instead of with other white men like themselves. I had on a rig of clean striped pyjamas—for, of course, I had dressed decent to go before the chiefs; but when I saw the missionary step out of this boat in the regular uniform, white duck clothes, pith helmet, white shirt and tie, and yellow boots to his feet, I could have bunged stones at him. As he came nearer, queering me pretty curious (because of the fight, I suppose), I saw he looked mortal sick, for the truth was he had a fever on, and had just had a chill in the boat.

'Mr Tarleton, I believe?' says I, for I had got his name.

'And you, I suppose, are the new trader?' says he.

'I want to tell you first that I don't hold with missions,' I went on, 'and that I think you and the likes of you do a sight of harm, filling up the natives with old wives' tales and bumptiousness.'

'You are perfectly entitled to your opinions,' says he, looking a bit ugly, 'but I have no call to hear them.'

'It so happens that you've got to hear them,' I said. 'I'm no missionary, nor missionary lover; I'm no Kanaka, nor favourer of Kanakas—I'm just a trader; I'm just a common, low-down, God-damned white man and British subject, the sort you would like to wipe your boots on. I hope that's plain!'

'Yes, my man,' said he. 'It's more plain than creditable. When you are sober, you'll be sorry for this.'

He tried to pass on, but I stopped him with my hand. The Kanakas were beginning to growl. Guess they didn't like my tone, for I spoke to that man as free as I would to you.

'Now, you can't say I've deceived you,' said I, 'and I can go on. I want a service—I want two services, in fact; and if you care to give me them, I'll perhaps take more stock in what you call your Christianity.'

He was silent for a moment. Then he smiled. 'You are rather a strange sort of man,' says he.

'I'm the sort of man God made me,' says I. 'I don't set up to be a gentleman,' I said.

'I am not quite so sure,' said he. 'And what can I do for you, Mr ——?'

'Wiltshire,' I says, 'though I'm mostly called Welsher; but Wiltshire is the way it's spelt, if the people on the beach could only get their tongues about it. And what do I want? Well, I'll tell you the first thing. I'm what you call a sinner—what I call a sweep—and I want you to help me make it up to a person I've deceived.'

He turned and spoke to his crew in the native. 'And now I am at your service,' said he, 'but only for the time my crew are dining. I must be much farther down the coast before night. I was delayed at Papa-Malulu till this morning, and I have an engagement in Fale-alii to-morrow night.'

I led the way to my house in silence, and rather pleased with myself for the way I had managed the talk, for I like a man to keep his self-respect.

'I was sorry to see you fighting,' says he.

'O, that's part of the yarn I want to tell you,' I said. 'That's service number two. After you've heard it you'll let me know whether you're sorry or not.'

We walked right in through the store, and I was surprised to find Uma had cleared away the dinner things. This was so unlike her ways that I saw she had done it out of gratitude, and liked her the better. She and Mr Tarleton called each other by name, and he was very civil to her seemingly. But I thought little of that; they can always find civility for a Kanaka, it's us white men they lord it over. Besides, I didn't want much Tarleton just then. I was going to do my pitch.

'Uma,' said I, 'give us your marriage certificate.' She looked put out. 'Come,' said I, 'you can trust me. Hand it up.'

She had it about her person, as usual; I believe she thought it was a pass to heaven, and if she died without having it handy she would go to hell. I couldn't see where she put it the first time, I couldn't see now where she took it from; it seemed to jump into her hand like that Blavatsky business in the papers. But it's the same way with all island women, and I guess they're taught it when young.

'Now,' said I, with the certificate in my hand, 'I was married to this girl by Black Joe the negro. The certificate was wrote by Case, and it's a dandy piece of literature, I promise you. Since then I've found out there's a kind of cry in the place against this wife of mine, and so long as I keep her I cannot trade. Now, what would any man do in my place, if he was a man?' I said. 'The first thing he would do is this, I guess.' And I took and tore up the certificate and bunged the pieces on the floor.

'*Aué!*'[1] cried Uma, and began to clap her hands; but I caught one of them in mine.

'And the second thing that he would do,' said I, 'if he was what I would call a man and you would call a man, Mr Tarleton, is to bring the girl right before you or any other missionary, and to up and say: "I was wrong married to this wife of mine, but I think a heap of her, and now I want to be married to her right." Fire away, Mr Tarleton. And I guess you'd better do it in native; it'll please the old lady,' I said, giving her the proper name of a man's wife upon the spot.

[1] Alas!

So we had in two of the crew for to witness, and were spliced in our own house; and the parson prayed a good bit, I must say—but not so long as some—and shook hands with the pair of us.

'Mr Wiltshire,' he says, when he had made out the lines and packed off the witnesses, 'I have to thank you for a very lively pleasure. I have rarely performed the marriage ceremony with more grateful emotions.'

That was what you would call talking. He was going on, besides, with more of it, and I was ready for as much taffy as he had in stock, for I felt good. But Uma had been taken up with something half through the marriage, and cut straight in.

'How your hand he get hurt?' she asked.

'You ask Case's head, old lady,' says I.

She jumped with joy, and sang out.

'You haven't made much of a Christian of this one,' says I to Mr Tarleton.

'We didn't think her one of our worst,' says he, 'when she was at Fale-alii; and if Uma bears malice I shall be tempted to fancy she has good cause.'

'Well, there we are at service number two,' said I. 'I want to tell you our yarn, and see if you can let a little daylight in.'

'Is it long?' he asked.

'Yes,' I cried; 'it's a goodish bit of a yarn!'

'Well, I'll give you all the time I can spare,' says he, looking at his watch. 'But I must tell you fairly, I haven't eaten since five this morning, and, unless you can let me have something, I am not likely to eat again before seven or eight to-night.'

'By God, we'll give you dinner,' I cried.

I was a little caught up at my swearing, just when all was going straight; and so was the missionary, I suppose, but he made believe to look out of the window, and thanked us.

So we ran him up a bit of a meal. I was bound to let the old lady have a hand in it, to show off, so I deputized her to brew the tea. I don't think I ever met such tea as she turned out. But that was not the worst, for she got round with the salt-box, which she considered an extra European touch, and turned my stew into sea-water. Altogether, Mr Tarleton had a devil of a dinner of it; but he had plenty entertainment by the way, for all the while that we were cooking, and afterwards, when he was making believe to eat, I kept posting him up on Master

Case and the beach of Falesá, and he putting questions that
showed he was following close.

'Well,' said he at last, 'I am afraid you have a dangerous
enemy. This man Case is very clever, and seems really wicked.
I must tell you I have had my eye on him for nearly a year,
and have rather had the worst of our encounters. About the
time when the last representative of your firm ran so suddenly
away, I had a letter from Namu, the native pastor, begging me
to come to Falesá at my earliest convenience, as his flock were
all "adopting Catholic practices". I had great confidence in
Namu; I fear it only shows how easily we are deceived. No
one could hear him preach and not be persuaded he was a
man of extraordinary parts. All our islanders easily acquire a
kind of eloquence, and can roll out and illustrate, with a great
deal of vigour and fancy, second-hand sermons; but Namu's
sermons are his own, and I cannot deny that I have found them
means of grace. Moreover, he has a keen curiosity in secular
things, does not fear work, is clever at carpentering, and has
made himself so much respected among the neighbouring
pastors that we call him, in a jest which is half serious, the
Bishop of the East. In short, I was proud of the man; all the
more puzzled by his letter, and took an occasion to come this
way. The morning before my arrival, Vigours had been sent
on board the *Lion*, and Namu was perfectly at his ease,
apparently ashamed of his letter, and quite unwilling to
explain it. This, of course, I could not allow, and he ended by
confessing that he had been much concerned to find his people
using the sign of the cross, but since he had learned the explanation his mind was satisfied. For Vigours had the Evil Eye, a
common thing in a country of Europe called Italy, where men
were often struck dead by that kind of devil, and it appeared
the sign of the cross was a charm against its power.

' "And I explain it, Misi," said Namu, "in this way: The
country in Europe is a Popey country, and the devil of the
Evil Eye may be a Catholic devil, or, at least, used to Catholic
ways. So then I reasoned thus: If this sign of the cross were used
in a Popey manner it would be sinful, but when it is used to
only protect men from a devil, which is a thing harmless in
itself, the sign too must be, as a bottle is neither good nor bad,
harmless. For the sign is neither good nor bad. But if the bottle
be full of gin, the gin is bad; and if the sign be made in idolatry

bad, so is the idolatry." And, very like a native pastor, he had a text apposite about the casting out of devils.

' "And who has been telling you about the Evil Eye?" I asked.

'He admitted it was Case. Now, I am afraid you will think me very narrow, Mr Wiltshire, but I must tell you I was displeased, and cannot think a trader at all a good man to advise or have an influence upon my pastors. And, besides, there had been some flying talk in the country of old Adams and his being poisoned, to which I had paid no great heed; but it came back to me at the moment.

' "And is this Case a man of a sanctified life?" I asked.

'He admitted he was not; for, though he did not drink, he was profligate with women, and had no religion.

' "Then," said I, "I think the less you have to do with him the better."

'But it is not easy to have the last word with a man like Namu. He was ready in a moment with an illustration. "Misi," said he, "you have told me there were wise men, not pastors, not even holy, who knew many things useful to be taught— about trees, for instance, and beasts, and to print books, and about the stones that are burned to make knives of. Such men teach you in your college, and you learn from them, but take care not to learn to be unholy. Misi, Case is my college."

'I knew not what to say. Mr Vigours had evidently been driven out of Falesá by the machinations of Case and with something not very unlike the collusion of my pastor. I called to mind it was Namu who had reassured me about Adams and traced the rumour to the ill-will of the priest. And I saw I must inform myself more thoroughly from an impartial source. There is an old rascal of a chief here, Faiaso, whom I daresay you saw to-day at the council; he has been all his life turbulent and sly, a great fomenter of rebellions, and a thorn in the side of the mission and the island. For all that he is very shrewd, and, except in politics or about his own misdemeanours, a teller of the truth. I went to his house, told him what I had heard, and besought him to be frank. I do not think I had ever a more painful interview. Perhaps you will understand me, Mr Wiltshire, if I tell you that I am perfectly serious in these old wives' tales with which you reproached me, and as anxious to do well for these islands as you can be to please and protect your pretty wife. And you are to remember that I thought Namu a paragon, and was proud of the man as one of the first ripe fruits of the mission. And now I was informed that he had fallen in a sort of dependence upon Case. The beginning of it was not corrupt; it began, doubtless, in fear and respect, produced by trickery and pretence; but I was shocked to find that another element had been lately added, that Namu helped himself in the store, and was believed to be deep in Case's debt. Whatever the trader said, that Namu believed with trembling. He was not alone in this; many in the village lived in a similar subjection; but Namu's case was the most influential, it was through Namu Case had wrought most evil; and with a certain following among the chiefs, and the pastor in his pocket, the man was as good as master of the village. You know something of Vigours and Adams, but perhaps you have never heard of old Underhill, Adams' predecessor. He was a quiet, mild old fellow, I remember, and we were told he had died suddenly: white men die very suddenly in Falesá. The truth, as I now heard it, made my blood run cold. It seems he was struck with a general palsy, all of him dead but one eye, which he continually winked. Word was started that this helpless old man was now a devil, and this vile fellow Case worked upon the natives' fears, which he professed to share, and pretended he durst not go into the house alone. At last a grave was dug, and the living body buried at the far end of the village. Namu, my pastor, whom I had helped to educate, offered up a prayer at the hateful scene.

'I felt myself in a very difficult position. Perhaps it was my duty to have denounced Namu and had him deposed. Perhaps I think so now, but at the time it seemed less clear. He had a great influence, it might prove greater than mine. The natives are prone to superstition; perhaps by stirring them up I might but ingrain and spread these dangerous fancies. And Namu besides, apart from this novel and accursed influence, was a good pastor, an able man, and spiritually minded. Where should I look for a better? How was I to find as good? At that moment, with Namu's failure fresh in my view, the work of my life appeared a mockery; hope was dead in me. I would rather repair such tools as I had than go abroad in quest of others that must certainly prove worse; and a scandal is, at the best, a thing to be avoided when humanly possible. Right or wrong, then, I determined on a quiet course. All that night I denounced and reasoned with the erring pastor, twitted him with his ignorance and want of faith, twitted him with his wretched attitude, making clean the outside of the cup and platter, callously helping at a murder, childishly flying in excitement about a few childish, unnecessary, and inconvenient gestures; and long before that day I had him on his knees and bathed in the tears of what seemed a genuine repentance. On Sunday I took the pulpit in the morning, and preached from First Kings, nineteenth, on the fire, the earthquake, and the voice, distinguishing the true spiritual power, and referring with such plainness as I dared to recent events in Falesá. The effect produced was great, and it was much increased when Namu rose in his turn and confessed that he had been wanting in faith and conduct, and was convinced of sin. So far, then, all was well; but there was one unfortunate circumstance. It was nearing the time of our "May" in the island, when the native contributions to the missions are received; it fell in my duty to make a notification on the subject, and this gave my enemy his chance, by which he was not slow to profit.

'News of the whole proceedings must have been carried to Case as soon as church was over, and the same afternoon he made an occasion to meet me in the midst of the village. He came up with so much intentness and animosity that I felt it would be damaging to avoid him.

' "So," says he, in native, "here is the holy man. He has been preaching against me, but that was not in his heart. He has been preaching upon the love of God; but that was not in his heart, it was between his teeth. Will you know what was in his heart?" cries he. "I will show it you!" And, making a snatch at my head, he made believe to pluck out a dollar, and held it in the air.

'There went that rumour through the crowd with which Polynesians receive a prodigy. As for myself, I stood amazed. The thing was a common conjuring trick which I have seen performed at home a score of times; but how was I to convince the villagers of that? I wished I had learned legerdemain instead of Hebrew, that I might have paid the fellow out with his own coin. But there I was; I could not stand there silent, and the best I could find to say was weak.

' "I will trouble you not to lay hands on me again," said I.

' "I have no such thought," said he, "nor will I deprive you of your dollar. Here it is," he said, and flung it at my feet. I am told it lay where it fell three days.'

'I must say it was well played,' said I.

'O! he is clever,' said Mr Tarleton, 'and you can now see for yourself how dangerous. He was a party to the horrid death of the paralytic; he is accused of poisoning Adams; he drove Vigours out of the place by lies that might have led to murder; and there is no question but he has now made up his mind to rid himself of you. How he means to try we have no guess; only be sure, it's something new. There is no end to his readiness and invention.'

'He gives himself a sight of trouble,' says I. 'And after all, what for?'

'Why, how many tons of copra may they make in this district?' asked the missionary.

'I daresay as much as sixty tons,' says I.

'And what is the profit to the local trader?' he asked.

'You may call it three pounds,' said I.

'Then you can reckon for yourself how much he does it for,' said Mr Tarleton. 'But the more important thing is to defeat him. It is clear he spread some report against Uma, in order to isolate and have his wicked will of her. Failing of that, and seeing a new rival come upon the scene, he used her in a different way. Now, the first point to find out is about Namu. Uma, when people began to leave you and your mother alone, what did Namu do?'

'Stop away all-e-same,' says Uma.

'I fear the dog has returned to his vomit,' said Mr Tarleton. 'And now what am I to do for you? I will speak to Namu, I will warn him he is observed; it will be strange if he allow anything to go on amiss when he is put upon his guard. At the same time, this precaution may fail, and then you must turn elsewhere. You have two people at hand to whom you might apply. There is, first of all, the priest, who might protect you by the Catholic interest; they are a wretchedly small body, but they count two chiefs. And then there is old Faiaso. Ah! if it had been some years ago you would have needed no one else; but his influence is much reduced, it has gone into Maea's hands, and Maea, I fear, is one of Case's jackals. In fine, if the worst comes to the worst, you must send up or come yourself to Fale-alii, and, though I am not due at this end of the island for a month, I will just see what can be done.'

So Mr Tarleton said farewell; and half an hour later the crew were singing and the paddles flashing in the missionary-boat.

Chapter IV

DEVIL-WORK

NEAR a month went by without much doing. The same night of our marriage Galoshes called round, and made himself mighty civil, and got into a habit of dropping in about dark and smoking his pipe with the family. He could talk to Uma, of course, and started to teach me native and French at the same time. He was a kind old buffer, though the dirtiest you would wish to see, and he muddled me up with foreign languages worse than the tower of Babel.

That was one employment we had, and it made me feel less lonesome; but there was no profit in the thing, for though the priest came and sat and yarned, none of his folks could be enticed into my store; and if it hadn't been for the other occupation I struck out, there wouldn't have been a pound of copra in the house. This was the idea: Fa'avao (Uma's mother) had a score of bearing trees. Of course we could get no labour, being all as good as tabooed, and the two women and I turned to and made copra with our own hands. It was copra to make your mouth water when it was done—I never understood how much the natives cheated me till I had made that four hundred pounds of my own hand—and it weighed so light I felt inclined to take and water it myself.

When we were at the job a good many Kanakas used to put in the best of the day looking on, and once that nigger turned up. He stood back with the natives and laughed and did the big don and the funny dog, till I began to get riled.

G

'Here, you nigger!' says I.

'I don't address myself to you, Sah,' says the nigger. 'Only speak to gen'le'um.'

'I know,' says I, 'but it happens I was addressing myself to you, Mr Black Jack. And all I want to know is just this: Did you see Case's figure-head about a week ago?'

'No, Sah,' says he.

'That's all right, then,' says I; 'for I'll show you the own brother to it, only black, in the inside of about two minutes.'

And I began to walk towards him, quite slow, and my hands down; only there was trouble in my eye, if anybody took the pains to look.

'You're a low, obstropulous fellow, Sah,' says he.

'You bet!' says I.

By that time he thought I was about as near as convenient, and lit out so it would have done your heart good to see him travel. And that was all I saw of that precious gang until what I am about to tell you.

It was one of my chief employments these days to go pot-hunting in the woods, which I found (as Case had told me) very rich in game. I have spoken of the cape which shut up the village and my station from the east. A path went about the end of it, and led into the next bay. A strong wind blew here daily, and as the line of the barrier reef stopped at the end of the cape, a heavy surf ran on the shores of the bay. A little cliffy hill cut the valley in two parts, and stood close on the beach; and at high water the sea broke right on the face of it, so that all passage was stopped. Woody mountains hemmed the place all round; the barrier to the east was particularly steep and leafy, the lower parts of it, along the sea, falling in sheer black cliffs streaked with cinnabar; the upper part lumpy with the tops of the great trees. Some of the trees were bright green, and some red, and the sand of the beach as black as your shoes. Many birds hovered round the bay, some of them snow-white; and the flying-fox (or vampire) flew there in broad daylight, gnashing its teeth.

For a long while I came as far as this shooting, and went no farther. There was no sign of any path beyond, and the cocoa palms in the front of the foot of the valley were the last this way. For the whole 'eye' of the island, as natives call the windward end, lay desert. From Falesá round about to Papa-malulu, there was neither house nor man, nor planted fruit-tree; and the reef being mostly absent, and the shores bluff, the sea beat direct among crags, and there was scarce a landing-place.

I should tell you that after I began to go in the woods, although no one offered to come near my store, I found people willing enough to pass the time of day with me where nobody could see them; and as I had begun to pick up native, and most of them had a word or two of English, I began to hold little odds and ends of conversation, not to much purpose to be sure, but they took off the worst of the feeling, for it's a miserable thing to be made a leper of.

It chanced one day towards the end of the month, that I was sitting in this bay in the edge of the bush, looking east, with a Kanaka. I had given him a fill of tobacco, and we were making out to talk as best we could; indeed, he had more English than most.

I asked him if there was no road going eastward.

'One time one road,' said he. 'Now he dead.'

'Nobody he go there?' I asked.

'No good,' said he. 'Too much devil he stop there.'

'Oho!' says I, 'got-um plenty devil, that bush?'

'Man devil, woman devil; too much devil,' said my friend. 'Stop there all-e-time. Man he go there, no come back.'

I thought if this fellow was so well posted on devils and spoke of them so free, which is not common, I had better fish for a little information about myself and Uma.

'You think me one devil?' I asked.

'No think devil,' said he soothingly. 'Think all-e-same fool.'

'Uma, she devil?' I asked again.

'No, no; no devil. Devil stop bush,' said the young man.

I was looking in front of me across the bay, and I saw the hanging front of the woods pushed suddenly open, and Case, with a gun in his hand, step forth into the sunshine on the black beach. He was got up in light pyjamas, near white, his gun sparkled, he looked mighty conspicuous; and the land-crabs scuttled from all round him to their holes.

'Hullo, my friend!' says I, 'you no talk all-e-same true. Ese he go, he come back.'

'Ese no all-e-same; Ese *Tiapolo*,' says my friend; and, with a 'Good-bye,' slunk off among the trees.

I watched Case all round the beach, where the tide was low; and let him pass me on the homeward way to Falesá. He was in deep thought, and the birds seemed to know it, trotting quite near him on the sand, or wheeling and calling in his ears. When he passed me I could see by the working of his lips that he was talking to himself, and what pleased me mightily, he had still my trade mark oh his brow. I tell you the plain truth: I had a mind to give him a gunful in his ugly mug, but I thought better of it.

All this time, and all the time I was following home, I kept repeating that native word, which I remembered by 'Polly, put the kettle on and make us all some tea,' tea-a-pollo.

'Uma,' says I, when I got back, 'what does *Tiapolo* mean?'

'Devil,' says she.

'I thought *aitu* was the word for that,' I said.

'*Aitu* 'nother kind of devil,' said she; 'stop bush, eat Kanaka. Tiapolo big chief devil, stop home; all-e-same Christian devil.'

'Well then,' said I, 'I'm no farther forward. How can Case be Tiapolo?'

'No all-e-same,' said she. 'Ese belong Tiapolo; Tiapolo too much like; Ese all-e-same his son. Suppose Ese he wish something, Tiapolo he make him.'

'That's mighty convenient for Ese,' says I. 'And what kind of things does he make for him?'

Well, out came a rigmarole of all sorts of stories, many of which (like the dollar he took from Mr Tarleton's head) were plain enough to me, but others I could make nothing of; and the thing that most surprised the Kanakas was what surprised me least—namely, that he would go in the desert among all the *aitus*. Some of the boldest, however, had accompanied him, and had heard him speak with the dead and give them orders, and, safe in his protection, had returned unscathed. Some said he had a church there, where he worshipped Tiapolo, and Tiapolo appeared to him; others swore that there was no sorcery at all, that he performed his miracles by the power of prayer, and the church was no church, but a prison, in which he had confined a dangerous *aitu*. Namu had been in the bush with him once, and returned glorifying God for these wonders. Altogether, I began to have a glimmer of the man's position, and the means by which he had acquired it, and though I saw he was a tough nut to crack, I was noways cast down.

'Very well,' said I, 'I'll have a look at Master Case's place of worship myself, and we'll see about the glorifying.'

At this Uma fell in a terrible taking; if I went in the high bush I should never return; none could go there but by the protection of Tiapolo.

'I'll chance it on God's,' said I. 'I'm a good sort of a fellow, Uma, as fellows go, and I guess God'll con me through.'

She was silent for a while. 'I think,' said she, mighty solemn—and then, presently—'Victoreea, he big chief?'

'You bet?' said I.

'He like you too much?' she asked again.

I told her with a grin, I believed the old lady was rather partial to me.

'All right,' said she. 'Victoreea he big chief, like you too much. No can help you here in Falesá; no can do—too far off. Maea he small chief—stop here. Suppose he like you—make you all right. All-e-same God and Tiapolo. God he big chief—got too much work. Tiapolo he small chief—he like too much make-see, work very hard.'

'I'll have to hand you over to Mr Tarleton,' said I. 'Your theology's out of its bearings, Uma.'

However, we stuck to this business all the evening, and, with the stories she told me of the desert and its dangers, she came near frightening herself into a fit. I don't remember half a quarter of them, of course, for I paid little heed; but two come back to me kind of clear.

About six miles up the coast there is a sheltered cove they call *Fanga-anaana*—'the haven full of caves'. I've seen it from the sea myself, as near as I could get my boys to venture in; and it's a little strip of yellow sand. Black cliffs overhang it, full of the black mouths of caves; great trees overhang the cliffs, and dangle-down lianas; and in one place, about the middle, a big brook pours over in a cascade. Well, there was a boat going by here, with six young men of Falesá, 'all very pretty,' Uma said, which was the loss of them. It blew strong, there was a heavy head sea and by the time they opened Fanga-anaana, and saw the white cascade and the shady beach, they were all tired and thirsty, and their water had run out. One proposed to land and get a drink, and, being reckless fellows, they were all of the same mind except the youngest.

Lotu was his name; he was a very good young gentleman, and
very wise; and he held out that they were crazy, telling them
the place was given over to spirits and devils and the dead,
and there were no living folk nearer than six miles the one way,
and may be twelve the other. But they laughed at his words,
and, being five to one, pulled in, beached the boat, and landed.
It was a wonderful pleasant place, Lotu said, and the water
excellent. They walked round the beach, but could see nowhere any way to mount the cliffs, which made them easier
in their mind; and at last they sat down to make a meal on the
food they had brought with them. They were scarce set,
when there came out of the mouth of one of the black caves
six of the most beautiful ladies ever seen: they had flowers in
their hair, and the most beautiful breasts, and necklaces of
scarlet seeds; and began to jest with these young gentlemen,
and the young gentlemen to jest back with them, all but Lotu.
As for Lotu, he saw there could be no living woman in such a
place, and ran, and flung himself in the bottom of the boat,
and covered his face, and prayed. All the time the business
lasted Lotu made one clean break of prayer, and that was all
he knew of it, until his friends came back, and make him sit
up, and they put to sea again out of the bay, which was now
quite desert, and no word of the six ladies. But, what frightened
Lotu, most, not one of the five remembered anything of what
had passed, but they were all like drunken men, and sang and
laughed in the boat, and skylarked. The wind freshened and
came squally, and the sea rose extraordinary high; it was such
weather as any man in the islands would have turned his back
to and fled home to Falesá; but these five were like crazy folk,
and cracked on all sail and drove their boat into the seas.
Lotu went to the bailing; none of the others thought to help
him, but sang and skylarked and carried on, and spoke
singular things beyond a man's comprehension, and laughed
out loud when they said them. So the rest of the day Lotu
bailed for his life in the bottom of the boat, and was all
drenched with sweat and cold sea-water; and none heeded
him. Against all expectation, they came safe in a dreadful
tempest to Papa-malulu, where the palms were singing out,
and the cocoa-nuts flying like cannon-balls about the village
green; and the same night the five young gentlemen sickened,
and spoke never a reasonable word until they died.

'And do you mean to tell me you can swallow a yarn like that?' I asked.

She told me the thing was well known, and with handsome young men alone it was even common; but this was the only case where five had been slain the same day and in a company by the love of the women-devils; and it had made a great stir in the island, and she would be crazy if she doubted.

'Well, anyway,' says I, 'you needn't be frightened about me. I've no use for the women-devils. You're all the women I want, and all the devil too, old lady.'

To this she answered there were other sorts, and she had seen one with her own eyes. She had gone one day alone to the next bay, and, perhaps, got too near the margin of the bad place. The boughs of the high bush overshadowed her from the cant of the hill, but she herself was outside on a flat place, very stony and growing full of young mummy-apples four and five feet high. It was a dark day in the rainy season, and now there came squalls that tore off the leaves and sent them flying, and now it was all still as in a house. It was in one of these still times that a whole gang of birds and flying foxes came pegging out of the bush like creatures frightened. Presently after she heard a rustle nearer hand, and saw, coming out of the margin of the trees, among the mummy-apples, the appearance of a lean grey old boar. It seemed to think as it came, like a person; and all of a sudden, as she looked at it coming, she was aware it was no boar but a thing that was a man with a man's thoughts. At that she ran, and the pig after her, and as the pig ran it holla'd aloud, so that the place rang with it.

'I wish I had been there with my gun,' said I. 'I guess that pig would have holla'd so as to surprise himself.'

But she told me a gun was of no use with the like of these, which were the spirits of the dead.

Well, this kind of talk put in the evening, which was the best of it; but of course it didn't change my notion, and the next day, with my gun and a good knife, I set off upon a voyage of discovery. I made, as near as I could, for the place where I had seen Case come out; for if it was true he had some kind of establishment in the bush I reckoned I should find a path. The beginning of the desert was marked off by a

wall, to call it so, for it was more of a long mound of stones.
They say it reaches right across the island, but how they know
it is another question, for I doubt if anyone has made the
journey in a hundred years, the natives sticking chiefly to the
sea and their little colonies along the coast, and that part being
mortal high and steep and full of cliffs. Up to the west side of
the wall, the ground has been cleared, and there are cocoa
palms and mummy-apples and guavas, and lots of sensitive.
Just across, the bush begins outright; high bush at that, trees
going up like the masts of ships, and ropes of liana hanging
down like a ship's rigging, and nasty orchids growing in the
forks like funguses. The ground where there was no underwood looked to be a heap of boulders. I saw many green
pigeons which I might have shot, only I was there with a
different idea. A number of butterflies flopped up and down
along the ground like dead leaves; sometimes I would hear a
bird calling, sometimes the wind overhead, and always the
sea along the coast.

But the queerness of the place it's more difficult to tell of,
unless to one who has been alone in the high bush himself.
The brightest kind of a day it is always dim down there. A man
can see to the end of nothing; whichever way he looks the
wood shuts up, one bough folding with another like the
fingers of your hand; and whenever he listens he hears always
something new—men talking, children laughing, the strokes
of an axe a far way ahead of him, and sometimes a sort of a
quick, stealthy scurry near at hand that makes him jump and
look to his weapons. It's all very well for him to tell himself
that he's alone, bar trees and birds; he can't make out to
believe it; whichever way he turns the whole place seems to be
alive and looking on. Don't think it was Uma's yarns that put
me out; I don't value native talk a four-penny-piece; it's a
thing that's natural in the bush, and that's the end of it.

As I got near the top of the hill, for the ground of the wood
goes up in this place steep as a ladder, the wind began to
sound straight on, and the leaves to toss and switch open and
let in the sun. This suited me better; it was the same noise all
the time, and nothing to startle. Well, I had got to a place
where there was an underwood of what they call wild cocoa-
nut—mighty pretty with its scarlet fruit—when there came a
sound of singing in the wind that I thought I had never heard

the like of. It was all very fine to tell myself it was the branches;
I knew better. It was all very fine to tell myself it was a bird; I
knew never a bird that sang like that. It rose and swelled, and
died away and swelled again; and now I thought it was like
someone weeping, only prettier; and now I thought it was like
harps; and there was one thing I made sure of, it was a sight
too sweet to be wholesome in a place like that. You may laugh
if you like; but I declare I called to mind the six young ladies
that came, with their scarlet necklaces, out of the cave at
Fanga-anaana, and wondered if they sang like that. We laugh
at the natives and their superstitions: but see how many
traders take them up, splendidly educated white men that
have been book-keepers (some of them) and clerks in the old
country. It's my belief a superstition grows up in a place like
the different kind of weeds; and as I stood there and listened
to that wailing I twittered in my shoes.

You may call me a coward to be frightened; I thought
myself brave enough to go on ahead. But I went mighty care-
fully, with my gun cocked, spying all about me like a hunter,
fully expecting to see a handsome young woman sitting somewhere in the bush, and fully determined (if I did) to try her
with a charge of duck-shot. And sure enough, I had not gone
far when I met with a queer thing. The wind came on the top
of the wood in a strong puff, the leaves in front of me burst
open, and I saw for a second something hanging in a tree. It
was gone in a wink, the puff blowing by and the leaves
closing. I tell you the truth: I had made up my mind to see an
aitu; and if the thing had looked like a pig or a woman, it
wouldn't have given me the same turn. The trouble was that
it seemed kind of square, and the idea of a square thing that
was alive and sang knocked me sick and silly. I must have
stood quite a while; and I made pretty certain it was right out
of the same tree that the singing came. Then I began to come
to myself a bit.

'Well,' says I, 'if this is really so, if this is a place where there
are square things that sing, I'm gone up anyway. Let's have
my fun for my money.'

But I thought I might as well take the off chance of a prayer
being any good; so I plumped on my knees and prayed out
loud; and all the time I was praying the strange sounds came
out of the tree, and went up and down, and changed, for all

the world like music, only you could see it wasn't human—
there was nothing there that you could whistle.

As soon as I had made an end in proper style, I laid down
my gun, stuck my knife between my teeth, walked right up to
that tree, and began to climb. I tell you my heart was like ice.
But presently, as I went up, I caught another glimpse of the
thing, and that relieved me, for I thought it seemed like a box;
and when I had got right up to it I near fell out of the tree
with laughing.

A box it was, sure enough, and a candle-box at that, with
the brand upon the side of it; and it had banjo strings stretched
so as to sound when the wind blew. I believe they call the thing
a Tyrolean[1] harp, whatever that may mean.

'Well, Mr Case,' said I, 'you've frightened me once, but I
defy you to frighten me again,' I says, and slipped down the
tree, and set out again to find my enemy's head office, which
I guessed would not be far away.

The undergrowth was thick in this part; I couldn't see
before my nose, and must burst my way through by main
force and ply the knife as I went, slicing the cords of the lianas
and slashing down whole trees at a blow. I call them trees for
the bigness, but in truth they were just big weeds, and sappy to
cut through like carrot. From all this crowd and kind of
vegetation, I was just thinking to myself, the place might
have once been cleared, when I came on my nose over a pile
of stones, and saw in a moment it was some kind of a work of
man. The Lord knows when it was made or when deserted, for
this part of the island has lain undisturbed since long before
the whites came. A few steps beyond I hit into the path I had
been always looking for. It was narrow, but well beaten, and
I saw that Case had plenty of disciples. It seems, indeed, it
was a piece of fashionable boldness to venture up here with the
trader, and a young man scarce reckoned himself grown till he
had got his breech tattooed, for one thing, and seen Case's
devils for another. This is mighty like Kanakas; but, if you
look at it another way, it's mighty like white folks too.

A bit along the path I was brought to a clear stand, and had
to rub my eyes. There was a wall in front of me, the path
passing it by a gap; it was tumbledown and plainly very old,
but built of big stones very well laid; and there is no native

[1] Æolian.

alive to-day upon that island that could dream of such a piece
of building. Along all the top of it was a line of queer figures,
idols or scarecrows, or what not. They had carved and painted
faces ugly to view, their eyes and teeth were of shell, their hair
and their bright clothes blew in the wind, and some of them
worked with the tugging. There are islands up west where
they make these kind of figures till to-day; but if ever they were
made in this island, the practice and the very recollection of it
are now long forgotten. And the singular thing was that all
these bogies were as fresh as toys out of a shop.

Then it came in my mind that Case had let out to me the
first day that he was a good forger of island curiosities, a thing
by which so many traders turn an honest penny. And with
that I saw the whole business, and how this display served the
man a double purpose, first of all, to season his curiosities, and
then to frighten those that came to visit him.

But I should tell you (what made the thing more curious)
that all the time the Tyrolean harps were harping round me
in the trees, and even while I looked, a green-and-yellow bird
(that, I suppose, was building) began to tear the hair off the
head of one of the figures.

A little farther on I found the best curiosity of the museum.
The first I saw of it was a longish mound of earth with a twist
to it. Digging off the earth with my hands, I found underneath tarpaulin stretched on boards, so that this was plainly
the roof of a cellar. It stood right on the top of the hill, and the
entrance was on the far side, between two rocks, like the
entrance to a cave. I went as far in as the bend, and, looking
round the corner, saw a shining face. It was big and ugly, like
a pantomine mask, and the brightness of it waxed and
dwindled, and at times it smoked.

'Oho!' says I, 'luminous paint!'

And I must say I rather admired the man's ingenuity. With
a box of tools and a few mighty simple contrivances he had
made out to have a devil of a temple. Any poor Kanaka
brought up here in the dark, with the harps whining all round
him, and shown that smoking face in the bottom of a hole,
would make no kind of doubt but he had seen and heard
enough devils for a lifetime. It's easy to find out what Kanakas
think. Just go back to yourself any way round from ten to
fifteen years old, and there's an average Kanaka. There are

some pious, just as there are pious boys; and the most of them, like the boys again, are middling honest and yet think it rather larks to steal, and are easy scared and rather like to be so. I remember a boy I was at school with at home who played the Case business. He didn't know anything, that boy; he couldn't do anything; he had no luminous paint and no Tyrolean harps; he just boldly said he was a sorcerer, and frightened us out of our boots, and we loved it. And then it came in my mind how the master had once flogged that boy and the surprise we were all in to see the sorcerer catch it and bum like anybody else. Thinks I to myself, 'I must find some way of fixing it so for Master Case.' And the next moment I had my idea.

I went back by the path, which, when once you had found it, was quite plain and easy walking; and when I stepped out on the black sands, who should I see but Master Case himself. I cocked my gun and held it handy, and we marched up and passed without a word, each keeping the tail of his eye on the other; and no sooner had we passed than we each wheeled round like fellows drilling, and stood face to face. We had each taken the same notion in his head, you see, that the other fellow might give him the load of his gun in the stern.

'You've shot nothing,' says Case.

'I'm not on the shoot to-day,' said I.

'Well, the devil go with you for me,' says he.

'The same to you,' says I.

But we stuck just the way we were; no fear of either of us moving.

Case laughed. 'We can't stop here all day, though,' said he.

'Don't let me detain you,' says I.

He laughed again. 'Look here, Wiltshire, do you think me a fool?' he asked.

'More of a knave, if you want to know,' says I.

'Well, do you think it would better me to shoot you here, on this open beach?' said he. 'Because I don't. Folks come fishing every day. There may be a score of them up the valley now, making copra; there might be half a dozen on the hill behind you, after pigeons; they might be watching us this minute, and I shouldn't wonder. I give you my word I don't want to shoot you. Why should I? You don't hinder me any. You haven't got one pound of copra but what you made with your own hands, like a negro slave. You're vegetating—that's what I call it—and I don't care where you vegetate, nor yet how long. Give me your word you don't mean to shoot me, and I'll give you a lead and walk away.'

'Well,' said I, 'you're frank and pleasant, ain't you? And I'll be the same. I don't mean to shoot you to-day. Why should I? This business is beginning; it ain't done yet, Mr Case. I've given you one turn already; I can see the marks of my knuckles on your head to this blooming hour, and I've more cooking for you. I'm not a paralee, like Underhill. My name ain't Adams, and it ain't Vigours; and I mean to show you that you've met your match.'

'This is a silly way to talk,' said he. 'This is not the talk to make me move on with.'

'All right,' said I, 'stay where you are. I ain't in any hurry, and you know it. I can put in a day on this beach and never mind. I ain't got any copra to bother with. I ain't got any luminous paint to see to.'

I was sorry I said that last, but it whipped out before I knew. I could see it took the wind out of his sails, and he stood and stared at me with his brow drawn up. Then I suppose he made up his mind he must get to the bottom of this.

'I take you at your word,' says he, and turned his back, and walked right into the devil's bush.

I let him go, of course, for I had passed my word. But I watched him as long as he was in sight, and after he was gone lit out for cover as lively as you would want to see, and went the rest of the way home under the bush, for I didn't trust him sixpence-worth. One thing I saw, I had been ass enough to give him warning, and that which I meant to do I must do at once.

You would think I had had about enough excitement for one morning, but there was another turn waiting me. As soon as I got far enough round the cape to see my house I made out there were strangers there; a little farther, and no doubt about it. There was a couple of armed sentinels squatting at my door. I could only suppose the trouble about Uma must have come to a head, and the station been seized. For aught I could think, Uma was taken up already, and these armed men were waiting to do the like with me.

However, as I came nearer, which I did at top speed, I saw there was a third native sitting on the verandah like a guest, and Uma was talking with him like a hostess. Nearer still I made out it was the big young chief, Maea, and that he was smiling away and smoking. And what was he smoking? None of your European cigarettes fit for a cat, not even the genuine big, knock-me-down native article that a fellow can really put in the time with if his pipe is broke—but a cigar, and one of my Mexicans at that, that I could swear to. At the sight of this my heart started beating, and I took a wild hope in my head that the trouble was over, and Maea had come round.

Uma pointed me out to him as I came up, and he met me at the head of my own stairs like a thorough gentleman.

'Vilivili,' said he, which was the best they could make of my name, 'I pleased.'

There is no doubt when an island chief wants to be civil he can do it. I saw the way things were from the word go. There was no call for Uma to say to me: 'He no 'fraid Ese now, come bring copra.' I tell you I shook hands with that Kanaka like as if he was the best white man in Europe.

The fact was, Case and he had got after the same girl; or Maea suspected it, and concluded to make hay of the trader on the chance. He had dressed himself up, got a couple of his retainers cleaned and armed to kind of make the thing more public, and, just waiting till Case was clear of the village, came round to put the whole of his business my way. He was rich as well as powerful. I suppose that man was worth fifty thousand nuts per annum. I gave him the price of the beach and a quarter cent better, and as for credit, I would have advanced him the inside of the store and the fittings besides, I was so pleased to see him. I must say he bought like a gentleman: rice and tins and biscuits enough for a week's feast, and stuffs by the bolt. He was agreeable besides; he had plenty of fun to him; and we cracked jests together, mostly through the interpreter, because he had mighty little English, and my native was still off colour. One thing I made out: he could never really have thought much harm of Uma; he could never have been really frightened, and must just have made believe from dodginess, and because he thought Case had a strong pull in the village and could help him on.

This set me thinking that both he and I were in a tightish place. What he had done was to fly in the face of the whole village, and the thing might cost him his authority. More than that, after my talk with Case on the beach, I thought it might very well cost me my life. Case had as good as said he would pot me if ever I got any copra; he would come home to find the best business in the village had changed hands; and the best thing I thought I could do was to get in first with the potting.

'See here, Uma,' says I, 'tell him I'm sorry I made him wait, but I was up looking at Case's Tiapolo store in the bush.'

'He want savvy if you no 'fraid?' translated Uma.

I laughed out. 'Not much!' says I. 'Tell him the place is a blooming toy-shop! Tell him in England we give these things to the kids to play with.'

'He want savvy if you hear devil sing?' she asked next.

'Look here,' I said, 'I can't do it now because I've got no banjo-strings in stock; but the next time the ship comes round I'll have one of these same contraptions right here in my verandah, and he can see for himself how much devil there is to it. Tell him, as soon as I can get the strings I'll make one for his picaninnies. The name of the concern is a Tyrolean harp; and you can tell him the name means in English that nobody but dam-fools give a cent for it.'

This time he was so pleased he had to try his English again. 'You talk true?' says he.

'Rather!' said I. 'Talk all-e-same Bible. Bring out a Bible here, Uma, if you've got such a thing, and I'll kiss it. Or, I'll tell you what's better still,' says I, taking a header, 'ask him if he's afraid to go up there himself by day.'

It appeared he wasn't; he could venture as far as that by day and in company.

'That's the ticket, then!' said I. 'Tell him the man's a fraud and the place foolishness, and if he'll go up there to-morrow he'll see all that's left of it. But tell him this, Uma, and mind he understands it: If he gets talking, it's bound to come to Case, and I'm a dead man! I'm playing his game, tell him, and if he says one word my blood will be at his door and be the damnation of him here and after.'

She told him, and he shook hands with me up to the hilt, and, says he: 'No talk. Go up to-mollow. You my friend?'

'No, sir,' says I, 'no such foolishness. I've come here to trade, tell him, and not to make friends. But, as to Case, I'll send that man to glory!'

So off Maea went, pretty well pleased, as I could see.

Chapter V

NIGHT IN THE BUSH

WELL, I was committed now; Tiapolo had to be smashed up before next day, and my hands were pretty full, not only with preparations, but with argument. My house was like a mechanics' debating society: Uma was so made up that I shouldn't go into the bush by night, or that, if I did, I was never to come back again. You know her style of arguing: you've had a specimen about Queen Victoria and the devil; and I leave you to fancy if I was tired of it before dark.

At last I had a good idea. What was the use of casting my pearls before her? I thought; some of her own chopped hay would be likelier to do the business.

'I'll tell you what, then,' said I. 'You fish out your Bible, and I'll take that up along with me. That'll make me right.'

She swore a Bible was no use.

'That's just your Kanaka ignorance,' said I. 'Bring the Bible out.'

She brought it, and I turned to the title-page, where I thought there would likely be some English, and so there was. 'There!' said I. 'Look at that! "*London: Printed for the British and Foreign Bible Society, Blackfriars,*" and the date, which I can't read, owing to its being in these X's. There's no devil in hell can look near the Bible Society, Blackfriars. Why, you silly!' I said, 'how do you suppose we get along with our own *aitus* at home? All Bible Society!'

'I think you no got any,' said she. 'White man, he tell me you no got.'

'Sounds likely, don't it?' I asked. 'Why would these islands all be chock full of them and none in Europe?'

'Well, you no got breadfruit,' said she.

I could have torn my hair. 'Now, look here, old lady,' said I, 'you dry up, for I'm tired of you. I'll take the Bible, which'll put me as straight as the mail, and that's the last word I've got to say.'

The night fell extraordinary dark, clouds coming up with sundown and overspreading all; not a star showed; there was only an end of a moon, and that not due before the small hours. Round the village, what with the lights and the fires in the open houses, and the torches of many fishers moving on the reef, it kept as gay as an illumination; but the sea and the mountains and woods were all clean gone. I suppose it might be eight o'clock when I took the road, laden like a donkey. First there was that Bible, a book as big as your head, which I had let myself in for by my own tomfoolery. Then there was my gun, and knife, and lantern, and patent matches, all necessary. And then there was the real plant of the affair in hand, a mortal weight of gunpowder, a pair of dynamite fishing bombs, and two or three pieces of slow match that I had hauled out of the tin cases and spliced together the best way I could; for the match was only trade stuff, and a man would be crazy that trusted it. Altogether, you see, I had the materials of a pretty good blow-up! Expense was nothing to me; I wanted that thing done right.

As long as I was in the open, and had the lamp in my house to steer by, I did well. But when I got to the path, it fell so dark I could make no headway, walking into trees and swearing there, like a man looking for the matches in his bed-room. I knew it was risky to light up, for my lantern would be visible all the way to the point of the cape, and as no one went there after dark, it would be talked about, and come to Case's ears. But what was I to do? I had either to give the business over and lose caste with Maea, or light up, take my chance, and get through the thing the smartest I was able.

As long as I was on the path I walked hard, but when I came to the black beach I had to run. For the tide was now nearly flowed; and to get through with my powder dry between the surf and the steep hill, took all the quickness I possessed. As it was, even, the wash caught me to the knees, and I came near falling on a stone. All this time the hurry I was in, and the free air and smell of the sea, kept my spirits lively; but when I was once in the bush and began to climb the path I took it easier. The fearsomeness of the wood had been a good bit rubbed off for me by Master Case's banjo-strings and graven images, yet I thought it was a dreary walk, and guessed, when the disciples went up there, they must be badly scared. The light of the lantern, striking among all these trunks, and forked branches and twisted rope-ends of lianas, made the whole place, or all that you could see of it, a kind of a puzzle of turning shadows. They came to meet you, solid and quick like giants, and then span off and vanished; they hove up over your head like clubs, and flew away into the night like birds. The floor of the bush glimmered with dead wood, the way the match-box used to shine after you had struck a lucifer. Big, cold drops fell on me from the branches overhead like sweat. There was no wind to mention; only a little icy breath of a land-breeze that stirred nothing; and the harps were silent.

The first landfall I made was when I got through the bush of wild cocoa-nuts, and came in view of the bogies on the wall. Mighty queer they looked by the shining of the lantern, with their painted faces and shell eyes, and their clothes and their hair hanging. One after another I pulled them all up and piled them in a bundle on the cellar roof, so as they might go to glory with the rest. Then I chose a place behind one of the big stones at the entrance, buried my powder and the two shells, and arranged my match along the passage. And then I had a look at the smoking head, just for good-bye. It was doing fine.

'Cheer up,' says I. 'You're booked.'

It was my first idea to light up and be getting homeward; the darkness and the glimmer of the dead wood and the shadows of the lantern made me lonely. But I knew where one of the harps hung; it seemed a pity it shouldn't go with the rest; and at the same time I couldn't help letting on to myself that I was mortal tired of my employment, and would like best to be at home and have the door shut. I stepped out of the cellar and argued it fore and back. There was a sound of the sea far down below me on the coast; nearer hand not a leaf stirred; I might have been the only living creature this side of Cape Horn. Well, as I stood there thinking, it seemed the bush woke and became full of little noises. Little noises they were, and nothing to hurt—a bit of a crackle, a bit of a rush—but the breath jumped right out of me and my throat went as dry as a biscuit. It wasn't Case I was afraid of, which would have been common-sense; I never thought of Case; what took me, as sharp as the colic, was the old wives' tales, the devil-women and the man-pigs. It was the toss of a penny whether I should run: but I got a purchase on myself, and stepped out and held up the lantern (like a fool) and looked all round.

In the direction of the village and the path there was nothing
to be seen; but when I turned inland it's a wonder to me I
didn't drop. There, coming right up out of the desert and the
bad bush—there, sure enough, was a devil-woman, just as the
way I had figured she would look. I saw the light shine on
her bare arms and her bright eyes, and there went out of me a
yell so big that I thought it was my death.

'Ah! No sing out!' says the devil-woman, in a kind of a high
whisper. 'Why you talk big voice? Put out light! Ese he come.'

'My God Almighty, Uma, is that you?' says I.

'*Ioe*,'[1] says she. 'I come quick. Ese here soon.

'You come alone?' I asked. 'You no 'fraid?'

'Ah, too much 'fraid!' she whispered, clutching me. 'I
think die.'

'Well,' says I, with a kind of a weak grin, 'I'm not the one
to laugh at you, Mrs Wiltshire, for I'm about the worst
scared man in the South Pacific myself.'

She told me in two words what brought her. I was scarce
gone, it seems, when Fa'avao came in, and the old woman
had met Black Joe running as hard as he was fit from our house
to Case's. Uma neither spoke nor stopped, but lit right out
to come and warn me. She was so close at my heels that the
lantern was her guide across the beach, and afterwards, by
the glimmer of it in the trees, she got her line up hill. It was
only when I had got to the top or was in the cellar that she
wandered Lord knews where! and lost a sight of precious time,
afraid to call out lest Case was at the heels of her, and falling
in the bush, so that she was all knocked and bruised. That
must have been when she got too far to the southward, and
how she came to take me in the flank at last and frighten me
beyond what I've got the words to tell of.

Well, anything was better than a devil-woman, but I
thought her yarn serious enough. Black Jack had no call to
be about my house, unless he was set there to watch; and it
looked to me as if my tomfool word about the paint, and perhaps some chatter of Maea's, had got us all in a clove hitch.
One thing was clear: Uma and I were here for the night; we
daren't try to go home before day, and even then it would be
safer to strike round up the mountain and come in by the back
of the village, or we might walk into an ambuscade. It was

[1] Yes.

plain, too, that the mine should be sprung immediately, or Case might be in time to stop it.

I marched into the tunnel, Uma keeping tight hold of me, opened my lantern and lit the match. The first length of it burned like a spill of paper, and I stood stupid, watching it burn, and thinking we were going aloft with Tiapolo, which was none of my views. The second took a better rate, though faster than I cared about; and at that I got my wits again, hauled Uma clear of the passage, blew out and dropped the lantern, and the pair of us groped our way into the bush until I thought it might be safe, and lay down together by a tree.

'Old lady,' I said, 'I won't forget this night. You're a trump and that's what's wrong with you.'

She humped herself close up to me. She had run out the way she was, with nothing on her but her kilt; and she was all wet with the dews and the sea on the black beach, and shook straight on with cold and the terror of the dark and the devils.

'Too much 'fraid,' was all she said.

The far side of Case's hill goes down near as steep as a precipice into the next valley. We were on the very edge of it, and I could see the dead wood shine and hear the sea sound far below. I didn't care about the position, which left me no retreat, but I was afraid to change. Then I saw I had made a worse mistake about the lantern, which I should have left lighted, so that I could have had a crack at Case when he stepped into the shine of it. And even if I hadn't had the wit to do that, it seemed a senseless thing to leave the good lantern to blow up with the graven images. The thing belonged to me, after all, and was worth money, and might come in handy. If I could have trusted the match, I might have run in still and rescued it. But who was going to trust the match? You know what trade is. The stuff was good enough for Kanakas to go fishing with, where they've got to look lively anyway, and the most they risk is only to have their hand blown off. But for anyone that wanted to fool around a blow-up like mine that match was rubbish.

Altogether the best I could do was to lie still, see my shotgun handy, and wait for the explosion. But it was a solemn kind of a business. The blackness of the night was like solid; the only thing you could see was the nasty bogy glimmer of the dead wood, and that showed you nothing but itself; and as for sounds, I stretched my ears till I thought I could have heard the match burn in the tunnel, and that bush was as silent as a coffin. Now and then there was a bit of a crack; but whether it was near or far, whether it was Case stubbing his toes within a few yard of me, or a tree breaking miles away, I knew no more than the babe unborn.

And then, all of a sudden, Vesuvius went off. It was a long time coming; but when it came (though I say it that shouldn't) no man could ask to see a better. At first it was just a son of a gun of a row, and a spout of fire, and the wood lighted up so that you could see to read. And then the trouble began. Uma and I were half buried under a wagonful of earth, and glad it was no worse, for one of the rocks at the entrance of the tunnel was fired clean into the air, fell within a couple of fathoms of where we lay, and bounded over the edge of the hill, and went pounding down into the next valley. I saw I had rather under-calculated our distance, or overdone the dynamite and powder, which you please.

And presently I saw I had made another slip. The noise of the thing began to die off, shaking the island; the dazzle was over; and yet the night didn't come back the way I expected. For the whole wood was scattered with red coals and brands from the explosion; they were all round me on the flat; some had fallen below in the valley, and some stuck and flared in the tree-tops. I had no fear of fire, for these forests were too wet to kindle. But the trouble was that the place was all lit up—not very bright, but good enough to get a shot by; and the way the coals were scattered, it was just as likely Case might have the advantage as myself. I looked all round for his white face, you may be sure; but there was not a sign of him. As for Uma, the life seemed to have been knocked right out of her by the bang and blaze of it.

There was one bad point in my game. One of the blessed graven images had come down all afire, hair and clothes and body, not four yards away from me. I cast a mighty noticing glance all round; there was still no Case, and I made up my mind I must get rid of that burning stick before he came, or I should be shot there like a dog.

It was my first idea to have crawled, and then I thought speed was the main thing, and stood half up to make a rush. The same moment from somewhere between me and the sea there came a flash and a report, and a rifle bullet screeched in my ear. I swung straight round and up with my gun, but the brute had a Winchester, and before I could as much as see him his second shot knocked me over like a ninepin. I seemed to fly in the air, then came down by the run and lay half a minute, silly; and then I found my hands empty, and my gun had flown over my head as I fell. It makes a man mighty wide awake to be in the kind of box that I was in. I scarcely knew where I was hurt, or whether I was hurt or not, but turned right over on my face to crawl after my weapon. Unless you have tried to get about with a smashed leg you don't know what pain is, and I let out a howl like a bullock's.

This was the unluckiest noise that ever I made in my life. Up to then Uma had stuck to her tree like a sensible woman, knowing she would be only in the way; but as soon as she heard me sing out, she ran forward. The Winchester cracked again, and down she went.

I had sat up, leg and all, to stop her; but when I saw her tumble I clapped down again where I was, lay still, and felt the handle of my knife. I had been scurried and put out before. No more of that for me. He had knocked over my girl, I had got to fix him for it; and I lay there and gritted my teeth, and footed up the chances. My leg was broke, my gun was gone. Case had still ten shots in his Winchester. It looked a kind of hopeless business. But I never despaired nor thought upon despairing: that man had got to go.

For a goodish bit not one of us let on. Then I heard Case begin to move nearer in the bush, but mighty careful. The image had burned out; there were only a few coals left here and there, and the wood was main dark, but had a kind of glow in it like a fire on its last legs. It was by this that I made out Case's head looking at me over a big tuft of ferns, and at the same time the brute saw me and shouldered his Winchester. I lay quite still, and as good as looked into the barrel: it was my last chance, but I thought my heart would have come right out of its bearings. Then he fired. Lucky for me it was no shot-gun, for the bullet struck within an inch of me and knocked the dirt in my eyes.

Just you try and see if you can lie quiet, and let a man take a sitting shot at you and miss you by a hair. But I did, and lucky too. A while Case stood with the Winchester at the port-arms; then he gave a little laugh to himself, and stepped round the ferns.

'Laugh!' thought I. 'If you had the wit of a louse you would be praying!'

I was all as taut as a ship's hawser or the spring of a watch, and as soon as he came within reach of me I had him by the ankle, plucked the feet right out from under him, laid him out, and was upon the top of him, broken leg and all, before he breathed. His Winchester had gone the same road as my shot-gun; it was nothing to me—I defied him now. I'm a pretty strong man anyway, but I never knew what strength was till I got hold of Case. He was knocked out of time by the rattle he came down with, and threw up his hands together, more like a frightened woman, so that I caught both of them with my left. This wakened him up, and he fastened his teeth in my forearm like a weasel. Much I cared. My leg gave me all the pain I had any use for, and I drew my knife and got it in the place.

'Now,' said I, 'I've got you; and you're gone up, and a good job too! Do you feel the point of that? That's for Underhill! And there's for Adams! And now here's for Uma, and that's going to knock your blooming soul right out of you!'

With that I gave him the cold steel for all I was worth. His body kicked under me like a spring sofa; he gave a dreadful kind of a long moan, and lay still.

'I wonder if you're dead? I hope so!' I thought, for my head was swimming. But I wasn't going to take chances; I had his own example too close before me for that, and I tried to draw the knife out to give it him again. The blood came over my hands, I remember, hot as tea; and with that I fainted clean away, and fell with my head on the man's mouth.

When I came to myself it was pitch dark; the cinders had burned out; there was nothing to be seen but the shine of the dead wood, and I couldn't remember where I was nor why I was in such pain nor what I was all wetted with. Then it came back, and the first thing I attended to was to give him the knife again a half-a-dozen times up to the handle. I believe he was dead already, but it did him no harm and did me good.

'I bet you're dead now,' I said, and then I called to Uma.

Nothing answered, and I made a move to go and grope for her, fouled my broken leg, and fainted again.

When I came to myself the second time the clouds had all cleared away, except a few that sailed there, white as cotton. The moon was up—a tropic moon. The moon at home turns a wood black, but even this old butt-end of a one showed up that forest as green as by day. The night birds—or, rather, they're a kind of early morning bird—sang out with their long, falling notes like nightingales. And I could see the dead man, that I was still half resting on, looking right up into the sky with his open eyes, no paler than when he was alive; and a little way off Uma tumbled on her side. I got over to her the best way I was able, and when I got there she was broad awake, and crying and sobbing to herself with no more noise than an insect. It appears she was afraid to cry out loud, because of the *aitus*. Altogether she was not much hurt, but scared beyond belief; she had come to her senses a long while ago, cried out to me, heard nothing in reply, made out we were both dead, and had lain there ever since, afraid to budge a finger. The ball had ploughed up her shoulder, and she had lost a main quantity of blood; but I soon had that tied up the way it ought to be with the tail of my shirt and a scarf I had on, got her head on my sound knee and my back against a trunk, and settled down to wait for morning. Uma was for neither use nor ornament, and could only clutch hold of me and shake and cry. I don't suppose there was ever anybody worse scared, and, to do her justice, she had had a lively night of it. As for me, I was in a good bit of pain and fever, but not so bad when I sat still; and every time I looked over to Case I could have sung and whistled. Talk about meat and drink! To see that man lying there dead as a herring filled me full.

The night birds stopped after a while; and then the light began to change, the east came orange, the whole wood began to whirr with singing like a musical box, and there was the broad day.

I didn't expect Maea for a long while yet; and, indeed, I thought there was an off-chance he might go back on the whole idea and not come at all. I was the better pleased when, about an hour after daylight, I heard sticks smashing and a lot of Kanakas laughing and singing out to keep their courage up.

Uma sat up quite brisk at the first word of it; and presently we saw a party come stringing out of the path, Maea in front, and behind him a white man in a pith helmet. It was Mr

Tarleton, who had turned up late last night in Falesá, having left his boat and walked the last stage with a lantern.

They buried Case upon the field of glory, right in the hole where he had kept the smoking head. I waited till the thing was done; and Mr Tarleton prayed, which I thought tomfoolery, but I'm bound to say he gave a pretty sick view of the dear departed's prospects, and seemed to have his own ideas of hell. I had it out with him afterwards, told him he had scamped his duty, and what he had ought to have done was to up like a man and tell the Kanakas plainly Case was damned, and a good riddance; but I never could get him to see it my way. Then they made me a litter of poles and carried me down to the station. Mr Tarleton set my leg, and made a regular missionary splice of it, so that I limp to this day. That done, he took down my evidence, and Uma's, and Maea's, wrote it all out fine, and had us sign it; and then he got the chiefs and marched over to Papa Randall's to seize Case's papers.

All they found was a bit of a diary, kept for a good many years, and all about the price of copra, and chickens being stolen, and that; and the books of the business and the will I told you of in the beginning, by both of which the whole thing (stock, lock, and barrel) appeared to belong to the Samoa woman. It was I that bought her out at a mighty reasonable figure, for she was in a hurry to get home. As for Randall and the black, they had to tramp; got into some kind of a station on the Papa-malulu side; did very bad business, for the truth is neither of the pair was fit for it, and lived mostly on fish, which was the means of Randall's death. It seems there was a nice shoal in one day, and papa went after them with the dynamite; either the match burned too fast, or papa was full, or both, but the shell went off (in the usual way) before he threw it, and where was papa's hand? Well, there's nothing to hurt in that; the islands up north are all full of one-handed men, like the parties in the 'Arabian Nights'; but either Randall was too old, or he drank too much, and the short and the long of it was that he died. Pretty soon after, the nigger was turned out of the island for stealing from white men, and went off to the west, where he found men of his own colour, in case he liked that, and the men of his own colour took and ate him at some kind of a corroborree, and I'm sure I hope he was to their fancy!

So there was I, left alone in my glory at Falesá; and when the schooner came round I filled her up, and gave her a deck cargo half as high as the house. I must say Mr Tarleton did the right thing by us; but he took a meanish kind of revenge.

'Now, Mr Wiltshire,' said he, 'I've put you all square with everybody here. It wasn't difficult to do, Case being gone; but I have done it, and given my pledge besides that you will deal fairly with the natives. I must ask you to keep my word.'

Well, so I did. I used to be bothered about my balances, and I reasoned it out this way: We all have queerish balances, and the natives all know it, and water their copra in a proportion so that it's fair all round; but the truth is, it did used to bother me, and, though I did well in Falesá, I was half glad when the firm moved me on to another station, where I was under no kind of a pledge and could look my balances in the face.

As for the old lady, you know her as well as I do. She's only the one fault. If you don't keep your eye lifting she would give away the roof off the station. Well, it seems it's natural in Kanakas. She's turned a powerful big woman now, and could throw a London bobby over her shoulder. But that's natural in Kanakas too, and there's no manner of doubt that she's an A1 wife.

Mr Tarleton's gone home, his trick being over. He was the best missionary I ever struck, and now, it seems, he's parsonizing down Somerset way. Well, that's best for him; he'll have no Kanakas there to get luny over.

My public-house? Not a bit of it, nor ever likely. I'm stuck here, I fancy. I don't like to leave the kids, you see: and—there's no use talking—they're better here than what they would be in a white man's country, though Ben took the eldest up to Auckland, where he's being schooled with the best. But what bothers me is the girls. They're only half-castes, of course; I know that as well as you do, and there's nobody thinks less of half-castes than I do; but they're mine, and about all I've got. I can't reconcile my mind to their taking up with Kanakas, and I'd like to know where I'm to find the whites?

WEIR OF HERMISTON

INTRODUCTORY

In the wild end of a moorland parish, far out of the sight of any house, there stands a cairn among the heather, and a little by east of it, in the going down of the brae-side, a monument with some little verses half defaced. It was here that Claverhouse shot with his own hand the Praying Weaver of Balweary, and the chisel of Old Mortality has clinked on that lonely gravestone. Public and domestic history have thus marked with a bloody finger this hollow among the hills; and since the Cameronian gave his life there, two hundred years ago, in a glorious folly, and without comprehension or regret, the silence of the moss has been broken once again by the report of firearms and the cry of the dying.

The Deil's Hags was the old name. But the place is now called Francie's Cairn. For a while it was told that Francie walked. Aggie Hogg met him in the gloaming by the cairnside, and he spoke to her, with chattering teeth, so that his words were lost. He pursued Rob Todd (if any one could have believed Robbie) for the space of half a mile with pitiful entreaties. But the age is one of incredulity; these superstitious decorations speedily fell off; and the facts of the story itself, like the bones of a giant buried there and half dug up, survived, naked and imperfect, in the memory of the scattered neighbours. To this day, of winter nights, when the sleet is on the window and the cattle are quiet in the byre, there will be told again, amid the silence of the young and the additions and corrections of the old, the tale of the Justice-Clerk and of his son, young Hermiston, that vanished from men's knowledge; of the two Kirsties and the Four Black Brothers of the Cauldstaneslap; and of Frank Innes, 'the young fool advocate', that came into these moorland parts to find his destiny.

Chapter I

LIFE AND DEATH OF MRS WEIR

THE Lord Justice-Clerk was a stranger in that part of the country; but his lady wife was known there from a child, as her race had been before her. The old 'riding Rutherfords of Hermiston', of whom she was the last descendant, had been famous men of yore, ill neighbours, ill subjects, and ill husbands to their wives though not their properties. Tales of them were rife for twenty miles about; and their name was even printed in the page of our Scots histories, not always to their credit. One bit the dust at Flodden; one was hanged at his peel door by James the Fifth; another fell dead in a carouse with Tom Dalyell; while a fourth (and that was Jean's own father) died presiding at a Hell-Fire Club, of which he was the founder. There were many heads shaken in Crossmichael at that judgment; the more so as the man had a villainous reputation among high and low, and both with the godly and the worldly. At that very hour of his demise, he had ten going pleas before the Session, eight of them oppressive. And the same doom extended even to his agents; his grieve, that had been his right hand in many a left-hand business, being cast from his horse one night and drowned in a peat-hag on the Kye-skairs; and his very doer (although lawyers have long spoons) surviving him not long, and dying on a sudden in a bloody flux.

In all these generations, while a male Rutherford was in the saddle with his lads, or brawling in a change-house, there would be always a white-faced wife immured at home in the old peel or the later mansion-house. It seemed this succession of martyrs bided long, but took their vengeance in the end, and that was in the person of the last descendant, Jean. She bore the name of the Rutherfords, but she was the daughter of their trembling wives. At the first she was not wholly without charm. Neighbours recalled in her, as a child, a strain of elfin wilfulness, gentle little mutinies, sad little gaieties, even a morning gleam of beauty that was not to be fulfilled. She withered in the growing, and (whether it was the sins of her sires or the sorrows of her mothers) came to her maturity depressed, and,

as it were, defaced; no blood of life in her, no grasp or gaiety;
pious, anxious, tender, tearful, and incompetent.

It was a wonder to many that she had married—seeming so
wholly of the stuff that makes old maids. But chance cast her
in the path of Adam Weir, then the new Lord-Advocate, a
recognised, risen man, the conqueror of many obstacles, and
thus late in the day beginning to think upon a wife. He was one
who looked rather to obedience than beauty, yet it would
seem he was struck with her at the first look. 'Wha's she?'
he said, turning to his host; and, when he had been told, 'Ay,'
says he, 'she looks menseful. She minds me—'; and then, after
a pause (which some have been daring enough to set down to
sentimental recollections), 'Is she releegious?' he asked, and
was shortly after, at his own request, presented. The acquaintance, which it seems profane to call a courtship, was pursued
with Mr Weir's accustomed industry, and was long a legend,
or rather a source of legends, in the Parliament House. He was
described coming, rosy with much port, into the drawing-
room, walking direct up to the lady, and assailing her with
pleasantries, to which the embarrassed fair one responded, in
what seemed a kind of agony, 'Eh, Mr Weir!' or 'O, Mr Weir!'
or 'Keep me, Mr Weir!' On the very eve of their engagement,
it was related that one had drawn near to the tender couple,
and had overheard the lady cry out, with the tones of one who
talked for the sake of talking, 'Keep me, Mr Weir, and what
became of him?' and the profound accents of the suitor reply,
'Haangit, mem, haangit.' The motives upon either side were
much debated. Mr Weir must have supposed his bride to be
somehow suitable; perhaps he belonged to that class of men
who think a weak head the ornament of women—an opinion
invariably punished in this life. Her descent and her estate
were beyond question. Her wayfaring ancestors and her
litigious father had done well by Jean. There was ready money
and there were broad acres, ready to fall wholly to the husband,
to lend dignity to his descendants, and to himself a title, when
he should be called upon the Bench. On the side of Jean, there
was perhaps some fascination of curiosity as to this unknown
male animal that approached her with the roughness of a
ploughman and the *aplomb* of an advocate. Being so tren-
chantly opposed to all she knew, loved, or understood, he may
well have seemed to her the extreme, if scarcely the ideal, of

his sex. And besides, he was an ill man to refuse. A little over forty at the period of his marriage, he looked already older, and to the force of manhood added the senatorial dignity of years; it was, perhaps, with an unreverend awe, but he was awful. The Bench, the Bar, and the most experienced and reluctant witness, bowed to his authority—and why not Jeannie Rutherford?

The heresy about foolish women is always punished, I have said, and Lord Hermiston began to pay the penalty at once. His house in George Square was wretchedly ill-guided; nothing answerable to the expense of maintenance but the cellar, which was his own private care. When things went wrong at dinner, as they continually did, my lord would look up the table at his wife: 'I think these broth would be better to sweem in than to sup.' Or else to the butler: 'Here, M'Killop, awa' wi' this Raadical gigot—tak it to the French, man, and bring me some puddocks! It seems rather a sore kind of business that I should be all day in Court haanging Raadicals, and get nawthing to my denner.' Of course this was but a manner of speaking, and he had never hanged a man for being a Radical in his life; the law, of which he was the faithful minister, directing otherwise. And of course these growls were in the nature of pleasantry, but it was of a recondite sort; and uttered as they were in his resounding voice, and commented on by that expression which they called in the Parliament House 'Hermiston's hanging face'—they struck mere dismay into the wife. She sat before him speechless and fluttering; at each dish, as at a fresh ordeal, her eye hovered toward my lord's countenance and fell again; if he but ate in silence, unspeakable relief was her portion; if there were complaint, the world was darkened. She would seek out the cook, who was always her *sister in the Lord*. 'O, my dear, this is the most dreidful thing that my lord can never be contented in his own house!' she would begin; and weep and pray with the cook; and then the cook would pray with Mrs Weir; and the next day's meal would never be a penny the better—and the next cook (when she came) would be worse, if anything, but just as pious. It was often wondered that Lord Hermiston bore it as he did; indeed, he was a stoical old voluptuary, contented with sound wine and plenty of it. But there were moments when he overflowed. Perhaps half a dozen times in the history of his married life—'Here! tak' it awa', and bring me a piece bread and kebbuck!' he had exclaimed, with an appalling explosion of his voice and rare gestures. None thought to dispute or to make excuses; the service was arrested; Mrs Weir sat at the head of the table whimpering without disguise; and his lordship opposite munched his bread and cheese in ostentatious disregard. Once only, Mrs Weir had ventured to appeal. He was passing her chair on his way into the study.

'O, Edom!' she wailed, in a voice tragic with tears, and reaching out to him both hands, in one of which she held a sopping pocket-handkerchief.

He paused and looked upon her with a face of wrath, into which there stole, as he looked, a twinkle of humour.

'Noansense!' he said. 'You and your noansense! What do I want with a Christian faim'ly? I want Christian broth! Get me a lass that can plain-boil a potato, if she was a whüre off the streets.' And with these words, which echoed in her tender ears like blasphemy, he had passed on to his study and shut the door behind him.

Such was the housewifery in George Square. It was better at Hermiston, where Kirstie Elliott, the sister of a neighbouring bonnet-laird, and an eighteenth cousin of the lady's, bore the charge of all, and kept a trim house and a good country table. Kirstie was a woman in a thousand, clean, capable, notable; once a moorland Helen, and still comely as a blood horse and healthy as the hill wind. High in flesh and voice and colour, she ran the house with her whole intemperate soul, in a bustle, not without buffets. Scarce more pious than decency in those days required, she was the cause of many an anxious thought and many a tearful prayer to Mrs Weir. Housekeeper and mistress renewed the parts of Martha and Mary; and though with a pricking conscience, Mary reposed on Martha's strength as on a rock. Even Lord Hermiston held Kirstie in a particular regard. There were few with whom he unbent so gladly, few whom he favoured with so many pleasantries. 'Kirstie and me maun have our joke,' he would declare in high good-humour, as he buttered Kirstie's scones, and she waited at table. A man who had no need either of love or of popularity, a keen reader of men and of events, there was perhaps only one truth for which he was quite unprepared: he would have been quite unprepared to learn that Kirstie hated him. He thought maid and master were well matched; hard, handy, healthy, broad Scots folk, without a hair of nonsense to the pair of them. And the fact was that she made a' goddess and an only child of the effete and tearful lady; and even as she waited at table her hands would sometimes itch for my lord's ears.

Thus, at least, when the family were at Hermiston, not only my lord, but Mrs Weir too, enjoyed a holiday. Free from the dreadful looking-for of the miscarried dinner, she would mind her seam, read her piety books, and take her walk (which was my lord's orders), sometimes by herself, sometimes with Archie, the only child of that scarce natural union. The child was her next bond to life. Her frosted sentiment bloomed again, she breathed deep of life, she let loose her heart, in that society. The miracle of her motherhood was ever new to her. The sight of the little man at her skirt intoxicated her with the sense of power, and froze her with the consciousness of her responsibility. She looked forward, and, seeing him in fancy grow up and play his diverse part on the world's theatre, caught in her breath and lifted up her courage with a lively effort. It was only with the child that she forgot herself and was at moments natural; yet it was only with the child that she had conceived and managed to pursue a scheme of conduct. Archie was to be a great man and a good; a minister if possible, a saint for certain. She tried to engage his mind upon her favourite books, Rutherford's *Letters*, Scougal's *Grace Abounding*, and the like. It was a common practice of hers (and strange to remember now) that she would carry the child to the Deil's Hags, sit with him on the Praying Weaver's stone, and talk of the Covenanters till their tears ran down. Her view of history was wholly artless, a design in snow and ink; upon one side, tender innocents with psalms upon their lips; upon the other, the persecutors, booted, bloody-minded, flushed with wine: a suffering Christ, a raging Beelzebub. *Persecutor* was a word that knocked upon the woman's heart; it was her highest thought of wickedness, and the mark of it was on her house. Her great-great-grandfather had drawn the sword against the Lord's anointed on the field of Rullion Green, and breathed his last (tradition said) in the arms of the detestable Dalyell. Nor could she blind herself to this, that had they lived in those old days, Hermiston himself would have been num-

17 Heriot Row, Stevenson's home in Edinburgh, 1857–79

Picture Post

Vailima, Samoa. (In the centre, left to right) Mrs Thomas Stevenson, Lloyd Osbourne, R.L.S., Fanny Stevenson, Isobel Strong with her son, Austin Strong.

bered alongside of Bloody MacKenzie and the politic Lauder-
dale and Rothes, in the band of God's immediate enemies.
The sense of this moved her to the more fervour; she had a
voice for that name of *persecutor* that thrilled in the child's
marrow; and when one day the mob hooted and hissed them
all in my lord's travelling carriage, and cried, 'Down with the
persecutor! down with Hanging Hermiston!' and mamma
covered her eyes and wept, and papa let down the glass and
looked out upon the rabble with his droll formidable face,
bitter and smiling, as they said he sometimes looked when he
gave sentence, Archie was for the moment too much amazed
to be alarmed, but he had scarce got his mother by herself
before his shrill voice was raised demanding an explanation:
why had they called papa a persecutor?

'Keep me my precious!' she exclaimed. 'Keep me, my
dear! this is poleetical. Ye must never ask me anything
poleetical, Erchie. Your faither is a great man, my dear, and
it's no for me or you to be judging him. It would be telling us
all, if we behaved ourselves in our several stations the way
your faither does in his high office; and let me hear no more
of any such disrespectful and undutiful questions! No that you
meant to be undutiful, my lamb; your mother kens that—she
kens it well, dearie!' And so slid off to safer topics, and left on
the mind of the child an obscure but ineradicable sense of
something wrong.

Mrs Weir's philosophy of life was summed in one expression
—tenderness. In her view of the universe, which was all lighted
up with a glow out of the doors of hell, good people must walk
there in a kind of ecstasy of tenderness. The beasts and plants
had no souls; they were here but for a day, and let their day
pass gently! And as for the immortal men, on what black,
downward path were many of them wending, and to what a
horror of an immortality! 'Are not two sparrows,' 'Whosoever
shall smite thee,' 'God sendeth His rain,' 'Judge not, that ye be
not judged'—these texts made by her body of divinity; she
put them on in the morning with her clothes and lay down to
sleep with them at night; they haunted her like a favourite
air, they clung about her like a favourite perfume. Their
minister was a marrowy expounder of the law, and my lord
sat under him with relish; but Mrs Weir respected him from
far off; heard him (like the cannon of a beleagured city) use-

H

fully booming outside on the dogmatic ramparts; and meanwhile, within and out of shot, dwelt in her private garden which
she watered with grateful tears. It seems strange to say of this
colourless and ineffectual woman, but she was a true enthusiast,
and might have made the sunshine and the glory of a cloister.
Perhaps none but Archie knew she could be eloquent; perhaps
none but he had seen her—her colour raised, her hands
clasped or quivering—glow with gentle ardour. There is a
corner of the policy of Hermiston, where you come suddenly
in view of the summit of Black Fell, sometimes like the mere
grass top of a hill, sometimes (and this is her own expression)
like a precious jewel in the heavens. On such days, upon the
sudden view of it, her hand would tighten on the child's
fingers, her voice rise like a song. '*I to the hills!*' she would
repeat. 'And O, Erchie, are nae these like the hills of Naphtali?'
and her tears would flow.

Upon an impressionable child the effect of this continual
and pretty accompaniment to life was deep. The woman's
quietism and piety passed on to his different nature undiminished; but whereas in her it was a native sentiment, in him
it was only an implanted dogma. Nature and the child's
pugnacity at times revolted. A cad from the Potterrow once
struck him in the mouth; he struck back, the pair fought it
out in the back stable lane towards the Meadows, and Archie
returned with a considerable decline in the number of his
front teeth, and unregenerately boasting of the losses of the
foe. It was a sore day for Mrs Weir; she wept and prayed over
infant backslider until my lord was due from Court, and she
must resume that air of tremulous composure with which she
always greeted him. The judge was that day in an observant
mood, and remarked upon the absent teeth.

'I am afraid Erchie will have been fechting with some of
they blagyard lads,' said Mrs Weir.

My lord's voice rang out as it did seldom in the privacy
of his own house. 'I'll have nonn of that, sir!' he cried. 'Do
you hear me?—nonn of that! No son of mine shall be speldering
in the glaur with any dirty raibble.'

The anxious mother was grateful for so much support; she
had even feared the contrary. And that night when she put
the child to bed—'Now, my dear, ye see!' she said, 'I told you
what your faither would think of it, if he heard ye had fallen

into this dreidful sin; and let you and me pray to God that ye may be keepit from the like temptation or stren'thened to resist it!'

The womanly falsity of this was thrown away. Ice and iron cannot be welded; and the points of view of the Justice-Clerk and Mrs Weir were not less unassimilable. The character and position of his father had long been a stumbling-block to Archie, and with every year of his age the difficulty grew more instant. The man was mostly silent; when he spoke at all, it was to speak of the things of the world, always in a worldly spirit, often in language that the child had been schooled to think coarse, and sometimes with words that he knew to be sins in themselves. Tenderness was the first duty, and my lord was invariably harsh. God was love; the name of my lord (to all who knew him) was fear. In the world, as schematized for Archie by his mother, the place was marked for such a creature. There were some whom it was good to pity and well (though very likely useless) to pray for; they were named reprobates, goats, God's enemies, brands for the burning; and Archie tallied every mark of identification, and drew the inevitable private inference that the Lord Justice-Clerk was the chief of sinners.

The mother's honesty was scarce complete. There was one influence she feared for the child and still secretly combated; that was my lord's; and half unconsciously, half in a wilful blindness, she continued to undermine her husband with his son. As long as Archie remained silent, she did so ruthlessly, with a single eye to heaven and the child's salvation; but the day came when Archie spoke. It was 1801, and Archie was seven, and beyond his years for curiosity and logic, when he brought the case up openly. If judging were sinful and forbidden, how came papa to be a judge? to have that sin for a trade? to bear the name of it for a distinction?

'I can't see it,' said the little Rabbi, and wagged his head.

Mrs Weir abounded in commonplace replies.

'No, I cannae see it,' reiterated Archie. 'And I'll tell you mamma, I don't think you and me's justifeed in staying with him.'

The woman awoke to remorse; she saw herself disloyal to her man, her sovereign and bread-winner, in whom (with what she had of worldliness) she took a certain subdued pride.

She expatiated in reply on my lord's honour and greatness; his useful services in this world of sorrow and wrong, and the place in which he stood, far above where babes and innocents could hope to see or criticize. But she had builded too well— Archie had his answers pat: Were not babes and innocents the type of the kingdom of heaven? Were not honour and greatness the badges of the world? And at any rate, how about the mob that had once seethed about the carriage?

'It's all very fine,' he concluded, 'but in my opinion papa has no right to be it. And it seems that's not the worst yet of it. It seems he's called "The Hanging Judge"—it seems he's crooool. I'll tell you what it is, mamma, there's a tex' borne in upon me: It were better for that man if a milestone were bound upon his back and him flung into the deepestmost pairts of the sea.'

'O, my lamb, ye must never say the like of that!' she cried. 'Ye're to honour faither and mother, dear, that your days may be long in the land. It's Atheists that cry out against him— French Atheists, Erchie! Ye would never surely even yourself down to be saying the same thing as French Atheists? It would break my heart to think of that of you. And O, Erchie, here are'na _you_ setting up to _judge_? And have ye no forgot God's plain command—the First with Promise, dear? Mind you upon the beam and the mote!'

Having thus carried the war into the enemy's camp, the terrified lady breathed again. And no doubt it is easy thus to circumvent a child with catchwords, but it may be questioned how far it is effectual. An instinct in his breast detects the quibble, and a voice condemns it. He will instantly submit, privately hold the same opinion. For even in this simple and antique relation of the mother and the child, hypocrisies are multiplied.

When the Court rose that year and the family returned to Hermiston, it was a common remark in all the country that the lady was sore failed. She seemed to loose and seize again her touch with life, now sitting inert in a sort of durable bewilderment, anon waking to feverish and weak activity. She dawdled about the lasses at their work, looking stupidly on; she fell to rummaging in old cabinets and presses, and desisted when half through; she would begin remarks with an air of animation and drop them without a struggle. Her common appearance was of one who has forgotten something and is trying to remember; and when she overhauled, one after another, the worthless and touching mementoes of her youth, she might have been seeking the clue to that lost thought. During this period, she gave many gifts to the neighbours and house lasses, giving them with a manner of regret that embarrassed the recipients.

The last night of all she was busy on some female work, and toiled upon it with so manifest and painful a devotion that my lord (who was not often curious) inquired as to its nature. She blushed to the eyes. 'O, Edom, it's for you!' she said. 'It's slippers. I—I hae never made ye any.'

'Ye daft auld wife!' returned his lordship. 'A bonny figure I would be, palmering about in bauchles!'

The next day, at the hour of her walk, Kirstie interfered. Kirstie took this decay of her mistress very hard; bore her a grudge, quarrelled with and railed upon her, the anxiety of a genuine love wearing the disguise of temper. This day of all days she insisted disrespectfully, with rustic fury, that Mrs Weir should stay at home. But, 'No, no,' she said, 'it's my lord's orders,' and set forth as usual. Archie was visible in the acre bog, engaged upon some childish enterprise, the instrument of which was mire; and she stood and looked at him a while like one about to call; then thought otherwise, sighed, and shook her head, and proceeded on her rounds alone. The house lasses were at the burnside washing, and saw her pass with her loose, weary, dowdy gait.

'She's a terrible feckless wife, the mistress!' said the one.

'Tut,' said the other, 'the wumman's seeck.'

'Weel, I canna see nae differ in her,' returned the first. 'A füshionless quean, a feckless carline.'

The poor creature thus discussed rambled a while in the grounds without a purpose. Tides in her mind ebbed and flowed, and carried her to and fro like seaweed. She tried a path, paused, returned, and tried another; questing, forgetting her quest; the spirit of choice extinct in her bosom, or devoid of sequency. On a sudden, it appeared as though she had remembered, or had formed a resolution, wheeled about, returned with hurried steps, and appeared in the dining-room, where Kirstie was at the cleaning, like one charged with an important errand.

'Kirstie!' she began, and paused; and then with conviction, 'Mr Weir isna speeritually minded, but he has been a good man to me.'

It was perhaps the first time since her husband's elevation that she had forgotten the handle to his name, of which the tender, inconsistent woman was not a little proud. And when Kirstie looked up at the speaker's face, she was aware of a change.

'Godsake, what's the maitter wi' ye, mem?' cried the house-keeper, starting from the rug.

'I do not ken,' answered her mistress, shaking her head. 'But he is not speeritually minded, my dear.'

'Here, sit down with ye! Godsake, what ails the wife?' cried Kirstie, and helped and forced her into my lord's own chair by the cheek of the hearth.

'Keep me, what's this?' she gasped. 'Kirstie, what's this? I'm frich'ened.'

They were her last words.

It was the lowering nightfall when my lord returned. He had the sunset in his back, all clouds and glory; and before him, by the wayside, spied Kirstie Elliott waiting. She was dissolved in tears, and addressed him in the high, false note of barbarous mourning, such as still lingers modified among Scots heather.

'The Lord peety ye, Hermiston! the Lord prepare ye!' she keened out. 'Weary upon me, that I should have to tell it!'

He reined in his horse and looked upon her with the hanging face.

'Has the French landit?' cried he.

'Man, man,' she said, 'is that a' ye can think of? The Lord prepare ye: the Lord comfort and support ye!'

'Is onybody deid?' said his lordship. 'It's no Erchie?'

'Bethankit, no!' exclaimed the woman, startled into a more natural tone. 'Na, na, it's no sae bad as that. It's the mistress, my lord; she just fair flittit before my e'en. She just gi'ed a sab and was by wi' it. Eh, my bonny Miss Jeannie, that I mind sae weel!' And forth again upon that pouring tide of lamentation in which women of her class excel and over-abound.

Lord Hermiston sat in the saddle beholding her. Then he seemed to recover command upon himself.

'Well, it's something of the suddenest,' said he. 'But she was a dwaibly body from the first.'

And he rode home at a precipitate amble with Kirstie at his horse's heels.

Dressed as she was for her last walk, they had laid the dead lady on her bed. She was never interesting in life; in death she was not impressive; and as her husband stood before her, with his hands crossed behind his powerful back, that which he looked upon was the very image of the insignificant.

'Her and me were never cut out for one another,' he remarked at last. 'It was a daft-like marriage,' And then, with a most unusual gentleness of tone, 'Puir bitch,' said he, 'puir bitch!' Then suddenly: 'Where's Erchie?'

Kirstie had decoyed him to her room and given him 'a jeely-piece'.

'Ye have some kind of gumption, too,' observed the judge, and considered his housekeeper grimly. 'When all's said,' he added, 'I micht have done waur—I micht have been marriet upon a skirling Jezebel like you!'

'There's naebody thinking of you, Hermiston!' cried the offended woman. 'We think of her that's out of her sorrows. And could *she* have done waur? Tell me that, Hermiston— tell me that before her clay-cauld corp!'

'Weel, there's some of them gey an' ill to please,' observed his lordship.

Chapter II

FATHER AND SON

MY Lord Justice-Clerk was known to many; the man Adam Weir perhaps to none. He had nothing to explain or to conceal; he sufficed wholly and silently to himself; and that part of our nature which goes out (too often with false coin) to acquire glory or love, seemed in him to be omitted. He did not try to be loved, he did not care to be; it is probable the very thought of it was a stranger to his mind. He was an admired lawyer, a highly unpopular judge; and he looked down upon those who were his inferiors in either distinction, who were lawyers of less grasp or judges not so much detested. In all the rest of his days and doings, not one trace of vanity appeared; and he went on through life with a mechanical movement, as of the unconscious, that was almost august.

He saw little of his son. In the childish maladies with which the boy was troubled, he would make daily inquiries and daily pay him a visit, entering the sick-room with a facetious and appalling countenance, letting off a few perfunctory jests, and going again swiftly, to the patient's relief. Once, a court holiday falling opportunely, my lord had his carriage, and drove the child himself to Hermiston, the customary place of convalescence. It is conceivable he had been more than usually anxious, for that journey always remained in Archie's memory as a thing apart, his father having related to him from beginning to end, and with much detail, three authentic murder cases. Archie went the usual round of other Edinburgh boys, the high school and the college; and Hermiston looked on, or rather looked away, with scarce an affectation of interest in his progress. Daily, indeed, upon a signal after dinner, he was brought in, given nuts and a glass of port, regarded sardonically, sarcastically questioned. 'Well, sir, and what have you donn with your book to-day?' my lord might begin, and set him posers in law Latin. To a child just stumbling into Corderius, Papinian and Paul proved quite invincible. But papa had memory of no other. He was not harsh to the little scholar, having a vast fund of patience learned upon the bench, and was at no pains whether to conceal or to express his disappointment. 'Well, ye have a long jaunt before ye yet!' he might observe, yawning, and fall back on his own thoughts (as like as not) until the time came for separation, and my lord would take the decanter and the glass, and be off to the back chamber looking on the Meadows, where he toiled on his cases till the hours were small. There was no 'fuller man' on the bench; his memory was marvellous, though wholly legal; if he had to 'advise' extempore, none did it better; yet there was none who more earnestly prepared. As he thus watched in the night, or sat at table and forgot the presence of his son, no doubt, but he tasted deeply of recondite pleasures. To be wholly devoted to some intellectual exercise is to have succeeded in life; and perhaps only in law and the higher mathematics may this devotion be maintained, suffice to itself without reaction, and find continual rewards without excitement. This atmosphere of his father's sterling industry was the best of Archie's education. Assuredly it did not attract him; assuredly it rather rebutted and depressed. Yet it was still present, unobserved like the ticking of a clock, an arid ideal, a tasteless stimulant in the boy's life.

But Hermiston was not all of one piece. He was, besides, a mighty toper; he could sit at wine until the day dawned, and pass directly from the table to the bench with a steady hand and a clear head. Beyond the third bottle, he showed the plebeian in a larger print; the low, gross accent, the low, foul mirth, grew broader and commoner; he became less formidable, and infinitely more disgusting. Now, the boy had inherited from Jean Rutherford a shivering delicacy, unequally mated with potential violence. In the playing-fields, and amongst his own companions, he repaid a coarse expression with a blow; at his father's table (when the time came for him to join these revels) he turned pale and sickened in silence. Of all the guests whom he there encountered, he had toleration for only one: David Keith Carnegie, Lord Glenalmond. Lord Glenalmond was tall and emaciated, with long features and long delicate hands. He was often compared with the statue of Forbes of Culloden in the Parliament House; and his blue eye, at more than sixty, preserved some of the fire of youth. His exquisite disparity with any of his fellow-guests, his appearance as of an artist and an aristocrat stranded in rude company, riveted the boy's attention; and as curiosity and interest are the things in the world that are the most immediately and certainly rewarded, Lord Glenalmond was attracted by the boy.

'And so this is your son, Hermiston?' he asked, laying his hand on Archie's shoulder. 'He's getting a big lad.'

'Hout!' said the gracious father, 'just his mother over again—daurna say boo to a goose!'

But the stranger retained the boy, talked to him, drew him out, found in him a taste for letters, and a fine, ardent, modest, youthful soul; and encouraged him to be a visitor on Sunday evenings in his bare, cold, lonely dining-room, where he sat and read in the isolation of a bachelor grown old in refinement.

The beautiful gentleness and grace of the old judge, and the delicacy of his person, thoughts, and language, spoke to Archie's heart in its own tongue. He conceived the ambition to be such another; and, when the day came for him to choose a profession, it was in emulation of Lord Glenalmond, not of Lord Hermiston, that he chose the Bar. Hermiston looked on at this friendship with some secret pride, but openly with the intolerance of scorn. He scarce lost an opportunity to put them down with a rough jape; and, to say truth, it was not difficult, for they were neither of them quick. He had a word of contempt for the whole crowd of poets, painters, fiddlers, and their admirers, the bastard race of amateurs, which was continually on his lips. 'Signor Feedle-eerie!' he would say. 'O, for Goad's sake, no more of the Signor!'

'You and my father are great friends, are you not?' asked Archie once.

'There is no man that I more respect, Archie,' replied Lord Glenalmond. 'He is two things of price. He is a great lawyer, and he is upright as the day.'

'You and he are so different,' said the boy, his eyes dwelling on those of his old friend, like a lover's on his mistress's.

'Indeed so,' replied the judge; 'very different. And so I fear are you and he. Yet I would like it very ill if my young friend were to misjudge his father. He has all the Roman virtues: Cato and Brutus were such; I think a son's heart might well be proud of such an ancestry of one.'

'And I would sooner he were a plaided herd,' cried Archie, with sudden bitterness.

'And that is neither very wise, nor I believe entirely true,' returned Glenalmond. 'Before you are done you will find some of these expressions rise on you like a remorse. They are merely literary and decorative; they do not aptly express your thought, nor is your thought clearly apprehended, and no doubt your father (if he were here) would say, "Signor Feedle-eerie"!'

With the infinitely delicate sense of youth, Archie avoided the subject from that hour. It was perhaps a pity. Had he but talked—talked freely—let himself gush out in words (the way youth loves to do and should), there might have been no tale to write upon the Weirs of Hermiston. But the shadow of a threat of ridicule sufficed; in the slight tartness of these words

he read a prohibition; and it is likely that Glenalmond meant
it so.

Besides the veteran, the boy was without confidant or
friend. Serious and eager, he came through school and college,
and moved among a crowd of the indifferent, in the seclusion
of his shyness. He grew up handsome, with an open, speaking
countenance, with graceful, youthful ways; he was clever, he
took prizes, he shone in the Speculative Society. It should
seem he must become the centre of a crowd of friends; but
something that was in part the delicacy of his mother, in part
the austerity of his father, held him aloof from all. It is a fact,
and a strange one, that among his contemporaries Hermiston's
son was thought to be a chip of the old block. 'You're a friend
of Archie Weir's?' said one to Frank Innes; and Innes replied,
with his usual flippancy and more than his usual insight: 'I
know Weir, but I never met Archie.' No one had met Archie,
a malady most incident to only sons. He flew his private
signal, and none heeded it; it seemed he was abroad in a
world from which the very hope of intimacy was banished; and
he looked round about him on the concourse of his fellow-
students, and forward to the trivial days and acquaintances
that were to come, without hope or interest.

As time went on, the tough and rough old sinner felt himself
drawn to the son of his loins and sole continuator of his new
family, with softnesses of sentiment that he could hardly credit
and was wholly impotent to express. With a face, voice, and
manner trained through forty years to terrify and repel,
Rhadamanthus may be great, but he will scarce be engaging.
It is a fact that he tried to propitiate Archie, but a fact that
cannot be too lightly taken; the attempt was so inconspicu-
ously made, the failure so stoically supported. Sympathy is
not due to these steadfast iron natures. If he failed to gain his
son's friendship, or even his son's toleration, on he went up
the great, bare staircase of his duty, uncheered and undepressed. There might have been more pleasure in his relations with Archie, so much he may have recognized at
moments; but pleasure was a by-product of the singular
chemistry of life, which only fools expected.

An idea of Archie's attitude, since we are all grown up and
have forgotten the days of our youth, it is more difficult to
convey. He made no attempt whatsoever to understand the

man with whom he dined and breakfasted. Parsimony of pain,
glut of pleasure, these are the two alternating ends of youth;
and Archie was of the parsimonious. The wind blew cold out
of a certain quarter—he turned his back upon it; stayed as
little as was possible in his father's presence; and when there,
averted his eyes as much as was decent from his father's face.
The lamp shone for many hundred days upon these two at
table—my lord, ruddy, gloomy, and unreverent; Archie with
a potential brightness that was always dimmed and veiled in
that society; and there were not, perhaps, in Christendom
two men more radically strangers. The father, with a grand
simplicity, either spoke of what interested himself, or maintained an unaffected silence. The son turned in his head for
some topic that should be quite safe, that would spare him
fresh evidence either of my lord's inherent grossness or of the
innocence of his inhumanity; treading gingerly the ways of
intercourse, like a lady gathering up her skirts in a by-path.
If he made a mistake, and my lord began to abound in matter
of offence, Archie drew himself up, his brow grew dark, his
share of the talk expired; but my lord would faithfully and
cheerfully continue to pour out the worst of himself before his
silent and offended son.

'Well, it's a poor hert that never rejoices!' he would say, at
the conclusion of such a nightmare interview. 'But I must get
to my plew-stilts.' And he would seclude himself as usual in
his back room, and Archie go forth into the night and the city
quivering with animosity and scorn.

Chapter III

IN THE MATTER OF THE HANGING OF
DUNCAN JOPP

IT chanced in the year 1813 that Archie strayed one day into
the Justiciary Court. The macer made room for the son of the
presiding judge. In the dock, the centre of men's eyes, there
stood a whey-coloured, misbegotten caitiff, Duncan Jopp, on

trial for his life. His story, as it was raked out before him in
that public scene, was one of disgrace and vice and cowardice,
the very nakedness of crime; and the creature heard and it
seemed at times as though he understood—as if at times he
forgot the horror of the place he stood in, and remembered
the shame of what had brought him there. He kept his head
bowed and his hands clutched upon the rail; his hair dropped
in his eyes and at times he flung it back; and now he glanced
about the audience in a sudden fellness of terror, and now
looked in the face of his judge and gulped. There was pinned
about his throat a piece of dingy flannel; and this it was perhaps that turned the scale in Archie's mind between disgust
and pity. The creature stood in a vanishing point; yet a little
while, and he was still a man, and had eyes and apprehension;
yet a little longer, and with a last sordid piece of pageantry, he
would cease to be. And here, in the meantime, with a trait
of human nature that caught at the beholder's breath, he was
tending a sore throat.

Over against him, my Lord Hermiston occupied the bench
in the red robes of criminal jurisdiction, his face framed in the
white wig. Honest all through, he did not affect the virtue of
impartiality; this was no case for refinement; there was a man
to be hanged, he would have said, and he was hanging him.
Nor was it possible to see his lordship, and acquit him of gusto
in the task. It was plain he gloried in the exercise of his
trained faculties, in the clear sight which pierced at once into
the joint of fact, in the rude, unvarnished gibes with which he
demolished every figment of defence. He took his ease and
jested, unbending in that solemn place with some of the
freedom of the tavern; and the rag of man with the flannel
round his neck was hunted gallowsward with jeers.

Duncan had a mistress, scarce less forlorn and greatly
older than himself, who came up, whimpering and curtseying,
to add the weight of her betrayal. My lord gave her the oath
in his most roaring voice, and added an intolerant warning.

'Mind what ye say now, Janet,' said he. 'I have an e'e upon
ye, I'm ill to jest with.'

Presently, after she was tremblingly embarked on her story,
'And what made ye do this, ye auld runt?' the Court interposed.
'Do ye mean to tell me ye was the panel's mistress?'

'If you please, ma loard,' whined the female.

'Godsake! ye made a bonny couple,' observed his lordship; and there was something so formidable and ferocious in his scorn that not even the galleries thought to laugh.

The summing up contained some jewels.

'These two peetiable creatures seem to have made up thegither, it's not for us to explain why.'—'The panel, who (whatever else he may be) appears to be equally ill set-out in mind and boady.'—'Neither the panel nor yet the old wife appears to have had so much common sense as even to tell a lie when it was necessary.' And in the course of sentencing, my lord had this *obiter dictum*: 'I have been the means, under God, of haanging a great number, but never just such a disjaskit rascal as yourself.' The words were strong in themselves; the light and heat and detonation of their delivery, and the savage pleasure of the speaker in his task, made them tingle in the ears.

When all was over, Archie came forth again into a changed world. Had there been the least redeeming greatness in the crime, any obscurity, any dubiety, perhaps he might have understood. But the culprit stood, with his sore throat, in the sweat of his mortal agony, without defence or excuse: a thing to cover up with blushes: a being so much sunk beneath the zones of sympathy that pity might seem harmless. And the judge had pursued him with a monstrous, relishing gaiety, horrible to be conceived, a trait for nightmares. It is one thing to spear a tiger, another to crush a toad; there are æsthetics even of the slaughter-house; and the loathsomeness of Duncan Jopp enveloped and infected the image of his judge.

Archie passed by his friends in the High Street with incoherent words and gestures. He saw Holyrood in a dream, remembrance of its romance awoke in him and faded; he had a vision of the old radiant stories, of Queen Mary and Prince Charlie, of the hooded stag, of the splendour and crime, the velvet and bright iron of the past; and dismissed them with a cry of pain. He lay and moaned in the Hunter's Bog, and the heavens were dark above him and the grass of the field an offence. 'This is my father,' he said. 'I draw my life from him; the flesh upon my bones is his, the bread I am fed with is the wages of these horrors.' He recalled his mother, and ground his forehead in the earth. He thought of flight, and where was he to flee to? of other lives, but was there any life worth living in this den of savage and jeering animals?

The interval before the execution was like a violent dream. He met his father; he would not look at him, he could not speak to him. It seemed there was no living creature but must have been swift to recognize that imminent animosity; but the hide of the Justice-Clerk remained impenetrable. Had my lord been talkative, the truce could never have subsisted; but he was by fortune in one of his humours of sour silence; and under the very guns of his broadside, Archie nursed the enthusiasm of rebellion. It seemed to him, from the top of his nineteen years' experience, as if he were marked at birth to be the perpetrator of some signal action, to set back fallen Mercy, to overthrow the usurping devil that sat, horned and hoofed, on her throne. Seductive Jacobin figments, which he had often refuted at the Speculative, swam up in his mind and startled him as with voices: and he seemed to himself to walk accompanied by an almost tangible presence of new beliefs and duties.

On the named morning he was at the place of execution. He saw the fleering rabble, the flinching wretch produced. He looked on for a while at a certain parody of devotion, which seemed to strip the wretch of his last claim to manhood. Then followed the brutal instant of extinction, and the paltry dangling of the remains like a broken jumping-jack. He had been prepared for something terrible, not for this tragic meanness. He stood a moment silent, and then—'I denounce this God-defying murder,' he shouted; and his father, if he must have disclaimed the sentiment, might have owned the stentorian voice with which it was uttered.

Frank Innes dragged him from the spot. The two handsome lads followed the same course of study and recreation, and felt a certain mutual attraction, founded mainly on good looks. It had never gone deep; Frank was by nature a thin, jeering creature, not truly susceptible whether of feeling or inspiring friendship; and the relation between the pair was altogether on the outside, a thing of common knowledge and the pleasantries that spring from a common acquaintance. The more credit to Frank that he was appalled by Archie's outburst, and at least conceived the design of keeping him in sight, and, if possible, in hand, for the day. But Archie, who had just defied—was it God or Satan?—would not listen to the word of a college companion.

'I will not go with you,' he said. 'I do not desire your company, sir; I would be alone.'

'Here, Weir, man, don't be absurd,' said Innes, keeping a tight hold upon his sleeve. 'I will not let you go until I know what you mean to do with yourself; it's no use brandishing that staff.' For indeed at that moment Archie had made a sudden—perhaps a warlike—movement. 'This has been the most insane affair; you know it has. You know very well that I'm playing the good Samaritan. All I wish is to keep you quiet.'

'If quietness is what you wish, Mr Innes,' said Archie, 'and you will promise to leave me entirely to myself, I will tell you so much, that I am going to walk in the country and admire the beauties of nature.'

'Honour bright?' asked Frank.

'I am not in the habit of lying, Mr Innes,' retorted Archie. 'I have the honour of wishing you good-day.'

'You won't forget the Spec.?' asked Innes.

'The Spec.?' said Archie. 'O no, I won't forget the Spec.'

And the young man carried his tortured spirit forth of the city and all the day long, by one road and another, in an endless pilgrimage of misery; while the other hastened smilingly to spread the news of Weir's access of insanity, and to drum up for that night a full attendance at the Speculative, where further eccentric developments might certainly be looked for. I doubt if Innes had the least belief in his prediction; I think it flowed rather from a wish to make the story as good and the scandal as great as possible; not from any ill-will to Archie—from the mere pleasure of beholding interested faces. But for all that his words were prophetic. Archie did not forget the Spec.; he put in an appearance there at the due time, and, before the evening was over, had dealt a memorable shock to his companions. It chanced he was the president of the night. He sat in the same room where the Society still meets—only the portraits were not there: the men who afterwards sat for them were then but beginning their career. The same lustre of many tapers shed its light over the meeting; the same chair, perhaps, supported him that so many of us have sat in since. At times he seemed to forget the business of the evening, but even in these periods he sat with a great air of energy and determination. At times he meddled bitterly, and launched with defiance those fines which are the precious and rarely used artillery of the president. He little thought, as he did so, how he resembled his father, but his friends remarked upon it, chuckling. So far, in his high place above his fellow-students, he seemed set beyond the possibility of any scandal; but his mind was made up—he was determined to fulfil the sphere of his offence. He signed to Innes (whom he had just fined, and who just impeached his ruling) to succeed him in the chair, stepped down from the platform, and took his place by the chimney-piece, the shine of many wax tapers from above illuminating his pale face, the glow of the great red fire relieving from behind his slim figure. He had to propose, as an amendment to the next subject in the case-book, 'Whether capital punishment be consistent with God's will or man's policy?'

A breath of embarrassment, of something like alarm, passed round the room, so daring did these words appear upon the lips of Hermiston's only son. But the amendment was not seconded; the previous question was promptly moved and unanimously voted, and the momentary scandal smuggled by. Innes triumphed in the fulfilment of his prophecy. He and Archie were now become the heroes of the night; but whereas every one crowded about Innes, when the meeting broke up, but one of all his companions came to speak to Archie.

'Weir, man! That was an extraordinary raid of yours!' observed this courageous member, taking him confidentially by the arm as they went out.

'I don't think it a raid,' said Archie grimly. 'More like a war. I saw that poor brute hanged this morning, and my gorge rises at it yet.'

'Hut-tut,' returned his companion, and, dropping his arm like something hot, he sought the less tense society of others.

Archie found himself alone. The last of the faithful—or was it only the boldest of the curious?—had fled. He watched the black huddle of his fellow-students draw off down and up the street, in whispering or boisterous gangs. And the isolation of the moment weighed upon him like an omen and an emblem of his destiny in life. Bred up in unbroken fear himself, among trembling servants, and in a house which (at the least ruffle in the master's voice) shuddered into silence, he saw himself on the brink of the red valley of war, and measured the danger and length of it with awe. He made a detour in the glimmer and shadow of the streets, came into the back stable lane, and watched for a long while the light burn steady in the Judge's room. The longer he gazed upon that illuminated window-blind, the more blank became the picture of the man who sat behind it, endlessly turning over sheets of process, pausing to sip a glass of port, or rising and passing heavily about his book-lined walls to verify some reference. He could not combine the brutal judge and the industrious, dispassionate student; the connecting link escaped him; from such a dual nature, it was impossible he should predict behaviour; and he asked himself if he had done well to plunge into a business of which the end could not be foreseen? and presently after, with a sickening decline of confidence, if he had done loyally to strike his father? For he had struck him—defied him twice over and before a cloud of witnesses—struck him a public buffet before crowds. Who had called him to judge his father in these precarious and high questions? The office was usurped. It might have become a stranger; in a son—there was no blinking it—in a son, it was disloyal. And now, between these two natures so antipathetic, so hateful to each other, there was depending an unpardonable affront: and the providence of God alone might foresee the manner in which it would be resented by Lord Hermiston.

These misgivings tortured him all night and arose with him in the winter's morning; they followed him from class to class, they made him shrinkingly sensitive to every shade of manner in his companions, they sounded in his ears through the current voice of the professor; and he brought them home with him at night unabated and indeed increased. The cause of this increase lay in a chance encounter with the celebrated Dr Gregory. Archie stood looking vaguely in the lighted window of a book shop, trying to nerve himself for the approaching ordeal. My lord and he had met and parted in the morning as they had now done for long, with scarcely the ordinary civilities of life; and it was plain to the son that nothing had yet reached the father's ears. Indeed, when he recalled the awful countenance of my lord, a timid hope sprang up in him that perhaps there would be found no one bold enough to carry tales. If this were so, he asked himself, would he begin again? and he found no answer. It was at this moment that a hand was laid upon his arm, and a voice said in his ear, 'My dear Mr Archie, you had better come and see me.'

He started, turned round, and found himself face to face with Dr Gregory. 'And why should I come to see you?' he asked, with the defiance of the miserable.

'Because you are looking exceedingly ill,' said the doctor, 'and you very evidently want looking after, my young friend. Good folk are scarce, you know; and it is not every one that would be quite so much missed as yourself. It is not every one that Hermiston would miss.'

And with a nod and a smile, the doctor passed on.

A moment after, Archie was in pursuit, and had in turn, but more roughly, seized him by the arm.

'What do you mean? what did you mean by saying that? What makes you think that Hermis—my father would have missed me?'

The doctor turned about and looked him all over with a clinical eye. A far more stupid man than Dr Gregory might have guessed the truth; but ninety-nine out of a hundred, even if they had been equally inclined to kindness, would have blundered by some touch of charitable exaggeration. The doctor was better inspired. He knew the father well; in that white face of intelligence and suffering, he divined something of the son; and he told, without apology or adornment, the plain truth.

'When you had the measles, Mr Archibald, you had them gey and ill; and I thought you were going to slip between my fingers,' he said. 'Well, your father was anxious. How did I know it? says you. Simply because I am a trained observer. The sign that I saw him make, ten thousand would have missed; and perhaps—*perhaps*, I say, because he's a hard man to judge of—but perhaps he never made another. A strange thing to consider! It was this. One day I came to him: "Hermiston," said I, "there's a change." He never said a word, just glowered at me (if ye'll pardon the phrase) like a wild beast. "A change for the better," said I. And I distinctly heard him take his breath.'

The doctor left no opportunity for anti-climax; nodding his cocked hat (a piece of antiquity to which he clung) and repeating 'Distinctly' with raised eyebrows, he took his departure, and left Archie speechless in the street.

The anecdote might be called infinitely little, and yet its

meaning for Archie was immense. 'I did not know the old man had so much blood in him.' He had never dreamed this sire of his, this aboriginal antique, this adamantine Adam, had even so much of a heart as to be moved in the least degree for another —and that other himself, who had insulted him! With the generosity of youth, Archie was instantly under arms upon the other side: had instantly created a new image of Lord Hermiston, that of a man who was all iron without and all sensibility within. The mind of the vile jester, the tongue that had pursued Duncan Jopp with unmanly insults, the unbeloved countenance that he had known and feared for so long, were all forgotten; and he hastened home, impatient to confess his misdeeds, impatient to throw himself on the mercy of this imaginary character.

He was not to be long without a rude awakening. It was in the gloaming when he drew near the door-step of the lighted house, and was aware of the figure of his father approaching from the opposite side. Little daylight lingered; but on the door being opened, the strong yellow shine of the lamp gushed out upon the landing and shone full on Archie, as he stood, in the old-fashioned observance of respect, to yield precedence. The Judge came without haste, stepping stately and firm; his chin raised, his face (as he entered the lamplight) strongly illumined, his mouth set hard. There was never a wink of change in his expression; without looking to the right or left, he mounted the stair, passed close to Archie, and entered the house. Instinctively, the boy, upon his first coming, had made a movement to meet him; instinctively he recoiled against the railing, as the old man swept by him in a pomp of indignation. Words were needless; he knew all—perhaps more than all—and the hour of judgment was at hand.

It is possible that, in this sudden revulsion of hope, and before these symptoms of impending danger, Archie might have fled. But not even that was left to him. My lord, after hanging up his cloak and hat, turned round in the lighted entry, and made him an imperative and silent gesture with his thumb, and with the strange instinct of obedience, Archie followed him into the house.

All dinner-time there reigned over the Judge's table a palpable silence, and as soon as the solids were despatched he rose to his feet.

'M'Killup, tak' the wine into my room,' said he; and then to his son: 'Archie, you and me has to have a talk.'

It was at this sickening moment that Archie's courage, for first and last time, entirely deserted him. 'I have an appointment,' said he.

'It'll have to be broken, then,' said Hermiston, and led the way into his study.

The lamp was shaded, the fire trimmed to a nicety, the table covered deep with orderly documents, the backs of law books made a frame upon all sides that was only broken by the window and the doors.

For a moment Hermiston warmed his hands at the fire, presenting his back to Archie; then suddenly disclosed on him the terrors of the Hanging Face.

'What's this I hear of ye?' he asked.

There was no answer possible to Archie.

'I'll have to tell ye, then,' pursued Hermiston. 'It seems ye've been skirling against the father that begot ye, and one of his Maijesty's Judges in this land; and that in the public street, and while an order of the Court was being executit. Forbye which, it would appear that ye've been airing your opeenions in a Coallege Debatin' Society ; he paused a moment: and then, with extraordinary bitterness, added: 'Ye damned eediot.'

'I had meant to tell you,' stammered Archie. 'I see you are well informed.'

'Muckle obleeged to ye,' said his lordship, and took his usual seat. 'And so you disapprove of Caapital Punishment?' he added.

'I am sorry, sir, I do,' said Archie.

'I am sorry, too,' said his lordship. 'And now, if you please, we shall approach this business with a little more parteecularity. I hear that at the hanging of Duncan Jopp—and, man! ye had a fine client there—in the middle of all the riff-raff of the ceety, ye thought fit to cry out, "This is a damned murder, and my gorge rises at the man that haangit him." '

'No, sir, these were not my words,' cried Archie.

'What were yer words, then?' asked the Judge.

'I believe I said, "I denounce it as a murder!" ' said the son. 'I beg your pardon—a God-defying murder. I have no wish to conceal the truth.' he added, and looked his father for a moment in the face.

'God, it would only need that of it next!' cried Hermiston. 'There was nothing about your gorge rising, then?'

'That was afterwards, my lord, as I was leaving the Speculative. I said I had been to see the miserable creature hanged, and my gorge rose at it.'

'Did ye, though?' said Hermiston. 'And I suppose ye knew who haangit him?'

'I was present at the trial, I ought to tell you that, I ought to explain. I ask your pardon beforehand for any expression that may seem undutiful. The position in which I stand is wretched,' said the unhappy hero, now fairly face to face with the business he had chosen. 'I have been reading some of your cases. I was present when Jopp was tried. It was a hideous business. Father, it was a hideous thing! Grant he was vile, why should you hunt him with a vileness equal to his own? It was done with glee— that is the word—you did it with glee; and I looked on, God help me! with horror.'

'You're a young gentleman that doesna approve of Caapital Punishment,' said Hermiston. 'Weel, I'm an auld man that does. I was glad to get Jopp haangit, and what for would I pretend I wasna? You're all for honesty, it seems; you couldn't even steik your mouth on the public street. What for should I steik mines upon the bench, the King's officer, bearing the sword, a dreid to evil-doers, as I was from the beginning, and as I will be to the end! Mair than enough of it! Heedious! I never gave twa thoughts to heediousness, I have no call to be bonny. I'm a man that gets through with my day's business, and let that suffice.'

The ring of sarcasm had died out of his voice as he went on; the plain words became invested with some of the dignity of the Justice-seat.

'It would be telling you if you could say as much,' the speaker resumed. 'But ye cannot. Ye've been reading some of my cases, ye say. But it was not for the law in them, it was to spy out your faither's nakedness, a fine employment in a son. You're splairging; you're running at lairge in life like a wild nowt. It's impossible you should think any longer of coming to the Bar. You're not fit for it; no splairger is. And another thing: son of mines or no son of mines, you have flung fylement in public on one of the Senators of the Coallege of Justice, and I would make it my business to see that ye were never admitted there

yourself. There is a kind of decency to be observit. Then comes
the next of it—what am I to do with ye next? Ye'll have to find
some kind of a trade, for I'll never support ye in idleset. What
do ye fancy ye'll be fit for? The pulpit? Na, they could never
get diveenity into that bloackhead. Him that the law of man
whammles is no likely to do muckle better by the law of God.
What would ye make of hell? Wouldna your gorge rise at that?
Na, there's no room for splairgers under the fower quarters of
John Calvin. What else is there? Speak up. Have ye got nothing
of your own?'

'Father, let me go to the Peninsula,' said Archie. 'That's
all I'm fit for—to fight.'

'All? quo' he!' returned the Judge. 'And it would be enough
too, if I thought it. But I'll never trust ye so near the French,
you that's so Frenchifeed.'

'You do me injustice there, sir,' said Archie. 'I am loyal; I will
not boast; but any interest I may have ever felt in the French—'

'Have ye been so loyal to me?' interrupted his father.

There came no reply.

'I think not,' continued Hermiston. 'And I would send no
man to be a servant to the King, God bless him! that has
proved such a shauchling son to his own faither. You can
splairge here on Edinburgh street, and where's the hairm? It
doesna play buff on me! And if there were twenty thousand
eediots like yourself, sorrow a Duncan Jopp would hang the
fewer. But there's no splairging possible in a camp; and if ye
were to go to it, you would find out for yourself whether Lord
Well'n'ton approves of caapital punishment or not. You a
sodger!' he cried, with a sudden burst of scorn. 'Ye auld wife,
the sodgers would bray at ye like cuddies!'

As at the drawing of a curtain, Archie was aware of some
illogicality in his position, and stood abashed. He had a
strong impression, besides, of the essential valour of the old
gentleman before him, how conveyed it would be hard to say.

'Well, have ye no other proposeetion?' said my lord again.

'You have taken this so calmly, sir, that I cannot but stand
ashamed,' began Archie.

'I'm nearer voamiting, though, than you would fancy,' said
my lord.

The blood rose to Archie's brow.

'I beg your pardon, I should have said that you had accepted my affront. . . . I admit it was an affront; I did not think to apologize, but I do, I ask your pardon; it will not be so again, I pass you my word of honour. . . . I should have said that I admired your magnanimity with—this—offender,' Archie concluded with a gulp.

'I have no other son, ye see,' said Hermiston. 'A bonny one I have gotten! But I must just do the best I can wi' him, and what am I to do? If ye had been younger, I would have wheepit ye for this rideeculous exhibeetion. The way it is, I have just to grin and bear. But one thing is to be clearly understood. As a fairther, I must grin and bear it; but if I had been the Lord Advocate instead of the Lord Justice-Clerk, son or no son, Mr Erchibald Weir would have been in a jyle the night.'

Archie was now dominated. Lord Hermiston was coarse and cruel; and yet the son was aware of a bloomless nobility, an ungracious abnegation of the man's self in the man's office. At every word, this sense of the greatness of Lord Hermiston's spirit struck more home; and along with it that of his own impotence, who had struck—and perhaps basely struck—at his own father, and not reached so far as to have even nettled him.

'I place myself in your hands without reserve,' he said.

'That's the first sensible word I've had of ye the night,' said Hermiston. 'I can tell ye, that would have been the end of it, the one way or the other; but it's better ye should come there yourself, than what I would have had to hirstle ye. Weel, by my way of it—and my way is the best—there's just the one thing it's possible that ye might be with decency, and that's a laird. Ye'll be out of hairm's way at the least of it. If ye have to rowt, ye can rowt amang the kye; and the maist feck of the caapital punishment ye're like to come across'll be guddlin trouts. Now, I'm for no idle lairdies; every man has to work, if it's only at peddling ballants; to work, or to be wheeped, or to be haangit. If I set ye down at Hermiston I'll have to see you work that place the way it has never been workit yet; ye must ken about the sheep like a herd; ye must be my grieve there, and I'll see that I gain by ye. Is that understood?'

'I will do my best,' said Archie.

'Well, then, I'll send Kirstie word the morn, and ye can go yourself the day after,' said Hermiston. 'And just try to be less of an eediot!' he concluded with a freezing smile, and turned immediately to the papers on his desk.

Chapter IV

OPINIONS OF THE BENCH

LATE the same night, after a disordered walk, Archie was admitted into Lord Glenalmond's dining-room, where he sat with a book upon his knee, beside three frugal coals of fire. In his robes upon the bench, Glenalmond had a certain air of burliness: plucked of these, it was a may-pole of a man that rose unsteadily from his chair to give his visitor welcome. Archie had suffered much in the last days, he had suffered again that evening; his face was white and drawn, his eyes wild and dark. But Lord Glenalmond greeted him without the least mark of surprise or curiosity.

'Come in, come in,' said he. 'Come in and take a seat. Carstairs' (to his servant), 'make up the fire, and then you can bring a bit of supper,' and again to Archie, with a very trivial accent: 'I was half expecting you,' he added.

'No supper,' said Archie. 'It is impossible that I should eat.'

'Not impossible,' said the tall old man, laying his hand upon his shoulder, 'and, if you will believe me, necessary.'

'You know what brings me?' said Archie, as soon as the servant had left the room.

'I have a guess, I have a guess,' replied Glenalmond. 'We will talk of it presently—when Carstairs has come and gone, and you have had a piece of my good Cheddar cheese and a pull at the porter tankard: not before.'

'It is impossible I should eat,' repeated Archie.

'Tut, tut!' said Lord Glenalmond. 'You have eaten nothing to-day and I venture to add, nothing yesterday. There is no case that may not be made worse; this may be a very disagreeable business, but if you were to fall sick and die, it would be still more so, and for all concerned—for all concerned.'

'I see you must know all,' said Archie. 'Where did you hear it?'

'In the mart of scandal, in the Parliament House,' said Glenalmond. 'It runs riot below among the bar and the public, but it sifts up to us upon the bench, and rumour has some of her voices even in the divisions.'

Carstairs returned at this moment, and rapidly laid out a little supper; during which Lord Glenalmond spoke at large and a little vaguely on indifferent subjects, so that it might be rather said of him that he made a cheerful noise, than that he contributed to human conversation; and Archie sat upon the other side, not heeding him, brooding over his wrongs and errors.

But so soon as the servant was gone, he broke forth again at once. 'Who told my father? Who dared to tell him? Could it have been you?'

'No, it was not me,' said the Judge; 'although—to be quite frank with you, and after I had seen and warned you—it might have been me. I believe it was Glenkindie.'

'That shrimp!' cried Archie.

'As you say, that shrimp,' returned my lord; 'although really it is scarce a fitting mode of expression for one of the senators of the College of Justice. We were hearing the parties in a long, crucial case, before the fifteen; Creech was moving at some length for an infeftment; when I saw Glenkindie lean forward to Hermiston with his hand over his mouth and make him a secret communication. No one could have guessed its nature from your father: from Glenkindie, yes, his malice sparked out of him a little grossly. But your father, no. A man of granite. The next moment he pounced upon Creech. "Mr Creech," says he, "I'll take a look of that sasine," and for thirty minutes after,' said Glenalmond, with a smile, 'Messrs. Creech and Co. were fighting a pretty up-hill battle, which resulted, I need hardly add, in their total rout. The case was dismissed. No, I doubt if ever I heard Hermiston better inspired. He was literally rejoicing *in apicibus juris*.'

Archie was able to endure no longer. He thrust his plate away and interrupted the deliberate and insignificant stream of talk. 'Here,' he said, 'I have made a fool of myself, if I have not made something worse. Do you judge between us—judge between a father and a son. I can speak to you; it is not like . . . I will tell you what I feel and what I mean to do; and you shall be the judge,' he repeated.

'I decline jurisdiction,' said Glenalmond, with extreme seriousness. 'But, my dear boy, if it will do you any good to talk, and if it will interest you at all to hear what I may choose to say when I have heard you, I am quite at your command. Let an old man say it, for once, and not need to blush: I love you like a son.'

There came a sudden sharp sound in Archie's throat. 'Ay,'
he cried, 'and there it is! Love! Like a son! And how do you
think I love my father?'

'Quietly, quietly,' says my lord.

'I will be very quiet,' replied Archie. 'And I will be baldly
frank. I do not love my father; I wonder sometimes if I do not
hate him. There's my shame; perhaps my sin; at least, and in
the sight of God, not my fault. How was I to love him? He
has never spoken to me, never smiled upon me; I do not think
he ever touched me. You know the way he talks? You do not
talk so, yet you can sit and hear him without shuddering, and
I cannot. My soul is sick when he begins with it; I could smite
him in the mouth. And all that's nothing. I was at the trial
of this Jopp. You were not there, but you must have heard
him often; the man's notorious for it, for being—look at my
position! he's my father and this is how I have to speak of him
—notorious for being a brute and cruel and a coward. Lord
Glenalmond, I give you my word, when I came out of that
Court, I longed to die—the shame of it was beyond my
strength: but I—I—' he rose from his seat and began to pace
the room in a disorder. 'Well, who am I? A boy, who have
never been tried, have never done anything except this two-
penny impotent folly with my father. But I tell you, my lord,
and I know myself, I am at least that kind of a man—or that
kind of a boy, if you prefer it—that I could die in torments
rather than that any one should suffer as that scoundrel
suffered. Well, and what have I done? I see it now. I have made
a fool of myself, as I said in the beginning; and I have gone back
and asked my father's pardon, and placed myself wholly in his
hands—and he has sent me to Hermiston,' with a wretched
smile, 'for life, I suppose—and what can I say? he strikes me as
having done quite right, and let me off better than I had
deserved.'

'My poor, dear boy!' observed Glenalmond. 'My poor dear
and, if you will allow me to say so, very foolish boy! You are
only discovering where you are; to one of your temperament,
or of mine, a painful discovery. The world was not made for
us; it was made for ten hundred millions of men, all different
from each other and from us; there's no royal road there, we
just have to sclamber and tumble. Don't think that I am at all
disposed to be surprised; don't suppose that I ever think of

blaming you; indeed I rather admire! But there fall to be offered one or two observations on the case which occur to me and which (if you will listen to them dispassionately) may be the means of inducing you to view the matter more calmly. First of all, I cannot acquit you of a good deal of what is called intolerance. You seem to have been very much offended because your father talks a little sculduddery after dinner, which it is perfectly licit for him to do, and which (although I am not very fond of it myself) appears to be entirely an affair of taste. Your father, I scarcely like to remind you, since it is so trite a commonplace, is older than yourself. At least, he is *major* and *sui juris*, and may please himself in the matter of his conversation. And, do you know, I wonder if he might not have as good an answer against you and me? We say we sometimes find him *coarse*, but I suspect he might retort that he finds us always dull. Perhaps a relevant exception.'

He beamed on Archie, but no smile could be elicited.

'And now,' proceeded the Judge, 'for "Archibald on Capital Punishment." This is a very plausible academic opinion; of course I do not and I cannot hold it; but that's not to say that many able and excellent persons have not done so in the past. Possibly, in the past also, I may have a little dipped myself in the same heresy. My third client, or possibly my fourth, was the means of a return in my opinions. I never saw the man I more believed in; I would have put my hand in the fire, I would have gone to the cross for him; and when it came to trial he was gradually pictured before me, by undeniable probation, in the light of so gross, so cold-blooded, and so black-hearted a villain, that I had a mind to have cast my brief upon the table. I was then boiling against the man with even a more tropical temperature than I had been boiling for him. But I said to myself: "No, you have taken up his case; and because you have changed your mind it must not be suffered to let drop. All that rich tide of eloquence that you prepared last night with so much enthusiasm is out of place, and yet you must not desert him, you must say something." So I said something, and I got him off. It made my reputation. But an experience of that kind is formative. A man must not bring his passions to the bar—or to the bench,' he added.

The story had slightly rekindled Archie's interest. 'I could never deny,' he began—'I mean I can conceive that some men would be better dead. But who are we to know all the springs of God's unfortunate creatures? Who are we to trust ourselves where it seems that God Himself must think twice before He treads, and to do it with delight? Yes, with delight. *Tigris ut aspera.*'

'Perhaps not a pleasant spectacle,' said Glenalmond. 'And yet, do you know, I think somehow a great one.'

'I've had a long talk with him to-night,' said Archie.

'I was supposing so,' said Glenalmond.

'And he struck me—I cannot deny that he struck me as something very big,' pursued the son. 'Yes, he is big. He never spoke about himself; only about me. I suppose I admired him. The dreadful part——'

'Suppose we did not talk about that,' interrupted Glenalmond. 'You know it very well, it cannot in any way help that you should brood upon it, and I sometimes wonder whether you and I—who are a pair of sentimentalists—are quite good judges of plain men.'

'How do you mean?' asked Archie.

'*Fair* judges, I mean,' replied Glenalmond. 'Can we be just to them? Do we not ask too much? There was a word of yours just now that impressed me a little when you asked me who we were to know all the springs of God's unfortunate creatures. You applied that, as I understood, to capital cases only. But does it—I ask myself—does it not apply all through? Is it any less difficult to judge of a good man or of a half-good man, than of the worst criminal at the bar? And may not each have relevant excuses?'

'Ah, but we do not talk of punishing the good,' cried Archie.

'No, we do not talk of it,' said Glenalmond. 'But I think we do it. Your father, for instance.'

'You think I have punished him?' cried Archie.

Lord Glenalmond bowed his head.

'I think I have,' said Archie. 'And the worst is, I think he feels it! How much, who can tell, with such a being? But I think he does.'

'And I am sure of it,' said Glenalmond.

'Has he spoken to you, then?' cried Archie.

'O no,' replied the judge.

'I tell you honestly,' said Archie, 'I want to make it up to him. I will go, I have already pledged myself to go to Hermiston. That was to him. And now I pledge myself to you, in the sight of God, that I will close my mouth on capital punishment and all other subjects where our views may clash, for—how long shall I say? when shall I have sense enough?—ten years. Is that well?'

'It is well,' said my lord.

'As far as it goes,' said Archie. 'It is enough as regards myself, it is to lay down enough of my conceit. But as regards him, whom I have publicly insulted? What am I to do to him? How do you pay attentions to a—an Alp like that?'

'Only in one way,' replied Glenalmond. 'Only by obedience, punctual, prompt, and scrupulous.'

'And I promise that he shall have it,' answered Archie. 'I offer you my hand in pledge of it.'

'And I take your hand as a solemnity,' replied the judge. 'God bless you, my dear, and enable you to keep your promise. God guide you in the true way, and spare your days, and preserve to you your honest heart.' At that, he kissed the young man upon the forehead in a gracious, distant, antiquated way; and instantly launched, with a marked change of voice, into another subject. 'And now, let us replenish the tankard; and I believe if you will try my Cheddar again, you would find you had a better appetite. The Court has spoken, and the case is dismissed.'

'No, there is one thing I must say,' cried Archie. 'I must say it in justice to himself. I know—I believe faithfully, slavishly, after our talk—he will never ask me anything unjust. I am proud to feel it, that we have that much in common, I am proud to say it to you.'

The Judge, with shining eyes, raised his tankard. 'And I think perhaps that we might permit ourselves a toast,' said he. 'I should like to propose the health of a man very different from me and very much my superior—a man from whom I have often differed, who has often (in the trivial expression) rubbed me the wrong way, but whom I have never ceased to respect and, I may add, to be not a little afraid of. Shall I give you his name?'

'The Lord Justice-Clerk, Lord Hermiston,' said Archie, almost with gaiety; and the pair drank the toast deeply.

It was not precisely easy to re-establish, after these emotional passages, the natural flow of conversation. But the Judge eked out what was wanting with kind looks, produced his snuff-box (which was very rarely seen) to fill in a pause, and at last, despairing of any further social success, was upon the point of getting down a book to read a favourite passage, when there came a rather startling summons at the front door, and Carstairs ushered in my Lord Glenkindie, hot from a midnight supper. I am not aware that Glenkindie was ever a beautiful object, being short, and gross-bodied, and with an expression of sensuality comparable to a bear's. At that moment, coming in hissing from many potations, with a flushed countenance and blurred eyes, he was strikingly contrasted with the tall, pale, kingly figure of Glenalmond. A rush of confused thought came over Archie—of shame that this was one of his father's elect friends; of pride, that at the least of it Hermiston could carry his liquor; and last of all, of rage, that he should have here under his eyes the man that had betrayed him. And then that too passed away; and he sat quiet, biding his opportunity.

The tipsy senator plunged at once into an explanation with Glenalmond. There was a point reserved yesterday, he had been able to make neither head nor tail of it, and seeing lights in the house, he had just dropped in for a glass of porter—and at this point he became aware of the third person. Archie saw the cod's mouth and the blunt lips of Glenkindie gape at him for a moment, and the recognition twinkle in his eyes.

'Who's this?' said he. 'What? is this possibly you, Don Quickshot? And how are ye? And how's your father? And what's all this we hear of you? It seems you're a most extraordinary leveller, by all tales. No king, no parliaments, and your gorge rises at the macers, worthy men! Hoot, toot! Dear, dear me! Your father's son too! Most rideeculous!'

Archie was on his feet, flushing a little at the reappearance of his unhappy figure of speech, but perfectly self-possessed. 'My lord—and you, Lord Glenalmond, my dear friend,' he began, 'this is a happy chance for me, that I can make my confession and offer my apologies to two of you at once.'

'Ah, but I don't know about that. Confession? It'll be judeecial, my young friend,' cried the jocular Glenkindie. 'And I'm afraid to listen to ye. Think if ye were to make me a coanvert!'

'If you would allow me, my lord,' returned Archie, 'what I have to say is very serious to me; and be pleased to be humorous after I am gone!'

'Remember, I'll hear nothing against the macers!' put in the incorrigible Glenkindie.

But Archie continued as though he had not spoken. 'I have played, both yesterday and to-day, a part for which I can only offer the excuse of youth. I was so unwise as to go to an execution; it seems I made a scene at the gallows; not content with which, I spoke the same night in a college society against capital punishment. This is the extent of what I have done, and in case you hear more alleged against me, I protest my innocence. I have expressed my regret already to my father, who is so good as to pass my conduct over—in a degree, and upon the condition that I am to leave my law studies.' . . .

Chapter V

WINTER ON THE MOORS

1. *At Hermiston*

THE road to Hermiston runs for a great part of the way up the valley of a stream, a favourite with anglers and with midges, full of falls and pools, and shaded by willows and natural woods of birch. Here and there, but at great distances, a byway branches off, and a gaunt farmhouse may be described above in a fold of the hill; but the more part of the time, the road would be quite empty of passage and the hills of habitation. Hermiston parish is one of the least populous in Scotland; and, by the time you came that length, you would scarce be surprised at the inimitable smallness of the kirk, a dwarfish, ancient place seated for fifty, and standing in a green by the burn-side among two-score gravestones. The manse close by, although no more than a cottage, is surrounded by the bright-ness of a flower-garden and the straw roofs of bees; and the whole colony, kirk and manse, garden and graveyard, finds harbourage in a grove of rowans, and is all the year round in a great silence broken only by the drone of the bees, the tinkle

of the burn, and the bell on Sundays. A mile beyond the kirk
the road leaves the valley by a precipitous ascent, and brings
you a little after to the place of Hermiston, where it comes to an
end in the back-yard before the coach-house. All beyond and
about is the great field of the hills; the plover, the curlew, and
the lark cry there; the wind blows as it blows in a ship's
rigging, hard and cold and pure; and the hill-tops huddle one
behind another like a herd of cattle into the sunset.

The house was sixty years old, unsightly, comfortable; a
farmyard and a kitchen-garden on the left, with a fruit wall
where little hard green pears came to their maturity about the
end of October.

The policy (as who should say the park) was of some extent,
but very ill reclaimed; heather and moorfowl had crossed the
boundary wall and spread and roosted within; and it would
have tasked a landscape gardener to say where policy ended
and unpolicied nature began. My lord had been led by the
influence of Mr Sheriff Scott into a considerable design of
planting; many acres were accordingly set out with fir, and
the little feathery besoms gave a false scale and lent a strange
air of a toy-shop to the moors. A great, rooty sweetness of
bogs was in the air, and at all seasons an infinite melancholy
piping of hill birds. Standing so high and with so little shelter,
it was a cold, exposed house, splashed by showers, drenched
by continuous rains that made the gutters to spout, beaten upon
and buffeted by all the winds of heaven; and the prospect
would be often black with tempest, and often white with the
snows of winter. But the house was wind and weather proof,
the hearths were kept bright, and the rooms pleasant with live
fires of peat; and Archie might sit of an evening and hear the
squalls bugle on the moorland, and watch the fire prosper in
the earthy fuel, and the smoke winding up the chimney, and
drink deep of the pleasures of shelter.

Solitary as the place was, Archie did not want neighbours.
Every night, if he chose, he might go down to the manse and
share a 'brewst' of toddy with the minister—a hare-brained
ancient gentleman, long and light and still active, though his
knees were loosened with age, and his voice broke continually
in childish trebles—and his lady wife, a heavy, comely dame,
without a word to say for herself beyond good-even and good-
day. Harum-scarum, clodpole young lairds of the neighbour-

I

hood paid him the compliment of a visit. Young Hay of
Romanes rode down to call, on his crop-eared pony; young
Pringle of Drumanno came up on his bony grey. Hay
remained on the hospitable field, and must be carried to bed;
Pringle got somehow to his saddle about 3 a.m., and (as
Archie stood with the lamp on the upper doorstep) lurched,
uttered a senseless view-holloa, and vanished out of the small
circle of illumination like a wraith. Yet a minute or two
longer the clatter of his break-neck flight was audible, then it
was cut off by the intervening steepness of the hill; and again,
a great while after, the renewed beating of phantom horse-
hoofs, far in the valley of the Hermiston, showed that the
horse at least, if not his rider, was still on the homeward way.

There was a Tuesday club at the 'Cross-keys' in Crossmichael, where the young bloods of the countryside congregated and drank deep on a percentage of the expense, so that
he was left gainer who should have drunk the most. Archie
had no great mind to this diversion, but he took it like a duty
laid upon him, went with a decent regularity, did his man-
fullest with the liquor, held up his head in the local jests, and
got home again and was able to put up his horse, to the admiration of Kirstie and the lass that helped her. He dined at Driffel,
supped at Windielaws. He went to the new year's ball at
Huntsfield and was made welcome, and thereafter rode to
hounds with my Lord Muirfell, upon whose name, as that of
a legitimate Lord of Parliament, in a work so full of Lords of
Session, my pen should pause reverently. Yet the same fate
attended him here as in Edinburgh. The habit of solitude
tends to perpetuate itself, and an austerity of which he was
quite unconscious, and a pride which seemed arrogance, and
perhaps was chiefly shyness, discouraged and offended his new
companions. Hay did not return more than twice, Pringle
never at all, and there came a time when Archie even desisted
from the Tuesday Club, and became in all things—what he
had had the name of almost from the first—the Recluse of
Hermiston. High-nosed Miss Pringle of Drumanno and high-
stepping Miss Marshall of the Mains were understood to have
had a difference of opinion about him the day after the ball—
he was none the wiser, he could not suppose himself to be
remarked by these entrancing ladies. At the ball itself my
Lord Muirfell's daughter, the Lady Flora, spoke to him twice,

and the second time with a touch of appeal, so that her colour
rose and her voice trembled a little in his ear, like a passing
grace in music. He stepped back with a heart on fire, coldly
and not ungracefully excused himself, and a little after watched
her dancing with young Drumanno of the empty laugh, and
was harrowed at the sight, and raged to himself that this was a
world in which it was given to Drumanno to please, and to
himself only to stand aside and envy. He seemed excluded, as
of right, from the favour of such society—seemed to extinguish
mirth wherever he came, and was quick to feel the wound, and
desist, and retire into solitude. If he had but understood the
figure he presented, and the impression he made on these
bright eyes and tender hearts; if he had but guessed that the
Recluse of Hermiston, young, graceful, well spoken, but always
cold, stirred the maidens of the county with the charm of
Byronism when Byronism was new, it may be questioned
whether his destiny might not even yet have been modified.
It may be questioned, and I think it should be doubted. It
was in his horoscope to be parsimonious of pain to himself, or
of the chance of pain, even to the avoidance of any opportunity
of pleasure; to have a Roman sense of duty, an instinctive
aristocracy of manners and taste; to be the son of Adam Weir
and Jean Rutherford.

2. *Kirstie*

Kirstie was now over fifty, and might have sat to a sculptor.
Long of limb, and still light of foot, deep-breasted, robust-
loined, her golden hair not yet mingled with any trace of
silver, the years had but caressed and embellished her. By the
lines of a rich and vigorous maternity, she seemed destined to
be the bride of heroes and the mother of their children; and
behold, by the iniquity of fate, she had passed through her youth
alone, and drew near to the confines of age, a childless woman.
The tender ambitions that she had received at birth had been,
by time and disappointment, diverted into a certain barren
zeal of industry and fury of interference. She carried her
thwarted ardours into housework, she washed floors with her
empty heart. If she could not win the love of one with love,
she must dominate all by her temper. Hasty, wordy, and wrath-
ful, she had a drawn quarrel with most of her neighbours, and

with the others not much more than armed neutrality. The grieve's wife had been 'sneisty'; the sister of the gardener who kept house for him had shown herself 'upsitten'; and she wrote to Lord Hermiston about once a year demanding the discharge of the offenders, and justifying the demand by much wealth of detail. For it must not be supposed that the quarrel rested with the wife and did not take in the husband also—or with the gardener's sister, and did not speedily include the gardener himself. As the upshot of all this petty quarrelling and intemperate speech, she was practically excluded (like a lightkeeper on his tower) from the comforts of human association; except with her own indoor drudge, who, being but a lassie and entirely at her mercy, must submit to the shifty weather of 'the mistress's' moods without complaint, and be willing to take buffets or caresses according to the temper of the hour. To Kirstie, thus situate and in the Indian summer of her heart, which was slow to submit to age, the gods sent this equivocal good thing of Archie's presence. She had known him in the cradle and paddled him when he misbehaved; and yet, as she had not so much as set eyes on him since he was eleven and had his last serious illness, the tall, slender, refined, and rather melancholy young gentleman of twenty came upon her with the shock of a new acquaintance. He was 'Young Hermiston', 'the laird himsel' ': he had an air of distinctive superiority, a cold straight glance of his black eyes, that abashed the woman's tantrums in the beginning, and therefore the possibility of any quarrel was excluded. He was new, and therefore immediately aroused her curiosity; he was reticent, and kept it awake. And lastly he was dark and she fair, and he was male and she female, the everlasting fountains of interest.

Her feeling partook of the loyalty of a clanswoman, the hero-worship of a maiden aunt, and the idolatry due to a god. No matter what he had asked of her, ridiculous or tragic, she would have done it and joyed to do it. Her passion, for it was nothing less, entirely filled her. It was a rich physical pleasure to make his bed or light his lamp for him when he was absent, to pull off his wet boots or wait on him at dinner when he returned. A young man who should have so doted on the idea, moral and physical, of any woman, might be properly described as being in love, head and heels, and would have behaved himself accordingly. But Kirstie—though her heart leaped at his coming footsteps—though, when he patted her shoulder, her face brightened for the day—had not a hope or thought beyond the present moment and its perpetuation to the end of time. Till the end of time she would have had nothing altered, but still continue delightedly to serve her idol, and be repaid (say twice in the month) with a clap on the shoulder.

I have said her heart leaped—it is the accepted phrase. But rather, when she was alone in any chamber of the house, and heard his foot passing on the corridors, something in her bosom rose slowly until her breath was suspended, and as slowly fell again with a deep sigh, when the steps had passed and she was disappointed of her eyes' desire. This perpetual hunger and thirst of his presence kept her all day on the alert. When he went forth at morning, she would stand and follow him with admiring looks. As it grew late and drew to the time of his return, she would steal forth to a corner of the policy wall and be seen standing there sometimes by the hour together, gazing with shaded eyes, waiting the exquisite and barren pleasure of his view a mile off on the mountains. When at night she had trimmed and gathered the fire, turned down his bed, and laid out his night-gear—when there was no more to be done for the king's pleasure, but to remember him fervently in her usually very tepid prayers, and go to bed brooding upon his perfections, his future career, and what she should give him the next day for dinner—there still remained before her one more opportunity; she was still to take in the tray and say good-night. Sometimes Archie would glance up from his book with a preoccupied nod and a perfunctory salutation which was in truth a dismissal; sometimes—and by degrees more often—the volume would be laid aside, he would meet her coming with a look of relief; and the conversation would be engaged, last out the supper, and be prolonged till the small hours by the waning fire. It was no wonder that Archie was fond of company after his solitary days; and Kirstie, upon her side, exerted all the arts of her vigorous nature to ensnare his attention. She would keep back some piece of news during dinner to be fired off with the entrance of the supper tray, and form as it were the *lever de rideau* of the evening's entertainment. Once he had heard her tongue wag, she made sure of

the result. From one subject to another she moved by insidious
transitions, fearing the least silence, fearing almost to give
him time for an answer lest it should slip into a hint of separation. Like so many people of her class, she was a brave narrator;
her place was on the hearthrug and she made it a rostrum,
mimeing her stories as she told them, fitting them with vital
detail, spinning them out with endless 'quo' he's' and 'quo'
she's', her voice sinking into a whisper over the supernatural or
the horrific; until she would suddenly spring up in affected
surprise, and pointing to the clock, 'Mercy, Mr Archie!' she
would say, 'whatten a time o' night is this of it! God forgive
me for a daft wife!' So it befell, by good management, that she
was not only the first to begin these nocturnal conversations,
but invariably the first to break them off; so she managed to
retire and not to be dismissed.

3. *A Border Family*

Such an unequal intimacy has never been uncommon in
Scotland, where the clan spirit survives; where the servant
tends to spend her life in the same service, a helpmeet at first,
then a tyrant, and at last a pensioner; where, besides, she is
not necessarily destitute of the pride of birth, but is, perhaps,
like Kirstie, a connection of her master's, and at least knows
the legend of her own family, and may count kinship with
some illustrious dead. For that is the mark of the Scot of all
classes: that he stands in an attitude towards the past unthink-
able to Englishmen, and remembers and cherishes the memory
of his forebears, good or bad; and there burns alive in him a
sense of identity with the dead even to the twentieth generation. No more characteristic instance could be found than in
the family of Kirstie Elliott. They were all, and Kirstie the
first of all, ready and eager to pour forth the particulars of
their genealogy, embellished with every detail that memory
had handed down or fancy fabricated; and, behold! from every
ramification of that tree there dangled a halter. The Elliotts
themselves have had a chequered history; but these Elliotts
deduced, besides, from three of the most unfortunate of the
border clans—the Nicksons, the Ellwalds, and the Crozers.
One ancestor after another might be seen appearing a moment
out of the rain and the hill mist upon his furtive business,

speeding home, perhaps, with a paltry booty of lame horses and lean kine, or squealing and dealing death in some moorland feud of the ferrets and the wild cats. One after another closed his obscure adventures in mid-air, triced up to the arm of the royal gibbet or the Baron's dule-tree. For the rusty blunderbuss of Scots criminal justice, which usually hurt nobody but jurymen, became a weapon of precision for the Nicksons, the Ellwards, and the Crozers. The exhilaration of their exploits seemed to haunt the memories of their descendants alone, and the shame to be forgotten. Pride glowed in their bosoms to publish their relationship to 'Andrew Ellwald of the Laverockstanes, called "Unchancy Dand", who was justifeed wi' seeven mair of the same name at Jeddart in the days of King James the Sax.' In all this tissue of crime and misfortune, the Elliotts of Cauldstaneslap had one boast which must appear legitimate: the males were gallows-birds, born outlaws, petty thieves, and deadly brawlers; but, according to the same tradition, the females were all chaste and faithful. The power of ancestry on the character is not limited to the inheritance of cells. If I buy ancestors by the gross from the benevolence of Lyon King of Arms, my grandson (if he is Scottish) will feel a quickening emulation of their deeds. The men of the Elliotts were proud, lawless, violent as of right, cherishing and prolonging a tradition. In like manner with the women. And the woman, essentially passionate and reckless, who crouched on the rug, in the shine of the peat fire, telling these tales, had cherished through life a wild integrity of virtue.

Her father Gilbert had been deeply pious, a savage disciplinarian in the antique style, and withal a notorious smuggler. 'I mind when I was a bairn getting mony a skelp and being shoo'd to bed like pou'try,' she would say. 'That would be when the lads and their bit kegs were on the road. We've had the riffraff of two-three counties in our kitchen, mony's the time, betwix' the twelve and the three; and their lanterns would be standing in the forecourt, ay, a score o' them at once. But there was nae ungodly talk permitted at Cauldstaneslap. My faither was a consistent man in walk and conversation; just let slip an aith, and there was the door to ye! He had that zeal for the Lord, it was a fair wonder to hear him pray, but the family has aye had a gift that way.' This father was twice married, once to a dark woman of the old Ellwald stock, by whom he had Gilbert, presently of Cauldstaneslap; and, secondly, to the mother of Kirstie. 'He was an auld man when he married her, a fell auld man wi' a muckle voice—you could hear him rowting from the top o' the Kye-skairs,' she said; 'but for her, it appears she was a perfit wonder. It was gentle blood she had, Mr Archie, for it was your ain. The country-side gaed gyte about her and her gowden hair. Mines is not to be mentioned wi' it, and there's few weemen has mair hair than what I have, or yet a bonnier colour. Often would I tell my dear Miss Jeannie—that was your mother, dear, she was cruel ta'en up about her hair, it was unco' tender, ye see—"Houts, Miss Jeannie," I would say, "just fling your washes and your French dentifrishes in the back o' the fire, for that's the place for them; and awa' down to a burn side, and wash yersel' in cauld hill water, and dry your bonny hair in the caller wind o' the muirs, the way that my mother aye washed hers, and that I have aye made it a practice to have wishen mines—just you do what I tell ye, my dear, and ye'll give me news of it! Ye'll have hair, and routh of hair, a pigtail as thick's my arm," I said, "and the bonniest colour like the clear gowden guineas, so as the lads in kirk'll no can keep their eyes off it!" Weel, it lasted out her time, puir thing! I cuttit a lock of it upon her corp that was lying there sae cauld. I'll show it ye some of thir days if ye're good. But, as I was sayin', my mither——'

On the death of the father there remained golden-haired Kirstie, who took service with her distant kinsfolk, the Rutherfords, and black-a-vised Gilbert, twenty years older, who farmed the Cauldstaneslap, married, and begot four sons between 1773 and 1784, and a daughter, like a postscript, in '97, the year of Camperdown and Cape St Vincent. It seemed it was a tradition in the family to wind up with a belated girl. In 1804, at the age of sixty, Gilbert met an end that might be called heroic. He was due home from market any time from eight at night till five in the morning, and in any condition from the quarrelsome to the speechless, for he maintained to that age the goodly customs of the Scots farmer. It was known on this occasion that he had a good bit of money to bring home; the word had gone round loosely. The laird had shown his guineas, and if anybody had but noticed it, there was an ill-looking, vagabond crew, the scum of Edinburgh, that drew out of the market long ere it was dusk and took the hill-road by Hermiston, where it was not to be believed that they had lawful business. One of the country-side, one Dickieson, they took with them to be their guide, and dear he paid for it! Of a sudden in the ford of the Broken Dykes, this vermin clan fell on the laird, six to one, and him three parts asleep, having drunk hard. But it is ill to catch an Elliott. For a while, in the night and the black water that was deep as to his saddle-girths, he wrought with his staff like a smith at his stithy, and great was the sound of oaths and blows. With that the ambuscade was burst, and he rode for home with a pistol-ball in him, three knife wounds, the loss of his front teeth, a broken rib and bridle, and a dying horse. That was a race with death that the laird rode! In the mirk night, with his broken bridle and his head swimming, he dug his spurs to the rowels in the horse's side, and the horse, that was even worse off than himself, the poor creature! screamed out loud like a person as he went, so that the hills echoed with it, and the folks at Cauldstaneslap got to their feet about the table and looked at each other with white faces. The horse fell dead at the yard gate, the laird won the length of the house and fell there on the threshold. To the son that raised him he gave the bag of money. 'Hae,' said he. All the way up the thieves had seemed to him to be at his heels, but now the hallucination left him—he saw them again in the place of the ambuscade—and the thirst of vengeance seized on his dying mind. Raising himself and pointing with an imperious finger into the black night from which he had come, he uttered the single command, 'Brocken Dykes', and fainted. He had never been loved, but he had been feared in honour. At that sight, at that word, gasped out at them from a toothless and bleeding mouth, the old Elliott spirit awoke with a shout in the four sons. 'Wanting the hat,' continues my author, Kirstie, whom I but haltingly follow, for she told this tale like one inspired, 'wanting guns, for there wasna twa grains o' pouder in the house, wi' nae mair weepons than their sticks into their hands, the fower o' them took the road. Only Hob, and that was the eldest, hunkered at the doorsill where the blood had rin, fyled his hand wi' it, and haddit it up to Heeven in the way o' the auld Border aith. "Hell shall have her ain again this nicht!" he raired, and rode forth upon his earrand.' It was three miles to Broken Dykes, down hill, and a sore road. Kirstie has seen men from Edinburgh dismounting there in plain day to lead their horses. But the four brothers rode it as if Auld Hornie were behind and Heaven in front. Come to the ford, and there was Dickieson. By all tales, he was not dead, but breathed and reared upon his elbow, and cried out to them for help. It was at a graceless face that he asked mercy. As soon as Hob saw, by the glint of the lantern, the eyes shining and the whiteness of the teeth in the man's face, 'Damn you!' says he; 'ye hae your teeth, hae ye?' and rode his horse to and fro upon that human remnant. Beyond that, Dandie must dismount with the lantern to be their guide; he was the youngest son, scarce twenty at the time. 'A' nicht long they gaed in the wet heath and jennipers, and whaur they gaed they neither knew nor cared, but just followed the bluid-stains and the footprints o' their fairther's murderers. And a' nicht Dandie had his nose to the grund like a tyke, and the ithers followed and spak' naething, neither black nor white. There was nae noise to be heard, but just the sough of the swalled burns, and Hob, the dour yin, risping his teeth as he gaed.' With the first glint of the morning they saw they were on the drove road, and at that the four stopped and had a dram to their breakfasts, for they knew that Dand must have guided them right, and the rogues could be but little ahead, hot foot for Edinburgh by the way of the Pentland Hills. By eight o'clock they had word of them—a shepherd had seen four men 'uncoly mishandled' go by in the last hour. 'That's yin a piece,' says Clem, and swung his cudgel. 'Five o' them!' says Hob. 'God's death, but the faither was a man! And him drunk!' And then there befell them what my author termed 'a sair misbegowk', for they were overtaken by a posse of mounted neighbours come to aid in the pursuit. Four sour faces looked on the reinforcement. 'The Deil's broughten you!' said Clem, and they rode thenceforward in the rear of the party with hanging heads. Before ten they had found and secured the rogues, and by three of the afternoon, as they rode up the Vennel with their prisoners, they were aware of a concourse of people bearing in their midst something that dripped. 'For the boady of the saxt,' pursued Kirstie, 'wi' his head smashed like a hazelnit, had been a' that nicht in the chairge o' Hermiston Water, and it dunting it on the stanes, and grunding it on the shallows, and flinging the deid thing heels-ower-hurdie at the Fa's o'

Spango; and in the first o' the day, Tweed had got a hold o'
him and carried him off like a wind, for it was uncoly swalled,
and raced wi' him, bobbing under brae-sides, and was long
playing with the creature in the drumlie lynns under the
castle, and at the hinder end of all cuist him up on the starling
of Crossmichael brig. Sae there they were a'thegither at last
(for Dickieson had been brought in on a cart long syne), and
folk could see what mainner o' man my brither had been that
had held his head again sax and saved the siller, and him
drunk!' Thus died of honourable injuries and in the savour of
fame Gilbert Elliott of the Cauldstaneslap; but his sons had
scarce less glory out of the business. Their savage haste, the
skill with which Dand had found and followed the trail, the
barbarity to the wounded Dickieson (which was like an open
secret in the county), and the doom which it was currently
supposed they had intended for the others, struck and stirred
popular imagination. Some century earlier the last of the
minstrels might have fashioned the last of the ballads out of
that Homeric fight and chase; but the spirit was dead, or had
been reincarnated already in Mr Sheriff Scott, and the
degenerate moorsmen must be content to tell the tale in prose,
and to make of the 'Four Black Brothers' a unit after the
fashion of the 'Twelve Apostles' or the 'Three Musketeers.'

Robert, Gilbert, Clement, and Andrew—in the proper
Border diminutives, Hob, Gib, Clem, and Dand Elliott—
these ballad heroes, had much in common; in particular, their
high sense of the family and the family honour; but they went
diverse ways, and prospered and failed in different businesses.
According to Kirstie, 'they had a' bees in their bonnets but
Hob.' Hob the laird was, indeed, essentially a decent man. An
elder of the Kirk, nobody had heard an oath upon his lips, save
perhaps thrice or so at the sheep-washing, since the chase of
his father's murderers. The figure he had shown on that event-
ful night disappeared as if swallowed by a trap. He who had
ecstatically dipped his hand in the red blood, he who had
ridden down Dickieson, became, from that moment on, a stiff
and rather graceless model of the rustic proprieties; cannily
profiting by the high war prices, and yearly stowing away a
little nest-egg in the bank against calamity; approved of and
sometimes consulted by the greater lairds for the massive
and placid sense of what he said, when he could be induced to

say anything; and particularly valued by the minister, Mr
Torrance, as a right-hand man in the parish, and a model to
parents. The transfiguration had been for the moment only;
some Barbarossa, some old Adam of our ancestors, sleeps in all
of us till the fit circumstance shall call it into action; and, for as
sober as he now seemed, Hob had given once for all the measure
of the devil that haunted him. He was married, and, by reason
of the effulgence of that legendary night, was adored by his
wife. He had a mob of little lusty, barefoot children who
marched in a caravan the long miles to school, the stages of
whose pilgrimage were marked by acts of spoilation and mis-
chief, and who were qualified in the country-side as 'fair
pests'. But in the house, if 'faither was in', they were quiet as
mice. In short, Hob moved through life in a great peace—the
reward of any one who shall have killed his man, with any
formidable and figurative circumstance, in the midst of a
country gagged and swaddled with civilization.

It was a current remark that the Elliotts were 'guid and bad,
like sanguishes'; and certainly there was a curious distinction,
the men of business coming alternately with the dreamers. The
second brother, Gib, was a weaver by trade, had gone out
early into the world to Edinburgh, and come home again with
his wings singed. There was an exaltation in his nature which
had led him to embrace with enthusiasm the principles of the
French Revolution, and had ended by bringing him under the
hawse of my Lord Hermiston in that furious onslaught of his
upon the Liberals, which sent Muir and Palmer into exile and
dashed the party into chaff. It was whispered that my lord,
in his great scorn for the movement, and prevailed upon a
little by a sense of neighbourliness, had given Gib a hint.
Meeting him one day in the Potterrow, my lord had stopped
in front of him: 'Gib, ye eediot,' he had said, 'what's this I hear
of you? Poalitics, poalitics, poalitics, weaver's poalitics, is the
way of it, I hear. If ye arena a'thegither dozened with eediocy,
ye'll gang your ways back to Cauldstaneslap, and ca' your
loom, and ca' your loom, man!' And Gilbert had taken him at
the word and returned, with an expedition almost to be called
flight, to the house of his father. The clearest of his inheritance
was that family gift of prayer of which Kirstie had boasted;
and the baffled politician now turned his attention to religious
matters—or, as others said, to heresy and schism. Every Sunday

morning he was in Crossmichael, where he had gathered together, one by one, a sect of about a dozen persons, who called
themselves 'God's Remnant of the True Faithful', or, for
short, 'God's Remnant'. To the profane, they were known as
'Gib's Deils'. Bailie Sweedie, a noted humorist in the town,
vowed that the proceedings always opened to the tune of 'The
Deil Fly Away with the Exciseman', and that the sacrament
was dispensed in the form of hot whisky-toddy; both wicked
hits at the evangelist, who had been suspected of smuggling in
his youth, and had been overtaken (as the phrase went) on
the streets of Crossmichael one Fair day. It was known that
every Sunday they prayed for a blessing on the arms of Bonaparte. For this 'God's Remnant', as they were 'skailing' from
the cottage that did duty for a temple, had been repeatedly
stoned by the bairns, and Gib himself hooted by a squadron of
Border volunteers in which his own brother, Dand, rode in a
uniform and with a drawn sword. The 'Remnant' were
believed, besides, to be 'antinomian in principle', which
might otherwise have been a serious charge, but the way public
opinion then blew it was quite swallowed up and forgotten in
the scandal about Bonaparte. For the rest, Gilbert had set up
his loom in an outhouse at Cauldstaneslap, where he laboured
assiduously six days of the week. His brothers, appalled by his
political opinions, and willing to avoid dissension in the household, spoke but little to him; he less to them, remaining
absorbed in the study of the Bible and almost constant prayer.
The gaunt weaver was dry-nurse at Cauldstaneslap, and the
bairns loved him dearly. Except when he was carrying an
infant in his arms, he was rarely seen to smile—as, indeed,
there were few smilers in that family. When his sister-in-law
rallied him, and proposed that he should get a wife and bairns
of his own, since he was so fond of them, 'I have no clearness
of mind upon that point,' he would reply. If nobody called
him in to dinner, he stayed out. Mrs Hob, a hard, unsym-
pathetic woman, once tried the experiment. He went without
food all day, but at dusk, as the light began to fail him, he
came into the house of his own accord, looking puzzled. 'I've
had a great gale of prayer upon my speerit,' said he. 'I canna
mind sae muckle's what I had for denner.' The creed of God's
Remnant was justified in the life of its founder. 'And yet I
dinna ken,' said Kirstie. 'He's maybe no more stockfish than

his neeghbours! He rode wi' the rest o' them, and had a good stamach to the work, by a' that I hear! God's Remnant! The deil's clavers! There wasna muckle Christianity in the way Hob guided Johnny Dickieson, at the least of it; but Guid kens! Is he a Christian even? He might be a Mahommedan or a Deevil or a Fire-worshipper, for what I ken.'

The third brother had his name on a door-plate, no less, in the city of Glasgow, 'Mr Clement Elliott,' as long as your arm. In his case, that spirit of innovation which had shown itself timidly in the case of Hob by the admission of new manures, and which had run to waste with Gilbert in subversive politics and heretical religions, bore useful fruit in many ingenious mechanical improvements. In boyhood, from his addiction to strange devices of sticks and string, he had been counted the most eccentric of the family. But that was all by now; and he was a partner of his firm, and looked to die a bailie. He too had married, and was rearing a plentiful family in the smoke and din of Glasgow; he was wealthy, and could have bought out his brother, the cock-laird, six times over, it was whispered; and when he slipped away to Cauldstaneslap for a well-earned holiday, which he did as often as he was able, he astonished the neighbours with his broadcloth, his beaver hat, and the ample plies of his neckcloth. Though an eminently solid man at bottom, after the pattern of Hob, he had contracted a certain Glasgow briskness and *aplomb* which set him off. All the other Elliotts were as lean as a rake, but Clement was laying on fat, and he panted sorely when he must get into his boots. Dand said, chuckling: 'Ay, Clem has the elements of a corporation.' 'A provost and corporation,' returned Clem. And his readiness was much admired.

The fourth brother, Dand, was a shepherd to his trade, and by starts, when he could bring his mind to it, excelled in the business. Nobody could train a dog like Dandie; nobody, through the peril of great storms in the winter time, could do more gallantly. But if his dexterity were exquisite, his diligence was but fitful; and he served his brother for bed and board, and a trifle of pocket-money when he asked for it. He loved money well enough, knew very well how to spend it, and could make a shrewd bargain when he liked. But he preferred a vague knowledge that he was well to windward to any counted coins in the pocket; he felt himself richer so. Hob

would expostulate: 'I'm an amature herd.' Dand would reply,
'I'll keep your sheep to you when I'm so minded, but I'll
keep my liberty too. Thir's no man can coandescend on what
I'm worth.' Clem would expound to him the miraculous
results of compound interest, and recommend investments.
'Ay, man?' Dand would say; 'and do you think, if I took
Hob's siller, that I wouldna drink it or wear it on the lassies?
And, anyway, my kingdom is no of this world. Either I'm a
poet or else I'm nothing.' Clem would remind him of old age.
'I'll die young, like Robbie Burns,' he would say stoutly.
No question but he had a certain accomplishment in minor
verse. His 'Hermiston Burn', with its pretty refrain—

> 'I love to gang thinking whaur ye gang linking,
> Hermiston burn, in the howe;'

his 'Auld, auld Elliotts, clay-cauld Elliotts, dour, bauld
Elliotts of auld', and his really fascinating piece about the
Praying Weaver's Stone, had gained him in the neighbourhood
the reputation, still possible in Scotland, of a local bard; and,
though not printed himself, he was recognized by others who
were and who had become famous. Walter Scott owed to
Dandie the text of the 'Raid of Wearie' in the *Minstrelsy*; and
made him welcome at his house, and appreciated his talents,
such as they were, with all his usual generosity. The Ettrick
Shepherd was his sworn crony; they would meet, drink to
excess, roar out their lyrics in each other's faces, and quarrel
and make it up again till bedtime. And besides these recog-
nitions, almost to be called official, Dandie was made welcome
for the sake of his gift through the farmhouses of several
contiguous dales, and was thus exposed to manifold temptations which he rather sought than fled. He had figured on the
stool of repentance, for once fulfilling to the letter the tradition
of his hero and model. His humorous verses to Mr Torrance on
that occasion—'Kenspeckle here my lane I stand'—unfortunately too indelicate for further citation, ran through the
country like a fiery cross; they were recited, quoted, para-
phrased, and laughed over as far away as Dumfries on the one
hand and Dunbar on the other.

These four brothers were united by a close bond, the bond
of that mutual admiration—or rather mutual hero-worship—

which is so strong among the members of secluded families
who have much ability and little culture. Even the extremes
admired each other. Hob, who had as much poetry as the
tongs, professed to find pleasure in Dand's verses; Clem, who
had no more religion than Claverhouse, nourished a heartfelt,
at least an open-mouthed, admiration of Gib's prayers; and
Dandie followed with relish the rise of Clem's fortunes.
Indulgence followed hard on the heels of admiration. The laird,
Clem, and Dand, who were Tories and patriots of the hottest
quality, excused to themselves, with a certain bashfulness, the
radical and revolutionary heresies of Gib. By another division
of the family, the laird, Clem, and Gib, who were men exactly
virtuous, swallowed the dose of Dand's irregularities as a kind
of clog or drawback in the mysterious providence of God
affixed to bards, and distinctly probative of poetical genius. To
appreciate the simplicity of their mutual admiration it was
necessary to hear Clem, arrived upon one of his visits, and
dealing in a spirit of continuous irony with the affairs and
personalities of that great city of Glasgow where he lived and
transacted business. The various personages, ministers of the
church, municipal officers, mercantile big-wigs, whom he had
occasion to introduce, were all alike denigrated, all served but
as reflectors to cast back a flattering sidelight on the house of
Cauldstaneslap. The Provost, for whom Clem by exception
entertained a measure of respect, he would liken to Hob. 'He
minds me o' the laird there,' he would say. 'He has some of
Hob's grand, whunstane sense, and the same way with him of
steiking his mouth when he's no very pleased.' And Hob, all
unconscious, would draw down his upper lip and produce, as
if for comparison, the formidable grimace referred to. The
unsatisfactory incumbent of St Enoch's Kirk was thus briefly
dismissed: 'If he had but twa fingers o' Gib's, he would waken
them up.' And Gib, honest man! would look down and secretly
smile. Clem was a spy whom they had sent out into the world
of men. He had come back with the good news that there was
nobody to compare with the Four Black Brothers, no position
that they would not adorn, no official that it would not be
well they should replace, no interest of mankind, secular or
spiritual, which would not immediately bloom under their
supervision. The excuse of their folly is in two words: scarce
the breadth of a hair divided them from the peasantry. The

measure of their sense is this: that these symposia of rustic vanity were kept entirely within the family, like some secret ancestral practice. To the world their serious faces were never deformed by the suspicion of any simper of self-contentment. Yet it was known. 'They hae a guid pride o' themsel's!' was the word in the country-side.

Lastly, in a Border story, there should be added their 'two-names.' Hob was The Laird. 'Roy ne puis, prince ne daigne'; he was the laird of Cauldstaneslap—say fifty acres—*ipsissimus*. Clement was Mr Elliott, as upon his door-plate, the earlier Dafty having been discarded as no longer applicable, and indeed only a reminder of misjudgment and the imbecility of the public; and the youngest, in honour of his perpetual wanderings, was known by the sobriquet of Randy Dand.

It will be understood that not all this information was communicated by the aunt, who had too much of the family failing herself to appreciate it thoroughly in others. But as time went on, Archie began to observe an omission in the family chronicle.

'Is there not a girl too?' he asked.

'Ay: Kirstie. She was named for me, or my grandmother at least—it's the same thing,' returned the aunt, and went on again about Dand, whom she secretly preferred by reason of his gallantries.

'But what is your niece like?' said Archie at the next opportunity.

'Her? As black's your hat! But I dinna suppose she would maybe be what you would ca' *ill-looked* a'thegither. Na, she's a kind of a handsome jaud—a kind o' gipsy,' said the aunt, who had two sets of scales for men and women—or perhaps it would be more fair to say that she had three, and the third and the most loaded was for girls.

'How comes it that I never see her in church?' said Archie.

' 'Deed, and I believe she's in Glesgie with Clem and his wife. A heap good she's like to get of it! I dinna say for men folk, but where weemen folk are born, there let them bide. Glory to God, I was never far'er from here than Crossmichael.'

In the meanwhile it began to strike Archie as strange, that while she thus sang the praises of her kinsfolk, and manifestly relished their virtues and (I may say) their vices like a thing

creditable to herself, there should appear not the least sign of
cordiality between the house of Hermiston and that of Cauldstaneslap. Going to church of a Sunday, as the lady housekeeper stepped with her skirts kilted, three tucks of her white
petticoat showing below, and her best India shawl upon her
back (if the day were fine) in a pattern of radiant dyes, she
would sometimes overtake her relatives preceding her more
leisurely in the same direction. Gib of course was absent: by
skreigh of day he had been gone to Crossmichael and his
fellow-heretics; but the rest of the family would be seen
marching in open order: Hob and Dand, stiff-necked, straight-
backed six-footers, with severe dark faces, and their plaids
about their shoulders; the convoy of children scattering (in a
state of high polish) on the wayside, and every now and again
collected by the shrill summons of the mother; and the mother
herself, by a suggestive circumstance which might have
afforded matter of thought to a more experienced observer
than Archie, wrapped in a shawl nearly identical with
Kirstie's, but a thought more gaudy and conspicuously newer.
At the sight, Kirstie grew more tall—Kirstie showed her
classical profile, nose in air and nostril spread, the pure blood
came in her cheek evenly in a delicate living pink.

'A braw day to ye, Mistress Elliott,' said she, and hostility
and gentility were nicely mingled in her tones. 'A fine day,
mem,' the laird's wife would reply with a miraculous curtsey,
spreading the while her plumage—setting off, in other words
and with arts unknown to the mere man, the pattern of her
India shawl. Behind her, the whole Cauldstaneslap contingent
marched in closer order, and with an indescribable air of
being in the presence of the foe; and while Dandie saluted his
aunt with a certain familiarity as of one who was well in court,
Hob marched on in awful immobility. There appeared upon
the face of this attitude in the family the consequences of some
dreadful feud. Presumably the two women had been principals
in the original encounter, and the laird had probably been
drawn into the quarrel by the ears, too late to be included in
the present skin-deep reconciliation.

'Kirstie,' said Archie one day, 'what is this you have against
your family?'

'I dinna complean,' said Kirstie, with a flush. 'I say
naething.'

'I see you do not—not even good-day to your own nephew,' said he.

'I hae naething to be ashamed of,' said she. 'I can say the Lord's prayer with a good grace. If Hob was ill, or in preeson or poverty, I would see to him blithely. But for curtchying and complimenting and colloguing, thank ye kindly!'

Archie had a bit of a smile: he leaned back in his chair. 'I think you and Mrs Robert are not very good friends,' says he slyly, 'when you have your India shawls on?'

She looked upon him in silence, with a sparkling eye but an indecipherable expression; and that was all that Archie was ever destined to learn of the battle of the India shawls.

'Do none of them ever come here to see you?' he inquired.

'Mr Archie,' said she, 'I hope that I ken my place better. It would be a queer thing, I think, if I was to clamjamfry up your faither's house—that I should say it!—wi' a dirty, black-a-vised clan, no ane o' them it was worth while to mar soap upon but just mysel'! Na, they're all damnifeed wi' the black Ellwalds. I have nae patience wi' black folk.' Then, with a sudden consciousness of the case of Archie, 'No that it maitters for men sae muckle,' she made haste to add, 'but there's naebody can deny that it's unwomanly. Long hair is the ornament o' woman ony way; we've good warrandise for that—it's in the Bible—and wha can doubt that the Apostle had some gowden-haired lassie in his mind—Apostle and all, for what was he but just a man like yersel'?'

Chapter VI

A LEAF FROM CHRISTINA'S PSALM-BOOK

ARCHIE was sedulous at church. Sunday after Sunday he sat down and stood up with that small company, heared the voice of Mr Torrance leaping like an ill-played clarionet from key to key, and had an opportunity to study his moth-eaten gown and the black thread mittens that he joined together in prayer, and lifted up with a reverent solemnity in the act of benediction. Hermiston pew was a little square box, dwarfish in proportion with the kirk itself, and enclosing a table not much bigger than a footstool. There sat Archie, an apparent prince, the only undeniable gentleman and the only great heritor in the parish, taking his ease in the only pew, for no other in the kirk had doors. Thence he might command an undisturbed view of that congregation of solid plaided men, strapping wives and daughters, oppressed children, and uneasy sheep-dogs. It was strange how Archie missed the look of race; except the dogs, with their refined foxy faces and inimitably curling tails, there was no one present with the least claim to gentility. The Cauldstaneslap party was scarcely an exception; Dandie perhaps, as he amused himself making verses through the interminable burden of the service, stood out a little by the glow in his eye and a certain superior animation of face and alertness of body; but even Dandie slouched like a rustic. The rest of the congregation, like so many sheep, oppressed him with a sense of hob-nailed routine, day following day—of physical labour in the open air, oatmeal porridge, peas bannock, the somnolent fireside in the evening, and the night-long nasal slumbers in a box-bed. Yet he knew many of them to be shrewd and humorous, men of character, notable women, making a bustle in the world and radiating an influence from their low-browed doors. He knew besides they were like other men; below the crust of custom, rapture found a way; he had heard them beat the timbrel before Bacchus—had heard them shout and carouse over their whisky-toddy; and not the most Dutch-bottomed and severe faces among them all, not even the solemn elders themselves, but were capable of singular gambols at the voice of love. Men drawing near to an end of life's adventurous journey—maids thrilling with fear and curiosity on the threshold of entrance—women who had borne and perhaps buried children, who could remember the clinging of the small dead hands and the patter of the little feet now silent—he marvelled that among all those faces there should be no face of expectation, none that was mobile, none into which the rhythm and poetry of life had entered. 'O for a live face,' he thought; and at times he had a memory of Lady Flora; and at times he would study the living gallery before him with despair, and would see himself go on to waste his days in that joyless pastoral place, and death come to him, and his grave be dug under the rowans, and the Spirit of the Earth laugh out in a thunder-peal at the huge fiasco.

On this particular Sunday, there was no doubt but that the spring had come at last. It was warm, with a latent shiver in the air that made the warmth only the more welcome. The shallows of the stream glittered and tinkled among bunches of primrose. Vagrant scents of the earth arrested Archie by the way with moments of ethereal intoxication. The grey Quakerish dale was still only awakened in places and patches from the sobriety of its winter colouring; and he wondered at its beauty; an essential beauty of the old earth it seemed to him, not resident in particulars but breathing to him from the whole. He surprised himself by a sudden impulse to write poetry—he did so sometimes, loose, galloping octosyllabics in the vein of Scott—and when he had taken his place on a boulder, near some fairy falls and shaded by a whip of a tree that was already radiant with new leaves, it still more surprised him that he should have nothing to write. His heart perhaps beat in time to vast indwelling rhythm of the universe. By the time he came to a corner of the valley and could see the kirk, he had so lingered by the way that the first psalm was finishing. The nasal psalmody, full of turns and trills and graceless graces, seemed the essential voice of the kirk itself upraised in thanksgiving. 'Everything's alive,' he said; and again cries it aloud, 'thank God, everything's alive!' He lingered yet a while in the kirk-yard. A tuft of primroses was blooming hard by the leg of an old black table tombstone, and he stopped to contemplate the random apologue. They stood forth on the cold earth with a trenchancy of contrast; and he was struck with a sense of incompleteness in the day, the season, and the beauty that surrounded him—the chill there was in the warmth, the gross black clods about the opening primroses, the damp earthy smell that was everywhere intermingled with the scents. The voice of the aged Torrance within rose in an ecstasy. And he wondered if Torrance also felt in his old bones the joyous influence of the spring morning; Torrance, or the shadow of what once was Torrance, that must come so soon to lie outside here in the sun and rain with all his rheumatisms, while a new minister stood in his room and thundered from his own familiar pulpit? The pity of it, and something of the chill of the grave, shook him for a moment as he made haste to enter.

He went up the aisle reverently, and took his place in the pew with lowered eyes, for he feared he had already offended the kind old gentleman in the pulpit, and was sedulous to offend no further. He could not follow the prayer, not even the heads of it. Brightnesses of azure, clouds of fragrance, a tinkle of falling water and singing birds, rose like exhalations from some deeper, aboriginal memory, that was not his, but belonged to the flesh on his bones. His body remembered; and it seemed to him that his body was in no way gross, but ethereal and perishable like a strain of music; and he felt for it an exquisite tenderness as for a child, an innocent, full of beautiful instincts and destined to an early death. And he felt for old Torrance—of the many supplications, of the few days —a pity that was near to tears. The prayer ended. Right over him was a tablet in the wall, the only ornament in the roughly masoned chapel—for it was no more; the tablet commemorated, I was about to say the virtues, but rather the existence of a former Rutherford of Hermiston; and Archie, under that trophy of his long descent and local greatness, leaned back in the pew and contemplated vacancy with the shadow of a smile between playful and sad, that became him strangely. Dandie's sister, sitting by the side of Clem in her new Glasgow finery, chose that moment to observe the young laird. Aware of the stir of his entrance, the little formalist had kept her eyes fastened and her face prettily composed during the prayer. It was not hypocrisy, there was no one further from a hypocrite. The girl had been taught to behave: to look up, to look down, to look unconscious, to look seriously impressed in church, and in every conjuncture to look her best. That was the game of female life, and she played it frankly. Archie was the one person in church who was of interest, who was somebody new, reputed eccentric, known to be young, and a laird, and still unseen by Christina. Small wonder that, as she stood there in her attitude of pretty decency, her mind should run upon him! If he spared a glance in her direction, he should know she was a well-behaved young lady who had been to Glasgow. In reason he must admire her clothes, and it was possible that he should think her pretty. At that her heart beat the least thing in the world; and she proceeded, by way of a corrective, to call up and dismiss a series of fancied pictures of the young man who should now, by rights, be looking at her.

She settled on the plainest of them—a pink short young man with a dish face and no figure, at whose admiration she could afford to smile; but for all that, the consciousness of his gaze (which was really fixed on Torrance and his mittens) kept her in something of a flutter till the word Amen. Even then, she was far too well-bred to gratify her curiosity with any impatience. She resumed her seat languidly—this was a Glasgow touch—she composed her dress, rearranged her nosegay of primroses, looked first in front, then behind upon the other side, and at last allowed her eyes to move, without hurry, in the direction of the Hermiston pew. For a moment, they were riveted. Next she had plucked her gaze home again like a tame bird who should have meditated flight. Possibilities crowded on her; she hung over the future and grew dizzy; the image of this young man, slim, graceful, dark, with the inscrutable half-smile, attracted and repelled her like a chasm. 'I wonder, will I have met my fate?' she thought, and her heart swelled.

Torrance was got some way into his first exposition, positing a deep layer of texts as he went along, laying the foundations of his discourse, which was to deal with a nice point in divinity, before Archie suffered his eyes to wander. They fell first of all on Clem, looking insupportably prosperous, and patronizing Torrance with the favour of a modified attention, as of one who was used to better things in Glasgow. Though he had never before set eyes on him, Archie had no difficulty in identifying him, and no hesitation in pronouncing him vulgar, the worst of the family. Clem was leaning lazily forward when Archie first saw him. Presently he leaned nonchalantly back; and that deadly instrument, the maiden, was suddenly unmasked in profile. Though not quite in the front of the fashion (had anybody cared!), certain artful Glasgow mantua-makers, and her own inherent taste, had arrayed her to great advantage. Her accoutrement was, indeed, a cause of heart-burning, and almost of scandal, in that infinitesimal kirk company. Mrs Hob had said her say at Cauldstaneslap. 'Daftlike!' she had pronounced it. 'A jaiket that'll no meet! Whaur's the sense of a jaiket that'll no button upon you, if it should come to be weet? What do ye ca' thir things? Demmy brokens, d'ye say? They'll be brokens wi' a vengeance or ye can win back! Weel, I have naething to do wi' it—it's no good taste.' Clem, whose purse had thus

metamorphosed his sister, and who was not insensible to the
advertisement, had come to the rescue with a 'Hoot, woman!
What do you ken of good taste that has never been to the
ceety?' And Hob, looking on the girl with pleased smiles, as
she timidly displayed her finery in the midst of the dark kitchen,
had thus ended the dispute: 'The cutty looks weel,' he had
said, 'and it's no very like rain. Wear them the day, hizzie;
but it's no a thing to make a practice o'.' In the breasts of her
rivals, coming to the kirk very conscious of white under-linen,
and their faces splendid with much soap, the sight of the toilet
had raised a storm of varying emotion, from the mere un-
envious admiration that was expressed in a long-drawn 'Eh!'
to the angrier feeling that found vent in an emphatic 'Set her
up!' Her frock was of straw-coloured jaconet muslin, cut low
at the bosom and short at the ankle, so as to display her
demi-broquins of Regency violet, crossing with many straps
upon a yellow cobweb stocking. According to the pretty
fashion in which our grandmothers did not hesitate to appear,
and our great-aunts went forth armed for the pursuit and
capture of our great-uncles, the dress was drawn up so as to
mould the contour of both breasts, and in the nook between, a
cairngorm brooch maintained it. Here, too, surely in a very
enviable position, trembled the nosegay of primroses. She
wore on her shoulders—or rather on her back and not her
shoulders, which it scarcely passed—a French coat of sarsenet,
tied in front with Margate braces, and of the same colour with
her violet shoes. About her face clustered a disorder of dark
ringlets, a little garland of yellow French roses surmounted
her brow, and the whole was crowned by a village hat of
chipped straw. Amongst all the rosy and all the weathered
faces that surrounded her in church, she glowed like an open
flower—girl and raiment, and the cairngorm that caught the
daylight and returned it in a fiery flash, and the threads of
bronze and gold that played in her hair.

Archie was attracted by the bright thing like a child. He
looked at her again and yet again, and their looks crossed. The
lip was lifted from her little teeth. He saw the red blood work
vividly under her tawny skin. Her eye, which was great as a
stag's, struck and held his gaze. He knew who she must be—
Kirstie, she of the harsh diminutive, his housekeeper's niece,
the sister of the rustic prophet, Gib—and he found in her the
answer to his wishes.

Christina felt the shock of their encountering glances, and seemed to rise, clothed in smiles, into a region of the vague and bright. But the gratification was not more exquisite than it was brief. She looked away abruptly, and immediately began to blame herself for that abruptness. She knew what she should have done, too late—turned slowly with her nose in the air. And meantime his look was not removed, but continued to play upon her like a battery of cannon constantly aimed, and now seemed to isolate her alone with him, and now seemed to uplift her, as on a pillory, before the congregation. For Archie continued to drink her in with his eyes, even as a wayfarer comes to a well-head on a mountain, and stoops his face, and drinks with thirst unassuageable. In the cleft of her little breasts the fiery eye of the topaz and the pale florets of prim-rose fascinated him. He saw the breasts heave, and the flowers shake with the heaving, and marvelled what should so much discompose the girl. And Christina was conscious of his gaze— saw it, perhaps, with the dainty plaything of an ear that peeped among her ringlets; she was conscious of changing colour, conscious of her unsteady breath. Like a creature tracked, run down, surrounded, she sought in a dozen ways to give herself a countenance. She used her handkerchief—it was a really fine one—then she desisted in a panic: 'He would only think I was too warm.' She took to reading in the metrical psalms, and then remembered it was sermon-time. Last she put a 'sugar-bool' in her mouth, and the next moment repented of the step. It was such a homely-like thing! Mr Archie would never be eating sweeties in kirk; and, with a palpable effort, she swallowed it whole, and her colour flamed high. At this signal of distress Archie awoke to a sense of his ill-behaviour. What had he been doing? He had been exquisitely rude in church to the niece of his housekeeper; he had stared like a lackey and a libertine at a beautiful and modest girl. It was possible, it was even likely, he would be presented to her after service in the kirk-yard, and then how was he to look? And there was no excuse. He had marked the tokens of her shame, of her increasing indignation, and he was such a fool that he had not understood them. Shame bowed him down, and he looked resolutely at Mr Torrance; who little supposed, good, worthy man, as he continued to expound justification by faith, what was his true business: to play the part of derivative to a pair of children at the old game of falling in love.

Christina was greatly relieved at first. It seemed to her that
she was clothed again. She looked back on what had passed.
All would have been right if she had not blushed, a silly fool!
There was nothing to blush at, if she *had* taken a sugar-bool.
Mrs MacTaggart, the elder's wife in St Enoch's, took them
often. And if he had looked at her, what was more natural
than that a young gentleman should look at the best-dressed
girl in church? And at the same time, she knew far otherwise,
she knew there was nothing casual or ordinary in the look, and
valued herself on its memory like a decoration. Well, it was a
blessing he had found something else to look at! And presently
she began to have other thoughts. It was necessary, she fancied,
that she should put herself right by a repetition of the incident,
better managed. If the wish was father to the thought, she did
not know or she would not recognize it. It was simply as a
manœuvre of propriety, as something called for to lessen the
significance of what had gone before, that she should a second
time meet his eyes, and this time without blushing. And at the
memory of the blush, she blushed again, and became one
general blush burning from head to foot. Was ever anything
so indelicate, so forward, done by a girl before? And here she
was, making an exhibition of herself before the congregation
about nothing! She stole a glance upon her neighbours, and
behold! they were steadily indifferent, and Clem had gone to
sleep. And still the one idea was becoming more and more
potent with her, that in common prudence she must look
again before the service ended. Something of the same sort was
going forward in the mind of Archie, as he struggled with the
load of penitence. So it chanced that, in the flutter of the
moment when the last psalm was given out, and Torrance
was reading the verse, and the leaves of every psalm-book in
church were rustling under busy fingers, two stealthy glances
were sent out like antennæ among the pews and on the indifferent and absorbed occupants, and drew timidly nearer to
the straight line between Archie and Christina. They met,
they lingered together for the least fraction of time, and that
was enough. A charge as of electricity passed through Christina, and behold! the leaf of her psalm-book was torn across.

Archie was outside by the gate of the graveyard, conversing
with Hob and the minister and shaking hands all round with
the scattering congregation, when Clem and Christina were

brought up to be presented. The laird took off his hat and bowed to her with grace and respect. Christina made her Glasgow curtsey to the laird, and went on again up the road for Hermiston and Cauldstaneslap, walking fast, breathing hurriedly with a heightened colour, and in this strange frame of mind, that when she was alone she seemed in high happiness, and when any one addressed her she resented it like a contradiction. A part of the way she had the company of some neighbour girls and a loutish young man; never had they seemed so insipid, never had she made herself so disagreeable. But these struck aside to their various destinations or were out-walked and left behind; and when she had driven off with sharp words the proffered convoy of some of her nephews and nieces, she was free to go on alone up Hermiston brae, walking on air, dwelling intoxicated among clouds of happiness. Near to the summit she heard steps behind her, a man's steps, light and very rapid. She knew the foot at once and walked faster. 'If it's me he's wanting, he can run for it,' she thought, smiling.

Archie overtook her like a man whose mind was made up. 'Miss Kirstie,' he began.

'Miss Christina, if you please, Mr Weir,' she interrupted. 'I canna bear the contraction.'

'You forget it has a friendly sound for me. Your aunt is an old friend of mine, and a very good one. I hope we shall see much of you at Hermiston?'

'My aunt and my sister-in-law doesna agree very well. Not that I have much ado with it. But still when I'm stopping in the house, if I was to be visiting my aunt, it would not look considerate-like.'

'I am sorry,' said Archie.

'I thank you kindly, Mr Weir,' she said. 'I whiles think myself it's a great peety.'

'Ah, I am sure your voice would always be for peace!' he cried.

'I wouldna be too sure of that,' she said. 'I have my days like other folk, I suppose.'

'Do you know, in our old kirk, among our good old grey dames, you made an effect like sunshine.'

'Ah, but that would be my Glasgow clothes!'

'I did not think I was so much under the influence of pretty frocks.'

She smiled with a half look at him. 'There's more than you!' she said. 'But you see I'm only Cinderella. I'll have to put all these things by in my trunk; next Sunday I'll be as grey as the rest. They're Glasgow clothes, you see, and it would never do to make a practice of it. It would seem terrible conspicuous.'

By that they were come to the place where their ways severed. The old grey moors were all about them; in the midst a few sheep wandered; and they could see on the one hand the straggling caravan scaling the braes in front of them for Cauldstaneslap, and on the other, the contingent from Hermiston bending off and beginning to disappear by detachments into the policy gate. It was in these circumstances that they turned to say farewell, and deliberately exchanged a glance as they shook hands. All passed as it should, genteelly; and in Christina's mind, as she mounted the first steep ascent for Cauldstaneslap, a gratifying sense of triumph prevailed over the recollection of minor lapses and mistakes. She had kilted her gown, as she did usually at that rugged pass; but when she spied Archie still standing and gazing after her, the skirts came down again as if by enchantment. Here was a piece of nicety for that upland parish, where the matrons marched with their coats kilted in the rain, and the lasses walked barefoot to kirk through the dust of summer, and went bravely down by the burn-side, and sat on stones to make a public toilet before entering! It was perhaps an air wafted from Glasgow; or perhaps it marked a stage of that dizziness of gratified vanity, in which the instinctive act passed unperceived. He was looking after! She unloaded her bosom of a prodigious sigh that was all pleasure, and betook herself to run. When she had overtaken the stragglers of her family, she caught up the niece whom she had so recently repulsed, and kissed and slapped her, and drove her away again, and ran after her with pretty cries and laughter. Perhaps she thought the laird might still be looking! But it chanced the little scene came under the views of eyes less favourable; for she overtook Mrs Hob marching with Clem and Dand.

'You're shürely fey, lass!' quoth Dandie.

'Think shame to yersel', miss!' said the strident Mrs Hob. 'Is this the gait to guide yersel' on the way hame frae kirk? You're shürely no sponsible the day! And anyway I would mind my guid claes.'

'Hoot!' said Christina, and went on before them head in air, treading the rough track with the tread of a wild doe.

She was in love with herself, her destiny, the air of the hills, the benediction of the sun. All the way home, she continued under the intoxication of these sky-scraping spirits. At table she could talk freely of young Hermiston; gave her opinion of him off-hand and with a loud voice, that he was a handsome young gentleman, real well mannered and sensible-like, but it was a pity he looked doleful. Only—the moment after—a memory of his eyes in church embarrassed her. But for this inconsiderable check, all through meal-time she had a good appetite, and she kept them laughing at table, until Gib (who had returned before them from Crossmichael and his separative worship) reproved the whole of them for their levity.

Singing 'in to herself' as she went, her mind still in the turmoil of a glad confusion, she rose and tripped upstairs to a little loft, lighted by four panes in the gable, where she slept with one of her nieces. The niece, who followed her, presuming on 'Auntie's' high spirits, was flounced out of the apartment with small ceremony, and retired, smarting and half tearful, to bury her woes in the byre among the hay. Still humming, Christina divested herself of her finery, and put her treasures one by one in her great green trunk. The last of these was the psalm-book; it was a fine piece, the gift of Mistress Clem, in distinct old-faced type, on paper that had begun to grow foxy in the warehouse—not by service—and she was used to wrap it in a handkerchief every Sunday after its period of service was over, and bury it end-wise at the head of her trunk. As she now took it in hand the book fell open where the leaf was torn, and she stood and gazed upon that evidence of her by-gone discomposure. There returned again the vision of the two brown eyes staring at her, intent and bright, out of that dark corner of the kirk. The whole appearance and attitude, the smile, the suggested gesture of young Hermiston came before her in a flash at the sight of the torn page. 'I was surely fey!' she said, echoing the words of Dandie, and at the suggested doom her high spirits deserted her. She flung herself prone upon the bed, and lay there, holding the psalm-book in her hands for hours, for the more part in a mere stupor of unconsenting pleasure and unreasoning fear. The fear was superstitious; there came up again and again in her memory

Dandie's ill-omened words, and a hundred grisly and black tales out of the immediate neighbourhood read her a commentary on their force. The pleasure was never realized. You might say the joints of her body thought and remembered, and were gladdened, but her essential self, in the immediate theatre of consciousness, talked feverishly of something else like a nervous person at a fire. The image that she most complacently dwelt on was that of Miss Christina in her character of the Fair Lass of Cauldstaneslap, carrying all before her in the straw-coloured frock, the violet mantle, and the yellow cobweb stockings. Archie's image, on the other hand, when it presented itself was never welcomed—far less welcomed with any ardour, and it was exposed at times to merciless criticism. In the long vague dialogues she held in her mind, often with imaginary, often with unrealized interlocutors, Archie, if he were referred to at all, came in for savage handling. He was described as 'looking like a stork', 'staring like a caulf', 'a face like a ghaist's'. 'Do you call that manners?' she said; or, 'I soon put him in his place.' ' "*Miss Christina, if you please, Mr Weir!*" says I, and just flyped up my skirt tails.' With gabble like this she would entertain herself long whiles together, and then her eye would perhaps fall on the torn leaf, and the eyes of Archie would appear again from the darkness of the wall, and the voluble words deserted her, and she would lie still and stupid, and think upon nothing with devotion, and be sometimes raised by a quiet sigh. Had a doctor of medicine come into that loft, he would have diagnosed a healthy, well-developed, eminently vivacious lass lying on her face in a fit of the sulks; not one who had just contracted, or was just contracting, a mortal sickness of the mind which should yet carry her towards death and despair. Had it been a doctor of psychology, he might have been pardoned for divining in the girl a passion of childish vanity, self-love *in excelsis*, and no more. It is to be understood that I have been painting chaos and describing the inarticulate. Every lineament that appears is too precise, almost every word used too strong. Take a finger-post in the mountains on a day of rolling mists; I have but copied the names that appear upon the pointers, the names of definite and famous cities far distant, and now perhaps basking in sunshine; but Christina remained all these hours, as it were, at the foot of the post itself, not moving, and enveloped in mutable and blinding wreaths of haze.

The day was growing late and the sunbeams long and level, when she sat suddenly up, and wrapped in its handkerchief and put by that psalm-book which had already played a part so decisive in the first chapter of her love-story. In the absence of the mesmerist's eye, we are told nowadays that the head of a bright nail may fill his place, if it be steadfastly regarded. So that torn page had riveted her attention on what might else have been but little, and perhaps soon forgotten; while the ominous words of Dandie—heard, not heeded, and still remembered—had lent to her thoughts, or rather to her mood, a cast of solemnity, and that idea of Fate—a pagan Fate, uncontrolled by any Christian deity, obscure, lawless, and august—moving indissuadably in the affairs of Christian men. Thus even that phenomenon of love at first sight, which is so rare and seems so simple and violent, like a disruption of life's tissue, may be decomposed into a sequence of accidents happily concurring.

She put on a grey frock and a pink kerchief, looked at herself a moment with approval in the small square of glass that served her for a toilet mirror, and went softly downstairs through the sleeping house that resounded with the sound of afternoon snoring. Just outside the door, Dandie was sitting with a book in his hand, not reading, only honouring the Sabbath by a sacred vacancy of mind. She came near him and stood still.

'I m for off up the muirs, Dandie,' she said.

There was something unusually soft in her tones that made him look up. She was pale, her eyes dark and bright; no trace remained of the levity of the morning.

'Ay, lass? Ye'll have yer ups and downs like me, I'm thinkin',' he observed.

'What for do ye say that?' she asked.

'O, for naething,' says Dand. 'Only I think ye're mair like me than the lave of them. Ye've mair of the poetic temper, tho' Guid kens little enough of the poetic taalent. It's an ill gift at the best. Look at yoursel'. At denner you were all sunshine and flowers and laughter, and now you're like the star of evening on a lake.'

She drank in this hackneyed compliment like wine, and it glowed in her veins.

'But I'm saying, Dand'—she came nearer him—'I'm for the muirs. I must have a braith of air. If Clem was to be speiring for me, try and quaiet him, will ye no?'

'What way?' said Dandie. 'I ken but the ae way, and that's leein'. I'll say ye had a sair heid, if ye like.'

'But I havena,' she objected.

'I daursay no,' he returned. 'I said I would say ye had; and if ye like to nay-say me when ye come back, it'll no mateerially maitter, for my chara'ter's clean gane a'ready past reca'.'

'O, Dand, are ye a leear?' she asked, lingering.

'Folks say sae,' replied the bard.

'Wha says sae?' she pursued.

'Them that should ken the best,' he responded. 'The lassies, for ane.'

But, Dand, you would never lee to me?' she asked.

'I'll leave that for your pairt of it, ye girzie,' said he. 'Ye'll lee to me fast eneuch, when ye hae gotten a jo. I'm tellin' ye and it's true; when you have a jo, Miss Kirstie, it'll be for guid and ill. I ken: I was made that way mysel', but the deil was in my luck! Here, gang awa wi' ye to your muirs, and let me be; I'm in an hour of inspiraution, ye upsetting tawpie!'

But she clung to her brother's neighbourhood, she knew not why.

'Will ye no gie's a kiss, Dand?' she said. 'I aye likit ye fine.'

He kissed her and considered her a moment; he found something strange in her. But he was a libertine through and through, nourished equal contempt and suspicion of all womankind, and paid his way among them habitually with idle compliments.

'Gae wa' wi' ye!' said he. 'Ye're a dentie baby, and be content wi' that!'

That was Dandie's way; a kiss and a comfit to Jenny—a bawbee and my blessing to Jill—and good-night to the whole clan of ye, my dears! When anything approached the serious, it became a matter for men, he both thought and said. Women, when they did not absorb, were only children to be shoo'd away. Merely in his character of connoisseur, however, Dandie glanced carelessly after his sister as she crossed the meadow. 'The brat's no that bad!' he thought with surprise, for though he had just been paying her compliments, he had not really looked at her. 'Hey! what's yon?' For the grey dress was cut with short sleeves and skirts, and displayed her trim strong legs clad in pink stockings of the same shade as the kerchief she wore round her shoulders, and that shimmered as she went. This was not her way in undress; he knew her ways and the ways of the whole sex in the country-side, no one better; when they did not go barefoot, they wore stout 'rig and furrow' woollen hose of an invisible blue mostly, when they were not black outright; and Dandie, at sight of this daintiness, put two and two together. It was a silk handkerchief, then they would be silken hose; they matched—then the whole outfit was a present of Clem's, a costly present, and not something to be worn through bog and briar, or on a late afternoon of Sunday. He whistled. 'My denty May, either your heid's fair turned, or there's some ongoings!' he observed, and dismissed the subject.

She went slowly at first, but ever straighter and faster for the Cauldstaneslap, a pass among the hills to which the farm owed its name. The Slap opened like a doorway between two rounded hillocks; and through this ran the short cut to Hermiston. Immediately on the other side it went down through the Deil's Hags, a considerable marshy hollow of the hill tops, full of springs, and crouching junipers, and pools where the black peat-water slumbered. There was no view from here. A man might have sat upon the Praying Weaver's stone a half century, and seen none but the Cauldstaneslap children twice in the twenty-four hours on their way to the school and back again, an occasional shepherd, the irruption of a clan of sheep, or the birds who haunted about the springs, drinking and shrilly piping. So, when she had once passed the Slap, Kirstie was received into seclusion. She looked back a last time at the farm. It still lay deserted except for the figure of Dandie, who was now seen to be scribbling in his lap, the hour of expected inspiration having come to him at last. Thence she passed rapidly through the morass, and came to the farther end of it, where a sluggish burn discharges, and the path for Hermiston accompanies it on the beginning of its downward path. From this corner a wide view was opened to her of the whole stretch of braes upon the other side, still sallow and in places rusty with the winter, with the path marked boldly, here and there

K

by the burn-side a tuft of birches, and—two miles off as the
crow flies—from its enclosures and young plantations, the
windows of Hermiston glittering in the western sun.

Here she sat down and waited, and looked for a long time
at these far-away bright panes of glass. It amused her to have
so extended a view, she thought. It amused her to see the
house of Hermiston—to see 'folk'; and there was an indistin-
guishable human unit, perhaps the gardener, visibly sauntering
on the gravel paths.

By the time the sun was down and all the easterly braes lay
plunged in clear shadow, she was aware of another figure
coming up the path at a most unequal rate of approach, now
half running, now pausing and seeming to hesitate. She
watched him at first with a total suspension of thought. She
held her thought as a person holds his breathing. Then she
consented to recognize him. 'He'll no be coming here, he canna
be; it's no possible.' And there began to grow upon her a
subdued choking suspense. He *was* coming; his hesitations had
quite ceased, his step grew firm and swift; no doubt remained;
and the question loomed up before her instant: what was she
to do? It was all very well to say that her brother was a laird
himself: it was all very well to speak of casual intermarriages
and to count cousinship, like Auntie Kirstie. The difference
in their social station was trenchant; propriety, prudence, all
that she had ever learned, all that she knew, bade her flee.
But on the other hand the cup of life now offered to her was
too enchanting. For one moment, she saw the question
clearly, and definitely made her choice. She stood up and
showed herself an instant in the gap relieved upon the sky line;
and the next, fled trembling and sat down glowing with
excitement on the Weaver's stone. She shut her eyes, seeking,
praying for composure. Her hand shook in her lap, and her
mind was full of incongruous and futile speeches. What was
there to make a work about? She could take care of herself, she
supposed! There was no harm in seeing the laird. It was the
best thing that could happen. She would mark a proper
distance to him once and for all. Gradually the wheels of her
nature ceased to go round so madly, and she sat in passive
expectation, a quiet, solitary figure in the midst of the grey
moss. I have said she was no hypocrite, but here I am at
fault. She never admitted to herself that she had come up the

hill to look for Archie. And perhaps after all she did not know, perhaps came as a stone falls. For the steps of love in the young, and especially in girls, are instinctive and unconscious.

In the meantime Archie was drawing rapidly near, and he at least was consciously seeking her neighbourhood. The afternoon had turned to ashes in his mouth; the memory of the girl had kept him from reading and drawn him as with cords; and at last, as the cool of the evening began to come on, he had taken his hat and set forth, with a smothered ejaculation, by the moor path to Cauldstaneslap. He had no hope to find her; he took the off chance without expectation of result and to relieve his uneasiness. The greater was his surprise, as he surmounted the slope and came into the hollow of the Deil's Hags, to see there, like an answer to his wishes, the little womanly figure in the grey dress and the pink kerchief sitting little, and low, and lost, and acutely solitary, in these desolate surroundings and on the weather-beaten stone of the dead weaver. Those things that still smacked of winter were all rusty about her, and those things that already relished of the spring had put forth the tender and lively colours of the season. Even in the unchanging face of the death-stone, changes were to be remarked; and in the channeled lettering, the moss began to renew itself in jewels of green. By an afterthought that was a stroke of art, she had turned up over her head the back of the kerchief; so that it now framed becomingly her vivacious and yet pensive face. Her feet were gathered under her on the one side, and she leaned on her bare arm, which showed out strong and round, tapered to a slim wrist, and shimmered in the fading light.

Young Hermiston was struck with a certain chill. He was reminded that he now dealt in serious matters of life and death. This was a grown woman he was approaching, endowed with her mysterious potencies and attractions, the treasury of the continued race, and he was neither better nor worse than the average of his sex and age. He had a certain delicacy which had preserved him hitherto unspotted, and which (had either of them guessed it) made him a more dangerous companion when his heart should be really stirred. His throat was dry as he came near; but the appealing sweetness of her smile stood between them like a guardian angel.

For she turned to him and smiled, though without rising.

There was a shade in this cavalier greeting that neither of them perceived; neither he, who simply thought it gracious and charming as herself; nor yet she, who did not observe (quick as she was) the difference between rising to meet the laird, and remaining seated to receive the expected admirer.

'Are ye stepping west, Hermiston?' said she, giving him his territorial name after the fashion of the country-side.

'I was,' said he, a little hoarsely, 'but I think I will be about the end of my stroll now. Are you like me, Miss Christina? The house would not hold me. I came here seeking air.'

He took his seat at the other end of the tombstone and studied her, wondering what was she. There was infinite import in the question alike for her and him.

'Ay,' she said. 'I couldna bear the roof either. It's a habit of mine to come up here about the gloaming when it's quaiet and caller.'

'It was a habit of my mother's also,' he said gravely. The recollection half startled him as he expressed it. He looked around. 'I have scarce been here since. It's peaceful,' he said, with a long breath.

'It's no like Glasgow,' she replied. 'A weary place, yon Glasgow! But what a day have I had for my hame-coming, and what a bonny evening!'

'Indeed, it was a wonderful day,' said Archie. 'I think I will remember it years and years until I come to die. On days like this—I do not know if you feel as I do—but everything appears so brief, and fragile, and exquisite, that I am afraid to touch life. We are here for so short a time; and all the old people before us—Rutherfords of Hermiston, Elliotts of the Cauldstaneslap—that were here but a while since riding about and keeping up a great noise in this quiet corner—making love too, and marrying—why, where are they now? It's deadly commonplace, but, after all, the commonplaces are the great poetic truths.'

He was sounding her, semi-consciously, to see if she could understand him; to learn if she were only an animal the colour of flowers, or had a soul in her to keep her sweet. She, on her part, her means well in hand, watched, womanlike, for any opportunity to shine, to abound in his humour, whatever that might be. The dramatic artist, that lies dormant or only half awake in most human beings, had in her sprung to his feet

in a divine fury, and chance had served her well. She looked
upon him with a subdued twilight look that became the hour
of the day and the train of thought; earnestness shone through
her like stars in the purple west; and from the great but controlled upheaval of her whole nature there passed into her
voice, and rang in her lightest words, a thrill of emotion.

'Have you mind of Dand's song?' she answered. 'I think
he'll have been trying to say what you have been thinking.'

'No, I never heard it,' he said. 'Repeat it to me, can you?'

'It's nothing wanting the tune,' said Kirstie.

'Then sing it me,' said he.

'On the Lord's Day? That would never do, Mr Weir!'

'I am afraid I am not so strict a keeper of the Sabbath, and
there is no one in this place to hear us, unless the poor old
ancient under the stone.'

'No that I'm thinking that really,' she said. 'By my way of
thinking, it's just as serious as a psalm. Will I sooth it to ye,
then?'

'If you please,' said he, and, drawing near to her on the
tombstone, prepared to listen.

She sat up as if to sing. 'I'll only can sooth it to ye,' she
explained. 'I wouldna like to sing out loud on the Sabbath. I
think the birds would carry news of it to Gilbert,' and she
smiled. 'It's about the Elliotts,' she continued, 'and I think
there's few bonnier bits in the book-poets, though Dand has
never got printed yet.'

And she began, in the low, clear tones of her half voice, now
sinking almost to a whisper, now rising to a particular note
which was her best, and which Archie learned to wait for with
growing emotion:

'O they rade in the rain, in the days that are gane,
    In the rain and the wind and the lave,
They shoutit in the ha' and they routit on the hill,
    But they're a' quairit noo in the grave.
Auld, auld Elliotts, clay-cauld Elliotts, dour, bauld Elliotts of auld!'

All the time she sang she looked steadfastly before her, her
knees straight, her hands upon her knee, her head cast back
and up. The expression was admirable throughout, for had
she not learned it from the lips and under the criticism of the
author? When it was done, she turned upon Archie a face

softly bright, and eyes gently suffused and shining in the
twilight, and his heart rose and went out to her with boundless
pity and sympathy. His question was answered. She was a
human being tuned to a sense of the tragedy of life; there were
pathos and music and a great heart in the girl.

He arose instinctively, she also; for she saw she had gained
a point, and scored the impression deeper, and she had wit
enough left to flee upon a victory. They were but commonplaces that remained to be exchanged, but the low, moved
voices in which they passed made them sacred in the memory.
In the falling greyness of the evening he watched her figure
winding through the morass, saw it turn a last time and wave
a hand, and then pass through the Slap; and it seemed to him
as if something went along with her out of the deepest of his
heart. And something surely had come, and come to dwell
there. He had retained from childhood a picture, now half
obliterated by the passage of time and the multitude of fresh
impressions, of his mother telling him, with the fluttered
earnestness of her voice, and often with dropping tears, the
tale of the 'Praying Weaver', on the very scene of his brief
tragedy and long repose. And now there was a companion
piece; and he beheld, and he should behold for ever, Christina
perched on the same tomb, in the grey colours of the evening,
gracious, dainty, perfect as a flower, and she also singing—

> 'Of old, unhappy far off things,
> And battles long ago,'

of their common ancestors now dead, of their rude wars
composed, their weapons buried with them, and of these
strange changelings, their descendants, who lingered a little
in their places, and would soon be gone also, and perhaps sung
of by others at the gloaming hour. By one of the unconscious
arts of tenderness the two women were enshrined together in
his memory. Tears, in that hour of sensibility, came into his
eyes indifferently at the thought of either; and the girl, from
being something merely bright and shapely, was caught up
into the zone of things serious as life and death and his dead
mother. So that in all ways and on either side, Fate played his
game artfully with this poor pair of children. The generations
were prepared, the pangs were made ready, before the curtain
rose on the dark drama.

In the same moment of time that she disappeared from Archie, there opened before Kirstie's eyes the cup-like hollow in which the farm lay. She saw, some five hundred feet below her, the house making itself bright with candles, and this was a broad hint to her to hurry. For they were only kindled on a Sabbath night with a view to that family worship which rounded in the incomparable tedium of the day and brought on the relaxation of supper. Already she knew that Robert must be within-sides at the head of the table, 'waling the portions'; for it was Robert in his quality of family priest and judge, not the gifted Gilbert, who officiated. She made good time accordingly down the steep ascent, and came up to the door panting as the three younger brothers, all roused at last from slumber, stood together in the cool and the dark of the evening with a fry of nephews and nieces about them, chatting and awaiting the expected signal. She stood back; she had no mind to direct attention to her late arrival or to her labouring breath.

'Kirstie, ye have shaved it this time, my lass?' said Clem. 'Whaur were ye?'

'O, just taking a dander by mysel',' said Kirstie.

And the talk continued on the subject of the American War, without further reference to the truant who stood by them in the covert of the dusk, thrilling with happiness and the sense of guilt.

The signal was given, and the brothers began to go in one after another, amid the jostle and throng of Hob's children.

Only Dandie, waiting till the last, caught Kirstie by the arm. 'When did ye begin to dander in pink hosen, Mistress Elliott?' he whispered slyly.

She looked down; she was one blush. 'I maun have forgotten to change them,' said she; and went into prayers in her turn with a troubled mind, between anxiety as to whether Dand should have observed her yellow stockings at church, and should thus detect her in a palpable falsehood, and shame that she had already made good his prophecy. She remembered the words of it, it was to be when she had gotten a jo, and that that would be for good and evil. 'Will I have gotten my jo now?' she thought with a secret rapture.

And all through prayers, where it was her principal business to conceal the pink stockings from the eyes of the indifferent

Mrs Hob—and all through supper, as she made a feint of eating and sat at the table radiant and constrained—and again when she had left them and come into her chamber, and was alone with her sleeping niece, and could at last lay aside the armour of society—the same words sounded within her, the same profound note of happiness, of a world all changed and renewed, of a day that had been passed in Paradise, and of a night that was to be heaven opened. All night she seemed to be conveyed smoothly upon a shallow stream of sleep and waking, and through the bowers of Beulah; all night she cherished to her heart that exquisite hope; and if, towards morning, she forgot it a while in a more profound unconsciousness, it was to catch again the rainbow thought with her first moment of awaking.

Chapter VII

ENTER MEPHISTOPHELES

Two days later a gig from Crossmichael deposited Frank Innes at the doors of Hermiston. Once in a way, during the past winter, Archie, in some acute phase of boredom, had written him a letter. It had contained something in the nature of an invitation or a reference to an invitation—precisely what, neither of them now remembered. When Innes had received it, there had been nothing further from his mind than to bury himself in the moors with Archie; but not even the most acute political heads are guided through the steps of life with unerring directness. That would require a gift of prophecy which has been denied to man. For instance, who could have imagined that, not a month after he had received the letter, and turned it into mockery, and put off answering it, and in the end lost it, misfortunes of a gloomy cast should begin to thicken over Frank's career? His case may be briefly stated. His father, a small Morayshire laird with a large family, became recalcitrant and cut off the supplies; he had fitted himself out with the beginnings of quite a good law library, which, upon some sudden losses on the turf, he had been obliged to sell before they were paid for; and his bookseller, hearing some rumour of the event, took out a warrant for his arrest. Innes had early word of it, and was able to take precautions. In this immediate welter of his affairs, with an unpleasant charge hanging over him, he had judged it the part of prudence to be off instantly, had written a fervid letter to his father at Inverauld, and put himself in the coach for Crossmichael. Any port in a storm! He was manfully turning his back on the Parliament House and its gay babble, on porter and oysters, the race-course and the ring; and manfully prepared, until these clouds should have blown by, to share a living grave with Archie Weir at Hermiston.

To do him justice, he was no less surprised to be going than Archie was to see him come; and he carried off his wonder with an infinitely better grace.

'Well, here I am!' said he, as he alighted. 'Pylades has come to Orestes at last. By the way, did you get my answer? No? How very provoking! Well, here I am to answer for myself, and that's better still.'

'I am very glad to see you, of course,' said Archie. 'I make you heartily welcome, of course. But you surely have not come to stay, with the Courts still sitting; is that not most unwise?'

'Damn the Courts!' says Frank. 'What are the Courts to friendship and a little fishing?'

And so it was agreed that he was to stay, with no term to the visit but the term which he had privily set to it himself—the day, namely, when his father should have come down with the dust, and he should be able to pacify the bookseller. On such vague conditions there began for these two young men (who were not even friends) a life of great familiarity and, as the days drew on, less and less intimacy. They were together at meal times, together o' nights when the hour had come for whisky-toddy; but it might have been noticed (had there been any one to pay heed) that they were rarely so much together by day. Archie had Hermiston to attend to, multifarious activities in the hills, in which he did not require, and had even refused, Frank's escort. He would be off sometimes in the morning and leave only a note on the breakfast table to announce the fact; and sometimes, with no notice at all, he would not return for dinner until the hour was long past.

Innes groaned under these desertions; it required all his philosophy to sit down to a solitary breakfast with composure, and all his unaffected good-nature to be able to greet Archie with friendliness on the more rare occasions when he came home late for dinner.

'I wonder what on earth he finds to do, Mrs Elliott?' said he one morning, after he had just read the hasty billet and sat down to table.

'I suppose it will be business, sir,' replied the housekeeper drily, measuring his distance off to him by an indicated curtsy.

'But I can't imagine what business!' he reiterated.

'I suppose it will be *his* business,' retorted the austere Kirstie.

He turned to her with that happy brightness that made the charm of his disposition, and broke into a peal of healthy and natural laughter.

'Well played, Mrs Elliott!' he cried; and the housekeeper's face relaxed into the shadow of an iron smile. 'Well played indeed!' said he. 'But you must not be making a stranger of me like that. Why, Archie and I were at the High School together, and we've been to college together, and we were going to the Bar together, when—you know! Dear, dear me! what a pity that was! A life spoiled, a fine young fellow as good as buried here in the wilderness with rustics; and all for what? A frolic, silly, if you like, but no more. God, how good your scones are, Mrs Elliott!'

'They're no mines, it was the lassie made them,' said Kirstie; 'and, saving your presence, there's little sense in taking the Lord's name in vain about idle vivers that you fill your kyte wi'.'

'I daresay you're perfectly right, ma'am,' quoth the imperturbable Frank. 'But as I was saying, this is a pitiable business, this about poor Archie; and you and I might do worse than put our heads together, like a couple of sensible people, and bring it to an end. Let me tell you, ma'am, that Archie is really quite a promising young man, and in my opinion he would do well at the Bar. As for his father, no one can deny his ability, and I don't fancy any one would care to deny that he has the deil's own temper——'

'If you'll excuse me, Mr Innes, I think the lass is crying on me,' said Kirstie, and flounced from the room.

'The damned, cross-grained, old broomstick!' ejaculated Innes.

In the meantime, Kirstie had escaped into the kitchen, and before her vassal gave vent to her feelings.

'Here, ettercap! Ye'll have to wait on yon Innes! I canna haud myself in. "Puir Erchie!" I'd "puir Erchie" him, if I had my way! And Hermiston with the deil's ain temper! God, let him take Hermiston's scones out of his mouth first. There's no a hair on ayther o' the Weirs that hasna mair spunk and dirdum to it than what he has in his hale dwaibly body! Settin' up his snash to me! Let him gang to the black toon where he's mebbe wantit—birling in a curricle—wi' pimatum on his heid—making a mess o' himsel' wi' nesty hizzies—a fair disgrace!' It was impossible to hear without admiration Kirstie's graduated disgust, as she brought forth, one after another, these somewhat baseless charges. Then she remembered her immediate purpose, and turned again on her fascinated auditor. 'Do ye no hear me, tawpie? Do ye no hear what I'm tellin' ye? Will I have to shoo ye in to him? If I come to attend to ye, mistress!' And the maid fled the kitchen, which had become practically dangerous, to attend on Innes' wants in the front parlour.

Tantaene irae? Has the reader perceived the reason? Since Frank's coming there were no more hours of gossip over the supper tray! All his blandishments were in vain; he had started handicapped on the race for Mrs Elliott's favour.

But it was a strange thing how misfortune dogged him in his efforts to be genial. I must guard the reader against accepting Kirstie's epithets as evidence; she was more concerned for their vigour than for their accuracy. Dwaibly, for instance; nothing could be more calumnious. Frank was the very picture of good looks, good humour, and manly youth. He had bright eyes with a sparkle and a dance to them, curly hair, a charming smile, brilliant teeth, an admirable carriage of the head, the look of a gentleman, the address of one accustomed to please at first sight and to improve the impression. And with all these advantages, he failed with every one about Hermiston; with the silent shepherd, with the obsequious grieve, with the groom who was also the ploughman, with the gardener and the gardener's sister—a pious, down-hearted woman with a shawl over her ears—he failed equally and flatly. They did not like him, and they showed it. The little maid, indeed, was an exception; she admired him devoutly, probably dreamed of him in her private hours; but she was accustomed to play the part of silent auditor to Kirstie's tirades and silent recipient of Kirstie's buffets, and she had learned not only to be a very capable girl of her years, but a very secret and prudent one besides. Frank was thus conscious that he had one ally and sympathiser in the midst of that general union of disfavour that surrounded, watched, and waited on him in the house of Hermiston; but he had little comfort or society from that alliance, and the demure little maid (twelve on her last birthday) preserved her own counsel, and tripped on his service, brisk, dumbly responsive, but inexorably unconversational. For the others, they were beyond hope and beyond endurance. Never had a young Apollo been cast among such rustic barbarians. But perhaps the cause of his ill-success lay in one trait which was habitual and unconscious with him, yet diagnostic of the man. It was his practice to approach any one person at the expense of some one else. He offered you an alliance against the some one else; he flattered you by slighting him; you were drawn into a small intrigue against him before you knew how. Wonderful are the virtues of this process generally; but Frank's mistake was in the choice of the some one else. He was not politic in that; he listened to the voice of irritation. Archie had offended him at first by what he had felt to be rather a dry reception, had offended him since by his frequent absences. He was besides the one figure continually present in Frank's eye; and it was to his immediate dependants that Frank could offer the snare of his sympathy. Now the truth is that the Weirs, father and son, were surrounded by a posse of strenuous loyalists. Of my lord they were vastly proud. It was a distinction in itself to be one of the vassals of the 'Hanging Judge', and his gross, formidable joviality was far from unpopular in the neighbourhood of his home. For Archie they had, one and all, a sensitive affection and respect which recoiled from a word of belittlement.

Nor was Frank more successful when he went farther afield. To the Four Black Brothers, for instance, he was antipathetic in the highest degree. Hob thought him too light, Gib too profane. Clem, who saw him but for a day or two before he went to Glasgow, wanted to know what the fule's business was, and whether he meant to stay here all session time! 'Yon's a drone,' he pronounced. As for Dand, it will be enough to describe their first meeting, when Frank had been whipping a river and the rustic celebrity chanced to come along the path.

'I'm told you're quite a poet,' Frank had said.

'Wha tell't ye that, mannie?' had been the unconciliating answer.

'O, everybody!' says Frank.

'God! Here's fame!' said the sardonic poet, and he had passed on his way.

Come to think of it, we have here perhaps a truer explanation of Frank's failures. Had he met Mr Sheriff Scott he could have turned a neater compliment, because Mr Scott would have been a friend worth making. Dand, on the other hand, he did not value sixpence, and he showed it even while he tried to flatter. Condescension is an excellent thing, but it is strange how one-sided the pleasure of it is! He who goes fishing among the Scots peasantry with condescension for a bait will have an empty basket by evening.

In proof of this theory Frank made a great success of it at the Crossmichael Club, to which Archie took him immediately on his arrival; his own last appearance on that scene of gaiety. Frank was made welcome there at once, continued to go regularly, and had attended a meeting (as the members ever after loved to tell) on the evening before his death. Young Hay and young Pringle appeared again. There was another supper at Windielaws, another dinner at Driffel; and it resulted in Frank being taken to the bosom of the county people as unreservedly as he had been repudiated by the country folk. He occupied Hermiston after the manner of an invader in a conquered capital. He was perpetually issuing from it, as from a base, to toddy parties, fishing parties, and dinner parties, to which Archie was not invited, or to which Archie would not go. It was now that the name of The Recluse became general for the young man. Some say that Innes invented it; Innes, at least, spread it abroad.

'How's all with your Recluse to-day?' people would ask.

'O, reclusing away!' Innes would declare, with his bright air of saying something witty; and immediately interrupt the general laughter which he had provoked much more by his air than his words, 'Mind you, it's all very well laughing, but

I'm not very well pleased. Poor Archie is a good fellow, an excellent fellow, a fellow I always liked. I think it small of him to take his little disgrace so hard and shut himself up. "Grant that it is a ridiculous story, painfully ridiculous," I keep telling him. "Be a man! Live it down, man!" But not he. Of course, it's just solitude, and shame, and all that. But I confess I'm beginning to fear the result. It would be all the pities in the world if a really promising fellow like Weir was to end ill. I'm seriously tempted to write to Lord Hermiston, and put it plainly to him.'

'I would if I were you,' some of his auditors would say, shaking the head, sitting bewildered and confused at this new view of the matter, so deftly indicated by a single word. 'A capital idea!' they would add, and wonder at the *aplomb* and position of this young man, who talked as a matter of course of writing to Hermiston and correcting him upon his private affairs.

And Frank would proceed, sweetly confidential: 'I'll give you an idea, now. He's actually sore about the way that I'm received and he's left out in the county—actually jealous and sore. I've rallied him and I've reasoned with him, told him that every one was most kindly inclined towards him, told him even that *I* was received merely because I was his guest. But it's no use. He will neither accept the invitations he gets, nor stop brooding about the ones where he's left out. What I'm afraid of is that the wound's ulcerating. He had always one of those dark, secret, angry natures—a little underhand and plenty of bile—you know the sort. He must have inherited it from the Weirs, whom I suspect to have been a worthy family of weavers somewhere; what's the cant phrase?—sedentary occupation. It's precisely the kind of character to go wrong in a false position like what his father's made for him, or he's making for himself, whichever you like to call it. And for my part, I think it a disgrace,' Frank would say generously.

Presently the sorrow and anxiety of this disinterested friend took shape. He began in private, in conversations of two, to talk vaguely of bad habits and low habits. 'I must say I'm afraid he's going wrong altogether,' he would say. 'I'll tell you plainly, and between ourselves, I scarcely like to stay there any longer; only, man, I'm positively afraid to leave him alone. You'll see, I shall be blamed for it later on. I'm staying at a great sacrifice. I'm hindering my chances at the Bar, and I can't blind my eyes to it. And what I'm afraid of is that I'm going to get kicked for it all round before all's done. You see, nobody believes in friendship nowadays.'

'Well, Innes,' his interlocutor would reply, 'it's very good of you, I must say that. If there's any blame going, you'll always be sure of *my* good word, for one thing.'

'Well,' Frank would continue, 'candidly, I don't say it's pleasant. He has a very rough way with him; his father's son, you know. I don't say he's rude—of course, I couldn't be expected to stand that—but he steers very near the wind. No, it's not pleasant; but I tell ye, man, in conscience I don't think it would be fair to leave him. Mind you, I don't say there's anything actually wrong. What I say is that I don't like the looks of it, man!' and he would press the arm of his momentary confidant.

In the early stages I am persuaded there was no malice. He talked but for the pleasure of airing himself. He was essentially glib, as becomes the young advocate, and essentially careless of the truth, which is the mark of the young ass; and so he talked at random. There was no particular bias, but that one which is indigenous and universal, to flatter himself and to please and interest the present friend. And by thus milling air out of his mouth, he had presently built up a presentation of Archie which was known and talked of in all corners of the county. Wherever there was a residential house and a walled garden, wherever there was a dwarfish castle and a park, wherever a quadruple cottage by the ruins of a peel-tower showed an old family going down, and wherever a handsome villa with a carriage approach and a shrubbery marked the coming up of a new one—probably on the wheels of machinery —Archie began to be regarded in the light of a dark, perhaps a vicious mystery, and the future developments of his career to be looked for with uneasiness and confidential whispering. He had done something disgraceful, my dear. What, was not precisely known, and that good kind young man, Mr Innes, did his best to make light of it. But there it was. And Mr Innes was very anxious about him now; he was really uneasy, my dear; he was positively wrecking his own prospects because he dared not leave him alone. How wholly we all lie at the mercy of a single prater, not needfully with any malign purpose!

And if a man but talks of himself in the right spirit, refers to his virtuous actions by the way, and never applies to them the name of virtue, how easily his evidence is accepted in the court of public opinion!

All this while, however, there was a more poisonous ferment at work between the two lads, which came late indeed to the surface, but had modified and magnified their dissensions from the first. To an idle, shallow, easy-going customer like Frank, the smell of a mystery was attractive. It gave his mind something to play with, like a new toy to a child; and it took him on the weak side, for like many young men coming to the Bar, and before they had been tried and found wanting, he flattered himself he was a fellow of unusual quickness and penetration. They knew nothing of Sherlock Holmes in those days, but there was a good deal said of Talleyrand. And if you could have caught Frank off his guard, he would have confessed with a smirk that, if he resembled any one, it was the Marquis de Talleyrand-Périgord. It was on the occasion of Archie's first absence that this interest took root. It was vastly deepened when Kirstie resented his curiosity at breakfast, and that same afternoon there occurred another scene which clinched the business. He was fishing Swingleburn, Archie accompanying him, when the latter looked at his watch.

'Well, good-bye,' said he. 'I have something to do. See you at dinner.'

'Don't be in such a hurry,' cries Frank. 'Hold on till I get my rod up. I'll go with you; I'm sick of flogging this ditch.'

And he began to reel up his line.

Archie stood speechless. He took a long while to recover his wits under this direct attack; but by the time he was ready with his answer, and the angle was almost packed up, he had become completely Weir, and the hanging face gloomed on his young shoulders. He spoke with a laboured composure, a laboured kindness even; but a child could see that his mind was made up.

'I beg your pardon, Innes; I don't want to be disagreeable, but let us understand one another from the beginning. When I want your company, I'll let you know.'

'O!' cries Frank, 'you don't want my company, don't you?'

'Apparently not just now,' replied Archie. 'I even indicated to you when I did, if you'll remember—and that was at dinner.

If we two fellows are to live together pleasantly—and I see
no reason why we should not—it can only be by respecting
each other's privacy. If we begin intruding——'

'O, come! I'll take this at no man's hands. Is this the way
you treat a guest and an old friend?' cried Innes.

'Just go home and think over what I said by yourself,'
continued Archie, 'whether it's reasonable, or whether it's
really offensive or not; and let's meet at dinner as though
nothing had happened. I'll put it this way, if you like—that I
know my own character, that I'm looking forward (with great
pleasure, I assure you) to a long visit from you, and that I'm
taking precautions at the first. I see the thing that we—-that I,
if you like—might fall out upon, and I step in and *obsto
principiis*. I wager you five pounds you'll end by seeing that I
mean friendliness, and I assure you, Francie, I do,' he added,
relenting.

Bursting with anger, but incapable of speech, Innes shouldered
his rod, made a gesture of farewell, and strode off down the
burn-side. Archie watched him go without moving. He was
sorry, but quite unashamed. He hated to be inhospitable, but
in one thing he was his father's son. He had a strong sense that
his house was his own and no man else's; and to lie at a guest's
mercy was what he refused. He hated to seem harsh. But that
was Frank's lookout. If Frank had been commonly discreet,
he would have been decently courteous. And there was another
consideration. The secret he was protecting was not his own
merely; it was hers: it belonged to that inexpressible she who
was fast taking possession of his soul, and whom he would soon
have defended at the cost of burning cities. By the time he had
watched Frank as far as the Swingleburn-foot, appearing and
disappearing in the tarnished heather, still stalking at a fierce
gait but already dwindled in the distance into less than the
smallness of Lilliput, he could afford to smile at the occurrence.
Either Frank would go, and that would be a relief—or he
would continue to stay, and his host must continue to endure
him. And Archie was now free—by devious paths, behind
hillocks and in the hollow of burns—to make for the trysting-
place where Kirstie, cried about by the curlew and the plover,
waited and burned for his coming by the Covenanter's stone.

Innes went off down-hill in a passion of resentment, easy to
be understood, but which yielded progressively to the needs of

his situation. He cursed Archie for a cold-hearted, unfriendly, rude, rude dog; and himself still more passionately for a fool in having come to Hermiston when he might have sought refuge in almost any other house in Scotland. But the step once taken, was practically irretrievable. He had no more ready money to go anywhere else; he would have to borrow from Archie the next club-night; and ill as he thought of his host's manners, he was sure of his practical generosity. Frank's resemblance to Talleyrand strikes me as imaginary; but at least not Talleyrand himself could have more obediently taken his lesson from the facts. He met Archie at dinner without resentment, almost with cordiality. You must take your friends as you find them, he would have said. Archie couldn't help being his father's son, or his grandfather's, the hypothetical weaver's, grandson. The son of a hunks, he was still a hunks at heart, incapable of true generosity and consideration; but he had other qualities with which Frank could divert himself in the meanwhile, and to enjoy which it was necessary that Frank should keep his temper.

So excellently was it controlled that he awoke next morning with his head full of a different, though a cognate subject. What was Archie's little game? Why did he shun Frank's company? What was he keeping secret? Was he keeping tryst with somebody, and was it a woman? It would be a good joke and a fair revenge to discover. To that task he set himself with a great deal of patience, which might have surprised his friends, for he had been always credited not with patience so much as brilliancy; and little by little, from one point to another, he at last succeeded in piecing out the situation. First he remarked that, although Archie set out in all the directions of the compass, he always came home again from some point between the south and west. From the study of a map, and in consideration of the great expanse of untenanted moorland running in that direction towards the sources of the Clyde, he laid his finger on Cauldstaneslap and two other neighbouring farms, Kingsmuirs and Polintarf. But it was difficult to advance farther. With his rod for a pretext, he vainly visited each of them in turn; nothing was to be seen suspicious about this trinity of moorland settlements. He would have tried to follow Archie, had it been the least possible, but the nature of the land precluded the idea. He did the next best, ensconced himself in a quiet corner, and pursued his

movements with a telescope. It was equally in vain, and he
soon wearied of his futile vigilance, left the telescope at home,
and had almost given the matter up in despair, when, on the
twenty-seventh day of his visit, he was suddenly confronted
with the person whom he sought. The first Sunday Kirstie
had managed to stay away from kirk on some pretext of indis-
position, which was more truly modesty; the pleasure of
beholding Archie seeming too sacred, too vivid for that public
place. On the two following, Frank had himself been absent
on some of his excursions among the neighbouring families.
It was not until the fourth, accordingly, that Frank had
occasion to set eyes on the enchantress. With the first look, all
hesitation was over. She came with the Cauldstaneslap party;
then she lived at Cauldstaneslap. Here was Archie's secret,
here was the woman, and more than that—though I have need
here of every manageable attenuation of language—with the
first look he had already entered himself as rival. It was a good
deal in pique, it was a little in revenge, it was much in genuine
admiration: the devil may decide the proportions! I cannot,
and it is very likely that Frank could not.

'Mighty attractive milkmaid,' he observed, on the way home.

'Who?' said Archie.

'O, the girl you're looking at—aren't you? Forward there on
the road. She came attended by the rustic bard; presumably,
therefore, belongs to his exalted family. The single objection!
for the four black brothers are awkward customers. If anything were to go wrong, Gib would gibber, and Clem would
prove inclement; and Dand fly in danders, and Hob blow up
in gobbets. It would be a Helliott of a business!'

'Very humorous, I am sure,' said Archie.

'Well, I am trying to be so,' said Frank. 'It's none too easy
in this place, and with your solemn society, my dear fellow.
But confess that the milkmaid has found favour in your eyes,
or resign all claim to be a man of taste.'

'It is no matter,' returned Archie.

But the other continued to look at him, steadily and
quizzically, and his colour slowly rose and deepened under the
glance, until not impudence itself could have denied that he
was blushing. And at this Archie lost some of his control. He
changed his stick from one hand to the other, and—'O, for
God's sake, don't be an ass!' he cried.

'Ass? That's the retort delicate without doubt,' says Frank. 'Beware of the homespun brothers, dear. If they come into the dance, you'll see who's an ass. Think now, if they only applied (say) a quarter as much talent as I have applied to the question of what Mr Archie does with his evening hours, and why he is so unaffectedly nasty when the subject's touched on——'

'You are touching on it now,' interrupted Archie with a wince.

'Thank you. That was all I wanted, an articulate confession,' said Frank.

'I beg to remind you——' began Archie.

But he was interrupted in turn. 'My dear fellow, don't. It's quite needless. The subject's dead and buried.'

And Frank began to talk hastily on other matters, an art in which he was an adept, for it was his gift to be fluent on anything or nothing. But although Archie had the grace or the timidity to suffer him to rattle on, he was by no means done with the subject. When he came home to dinner, he was greeted with a sly demand, how things were looking 'Cauldstaneslap ways'. Frank took his first glass of port out after dinner to the toast of Kirstie, and later in the evening he returned to the charge again.

'I say, Weir, you'll excuse me for returning again to this affair. I've been thinking it over, and I wish to beg you very seriously to be more careful. It's not a safe business. Not safe, my boy,' said he.

'What?' said Archie.

'Well, it's your own fault if I must put a name on the thing; but really, as a friend, I cannot stand by and see you rushing head down into these dangers. My dear boy,' said he, holding up a warning cigar, 'consider! What is to be the end of it?'

'The end of what?'—Archie, helpless with irritation, persisted in this dangerous and ungracious guard.

'Well, the end of the milkmaid; or, to speak more by the card, the end of Miss Christina Elliott of the Cauldstaneslap.'

'I assure you,' Archie broke out, 'this is all a figment of your imagination. There is nothing to be said against that young lady; you have no right to introduce her name into the conversation.'

'I'll make a note of it,' said Frank. 'She shall henceforth be nameless, nameless, nameless, Grigalach! I make a note besides of your valuable testimony to her character. I only want to look at this thing as a man of the world. Admitted she's an angel—but, my good fellow, is she a lady?'

This was torture to Archie. 'I beg your pardon,' he said, struggling to be composed, 'but because you have wormed yourself into my confidence——'

'O, come!' cried Frank. 'Your confidence? It was rosy but unconsenting. Your confidence, indeed? Now look! This is what I must say, Weir, for it concerns your safety and good character, and therefore my honour as your friend. You say I wormed myself into your confidence. Wormed is good. But what have I done? I have put two and two together, just as the parish will be doing to-morrow, and the whole of Tweed-dale in two weeks, and the black brothers—well, I won't put a date on that; it will be a dark and stormy morning! Your secret, in other words, is poor Poll's. And I want to ask of you as a friend whether you like the prospect? There are two horns to your dilemma, and I must say for myself I should look mighty ruefully on either. Do you see yourself explaining to the four Black Brothers? or do you see yourself presenting the milkmaid to papa as the future lady of Hermiston? Do you? I tell you plainly, I don't!'

Archie rose. 'I will hear no more of this,' he said, in a trembling voice.

But Frank again held up his cigar. 'Tell me one thing first. Tell me if this is not a friend's part that I am playing?'

'I believe you think it so,' replied Archie. 'I can go as far as that. I can do so much justice to your motives. But I will hear no more of it. I am going to bed.'

'That's right, Weir,' said Frank heartily. 'Go to bed and think over it; and I say, man, don't forget your prayers! I don't often do the moral—don't go in for that sort of thing—but when I do there's one thing sure, that I mean it.'

So Archie marched off to bed, and Frank sat alone by the table for another hour or so, smiling to himself richly. There was nothing vindictive in his nature; but, if revenge came in his way, it might as well be good, and the thought of Archie's pillow reflections that night was indescribably sweet to him. He felt a pleasant sense of power. He looked down on Archie as on a very little boy whose strings he pulled—as on a horse whom he had backed and bridled by sheer power of intelligence, and whom he might ride to glory or the grave at pleasure. Which was it to be? He lingered long, relishing the details of schemes that he was too idle to pursue. Poor cork upon a torrent, he tasted that night the sweets of omnipotence, and brooded like a deity over the strands of that intrigue which was to shatter him before the summer waned.

Chapter VIII

A NOCTURNAL VISIT

KIRSTIE had many causes of distress. More and more as we grow old—and yet more and more as we grow old and are women, frozen by the fear of age—we come to rely on the voice as the single outlet of the soul. Only thus, in the curtailment of our means, can we relieve the straitened cry of the passion within us; only thus, in the bitter and sensitive shyness of advancing years, can we maintain relations with those vivacious figures of the young that still show before us and tend daily to become no more than the moving wall-paper of life. Talk is the last link, the last relation. But with the end of the conversation, when the voice stops and the bright face of the listener is turned away, solitude falls again on the bruised heart. Kirstie had lost her 'cannie hour at e'en'; she could no more wander with Archie, a ghost if you will, but a happy ghost, in fields Elysian. And to her it was as if the whole world had fallen silent; to him, but an unremarkable change of amusements. And she raged to know it. The effervescency of her passionate and irritable nature rose within her at times to bursting point.

This is the price paid by age for unseasonable ardours of feelings. It must have been so for Kirstie at any time when the occasion chanced; but it so fell out that she was deprived of this delight in the hour when she had most need of it, when she had most to say, most to ask, and when she trembled to recog-

nize her sovereignty not merely in abeyance but annulled.
For, with the clairvoyance of a genuine love, she had pierced
the mystery that had so long embarrassed Frank. She was
conscious, even before it was carried out, even on that Sunday
night when it began, of an invasion of her rights; and a voice
told her the invader's name. Since then, by arts, by accident,
by small things observed, and by the general drift of Archie's
humour, she had passed beyond all possibility of doubt. With
a sense of justice that Lord Hermiston might have envied, she
had that day in church considered and admitted the attractions of the younger Kirstie; and with the profound humanity
and sentimentality of her nature, she had recognized the
coming of fate. Not thus would she have chosen. She had seen,
in imagination, Archie wedded to some tall, powerful, and
rosy heroine of the golden locks, made in her own image, for
whom she would have strewed the bride-bed with delight; and
now she could have wept to see the ambition falsified. But the
gods had pronounced, and her doom was otherwise.

She lay tossing in bed that night, besieged with feverish
thoughts. There were dangerous matters pending, a battle was
toward, over the fate of which she hung in jealousy, sympathy, fear, and alternate loyalty and disloyalty to either side.
Now she was reincarnated in her niece, and now in Archie.
Now she saw, through the girl's eyes, the youth on his knees to
her, heard his persuasive instances with a deadly weakness,
and received his overmastering caresses. Anon, with a revulsion, her temper raged to see such utmost favours of fortune
and love squandered on a brat of a girl, one of her own house,
using her own name—a deadly ingredient—and that 'didna
ken her ain mind an' was as black's your hat'. Now she trembled lest her deity should plead in vain, loving the idea of
success for him like a triumph of nature; anon, with returning
loyalty to her own family and sex, she trembled for Kirstie and
the credit of the Elliotts. And again she had a vision of herself,
the day over for her old-world tales and local gossip, bidding
farewell to her last link with life and brightness and love; and
behind and beyond, she saw but the blank butt-end where she
must crawl to die. Had she then come to the lees? she, so great,
so beautiful, with a heart as fresh as a girl's and strong as
womanhood? It could not be, and yet it was so; and for a
moment her bed was horrible to her as the sides of the grave.

And she looked forward over a waste of hours, and saw herself go on to rage, and tremble, and be softened, and rage again, until the day came and the labours of the day must be renewed.

Suddenly she heard feet on the stairs—his feet, and soon after the sound of a window-sash flung open. She sat up with her heart beating. He had gone to his room alone, and he had not gone to bed. She might again have one of her night cracks; and at the entrancing prospect, a change came over her mind; with the approach of this hope of pleasure, all the baser metal became immediately obliterated from her thoughts. She rose, all woman, and all the best of woman, tender, pitiful, hating the wrong, loyal to her own sex—and all the weakest of that dear miscellany, nourishing, cherishing next her soft heart, voicelessly flattering, hopes that she would have died sooner than have acknowledged. She tore off her nightcap, and her hair fell about her shoulders in profusion. Undying coquetry awoke. By the faint light of her nocturnal rush, she stood before the looking-glass, carried her shapely arms above her head, and gathered up the treasures of her tresses. She was never backward to admire herself; that kind of modesty was a stranger to her nature; and she paused, struck with a pleased wonder at the sight. 'Ye daft auld wife!' she said, answering a thought that was not; and she blushed with the innocent consciousness of a child. Hastily she did up the massive and shining coils, hastily donned a wrapper, and with the rushlight in her hand, stole into the hall. Below stairs she heard the clock ticking the deliberate seconds, and Frank jingling with the decanters in the dining-room. Aversion rose in her, bitter and momentary. 'Nesty, tippling puggy!' she thought; and the next moment she had knocked guardedly at Archie's door and was bidden enter.

Archie had been looking out into the ancient blackness, pierced here and there with a rayless star; taking the sweet air of the moors and the night into his bosom deeply; seeking, perhaps finding, peace after the manner of the unhappy. He turned round as she came in, and showed her a pale face against the window-frame.

'Is that you, Kirstie?' he asked. 'Come in!'

'It's unco late, my dear,' said Kirstie, affecting unwillingness.

'No, no,' he answered, 'not at all. Come in, if you want a crack. I am not sleepy, God knows!'

She advanced, took a chair by the toilet table and the candle, and set the rushlight at her foot. Something—it might be in the comparative disorder of her dress, it might be the emotion that now welled in her bosom—had touched her with a wand of transformation, and she seemed young with the youth of goddesses.

'Mr Erchie,' she began, 'what's this that's come to ye?'

'I am not aware of anything that has come,' said Archie, and blushed, and repented bitterly that he had let her in.

'O, my dear, that'll no dae!' said Kirstie. 'It's ill to blend the eyes of love. O, Mr Erchie, tak a thocht ere it's ower late. Ye shouldna be impatient o' the braws o' life, they'll a' come in their saison, like the sun and the rain. Ye're young yet; ye've mony cantie years afore ye. See and dinna wreck yersel' at the outset like sae mony ithers! Hae patience—they telled me aye that was the owercome o' life—hae patience, there's a braw day coming yet. Gude kens it never cam to me; and here I am, wi' nayther man nor bairn to ca' my ain, wearying a' folks wi' my ill tongue, and you the first, Mr Erchie!'

'I have a difficulty in knowing what you mean,' said Archie.

'Weel, and I'll tell ye,' she said. 'It's just this, that I'm feared. I'm feared for ye, my dear. Remember, your faither is a hard man, reaping where he hasna sowed and gaithering where he hasna strawed. It's easy speakin', but mind! Ye'll have to look in the gurly face o'm, where it's ill to look, and vain to look for mercy. Ye mind me o' a bonny ship pitten oot into the black and gowsty seas—ye're a' safe still, sittin' quait and crackin' wi' Kirstie in your lown chalmer; but whaur will ye be the morn, and in whatten horror o' the fearsome tempest, cryin' on the hills to cover ye?'

'Why, Kirstie, you're very enigmatical to-night—and very eloquent,' Archie put in.

'And, my dear Mr Erchie,' she continued, with a change of voice, 'ye mauna think that I canna sympathize wi' ye. Ye mauna think that I havena been young mysel'. Lang syne, when I was a bit lassie, no twenty yet——' She paused and sighed. 'Clean and caller, wi' a fit like the hinney bee,' she continued. 'I was aye big and buirdly, ye maun understand; a bonny figure o' a woman, though I say it that suldna—built

to rear bairns—braw bairns they suld hae been, and grand I
would hae likit it! But I was young, dear, wi' the bonny glint
o' youth in my e'en, and little I dreamed I'd ever be tellin' ye
this, an auld, lanely, rudas wife! Weel, Mr Erchie, there was a
lad cam' courtin' me, as was but naetural. Mony had come
before, and I would nane o' them. But this yin had a tongue to
wile the birds frae the lift and the bees frae the foxglove bells.
Deary me, but it's lang syne! Folk have dee'd sinsyne and been
buried, and are forgotten, and bairns been born and got merrit
and got bairns o' their ain. Sinsyne woods have been plantit,
and have grawn up and are bonny trees, and the joes sit in
their shadow, and sinsyne auld estates have changed hands,
and there have been wars and rumours of wars on the face of
the earth. And here I'm still—like an auld droopit craw—
lookin' on and craikin'! But, Mr Erchie, do ye no think that I
have mind o' it a' still? I was dwalling then in my faither's
house; and it's a curious thing that we were whiles trysted in
the Deil's Hags. And do ye no think that I have mind of the
bonny simmer days, the lang miles o' the bluid-red heather,
the cryin' o' the whaups, and the lad and the lassie that was
trysted? Do ye no think that I mind how the hilly sweetness
ran about my hairt? Ay, Mr Erchie, I ken the way o' it—fine
do I ken the way—how the grace o' God takes them, like
Paul of Tarsus, when they think it least, and drives the pair o'
them into a land which is like a dream, and the world and the
folks in't are nae mair than clouds to the puir lassie, and heeven
nae mair than windle-straes, if she can but pleesure him!
Until Tam dee'd—that was my story,' she broke off to say,
'he dee'd, and I wasna at the buryin'. But while he was here,
I could take care o' mysel'. And can yon puir lassie?'

Kirstie, her eyes shining with unshed tears, stretched out her
hand towards him appealingly; the bright and the dull gold
of her hair flashed and smouldered in the coils behind her
comely head, like the rays of an eternal youth; the pure
colour had risen in her face; and Archie was abashed alike
by her beauty and her story. He came towards her slowly
from the window, took up her hand in his and kissed it.

'Kirstie,' he said hoarsely, 'you have misjudged me sorely.
I have always thought of her, I wouldna harm her for the
universe, my woman!'

'Eh, lad, and that's easy saying',' cried Kirstie, 'but it's

nane sae easy doin'! Man, do ye no comprehend that it's
God's wull we should be blendit and glamoured, and have nae
command over our ain members at a time like that? My
bairn,' she cried, still holding his hand, 'think o' the puir lass!
have pity upon her, Erchie! and O, be wise for twa! Think o'
the risk she rins! I have seen ye, and what's to prevent ithers!
I saw ye once in the Hags, in my ain howl, and I was wae to see
ye there—in pairt for the omen, for I think there's a weird on the
place—and in pairt for pure nakit envy and bitterness o' hairt.
It's strange ye should forgather there tae! God! but yon puir,
thrawn, auld Covenanter's seen a heap o' human natur since
he lookit his last on the musket barrels, if he never saw nane
afore,' she added, with a kind of wonder in her eyes.

'I swear by my honour I have done her no wrong,' said
Archie. 'I swear by my honour and the redemption of my
soul that there shall none be done her. I have heard of this
before. I have been foolish, Kirstie, not unkind, and, above all,
not base.'

'There's my bairn!' said Kirstie, rising. 'I'll can trust ye
noo, I'll can gang to my bed wi' an easy hairt.' And then she
saw in a flash how barren had been her triumph. Archie had
promised to spare the girl, and he would keep it; but who had
promised to spare Archie? What was to be the end of it? Over
a maze of difficulties she glanced, and saw, at the end of every
passage, the flinty countenance of Hermiston. And a kind of
horror fell upon her at what she had done. She wore a tragic
mask. 'Erchie, the Lord peety you, dear, and peety me! I
have buildit on this foundation'—laying her hand heavily on
his shoulder—'and buildit hie, and pit my hairt in the buildin'
of it. If the hale hypothec were to fa', I think, laddie, I would
dee! Excuse a daft wife that loves ye, and that kenned your
mither. And for His name's sake keep yersel' frae inordinate
desires; haud your heart in baith your hands, carry it canny
and laigh; dinna send it up like a bairn's kite into the collieshangie o' the wunds! Mind, Maister Erchie dear, that this
life's a' disappointment, and a mouthfu' o' mools is the
appointed end.'

'Ay, but Kirstie, my woman, you're asking me ower much
at last,' said Archie, profoundly moved, and lapsing into the
broad Scots. 'Ye're asking what nae man can grant ye, what
only the Lord of heaven can grant ye if He see fit. Ay! And

can even He! I can promise ye what I shall do, and you can depend on that. But how I shall feel—my woman, that is long past thinking of!'

They were both standing by now opposite each other. The face of Archie wore the wretched semblance of a smile; hers was convulsed for a moment.

'Promise me ae thing,' she cried in a sharp voice. 'Promise me ye'll never do naething without telling me.'

'No, Kirstie, I canna promise ye that,' he replied. 'I have promised enough, God kens!'

'May the blessing of God lift and rest upon ye dear!' she said.

'God bless ye, my old friend,' said he.

Chapter IX

AT THE WEAVER'S STONE

IT was late in the afternoon when Archie drew near by the hill path to the Praying Weaver's stone. The Hags were in shadow. But still, through the gate of the Slap, the sun shot a last arrow, which sped far and straight across the surface of the moss, here and there touching and shining on a tussock, and lighted at length on the gravestone and the small figure awaiting him there. The emptiness and solitude of the great moors seemed to be concentrated there, and Kirstie pointed out by that figure of sunshine for the only inhabitant. His first sight of her was thus excruciatingly sad, like a glimpse of a world from which all light, comfort, and society were on the point of vanishing. And the next moment, when she had turned her face to him and the quick smile had enlightened it, the whole face of nature smiled upon him in her smile of welcome. Archie's slow pace was quickened; his legs hasted to her though his heart was hanging back. The girl, upon her side, drew herself together slowly and stood up, expectant; she was all languor, her face was gone white; her arms ached for him, her soul was on tip-toes. But he deceived her, pausing a few steps away, not less white than herself, and holding up his hand with a gesture of denial.

'No, Christina, not to-day,' he said. 'To-day I have to talk to you seriously. Sit ye down, please, there where you were. Please!' he repeated.

The revulsion of feeling in Christina's heart was violent. To have longed and waited these weary hours for him, rehearsing her endearments—to have seen him at last come—to have been ready there, breathless, wholly passive, his to do what he would with—and suddenly to have found herself confronted with a grey-faced, harsh schoolmaster—it was too rude a shock. She could have wept, but pride withheld her. She sat down on the stone, from which she had arisen, part with the instinct of obedience, part as though she had been thrust there. What was this? Why was she rejected? Had she ceased to please? She stood here offering her wares, and he would none of them! And yet they were all his! His to take and keep, not his to refuse though! In her quick petulant nature, a moment ago on fire with hope, thwarted love and wounded vanity wrought. The schoolmaster that there is in all men, to the despair of all girls and most women, was now completely in possession of Archie. He had passed a night of sermons, a day of reflection; he had come wound up to do his duty; and the set mouth, which in him only betrayed the effort of his will, to her seemed the expression of an averted heart. It was the same with his constrained voice and embarrassed utterance; and if so—if it was all over—the pang of the thought took away from her the power of thinking.

He stood before her some way off. 'Kirstie, there's been too much of this. We've seen too much of each other.' She looked up quickly and her eyes contracted. 'There's no good ever comes of these secret meetings. They're not frank, not honest truly, and I ought to have seen it. People have begun to talk; and it's not right of me. Do you see?'

'I see somebody will have been talking to ye,' she said sullenly.

'They have, more than one of them,' replied Archie.

'And whae were they?' she cried. 'And what kind o' love do ye ca' that, that's ready to gang round like a whirligig at folk talking? Do ye think they havena talked to me?'

'Have they indeed?' said Archie, with a quick breath. 'That is what I feared. Who were they? Who has dared——?'

Archie was on the point of losing his temper.

As a matter of fact, not any one had talked to Christina on

the matter; and she strenuously repeated her own first question in a panic of self-defence.

'Ah, well! what does it matter?' he said. 'They were good folk that wished well to us, and the great affair is that there are people talking. My dear girl, we have to be wise. We must not wreck our lives at the outset. They may be long and happy yet, and we must see to it, Kirstie, like God's rational creatures and not like fool children. There is one thing we must see to before all. You're worth waiting for, Kirstie! worth waiting for a generation; it would be enough reward.'—And here he remembered the schoolmaster again, and very unwisely took to following wisdom. 'The first thing that we must see to, is that there shall be no scandal about for my father's sake. That would ruin all; do ye no see that?'

Kirstie was a little pleased, there had been some show of warmth of sentiment in what Archie had said last. But the dull irritation still persisted in her bosom; with the aboriginal instinct, having suffered herself, she wished to make Archie suffer.

And besides, there had come out the word she had always feared to hear from his lips, the name of his father. It is not to be supposed that, during so many days with a love avowed between them, some reference had not been made to their conjoint future. It had in fact been often touched upon, and from the first had been the sore point. Kirstie had wilfully closed the eye of thought; she would not argue even with herself; gallant, desperate little heart, she had accepted the command of that supreme attraction like the call of fate and marched blindfold on her doom. But Archie, with his masculine sense of responsibility, must reason; he must dwell on some future good, when the present good was all in all to Kirstie; he must talk—and talk lamely, as necessity drove him—of what was to be. Again and again he had touched on marriage; again and again been driven back into indistinctness by a memory of Lord Hermiston. And Kirstie had been swift to understand and quick to choke down and smother the understanding; swift to leap up in flame at a mention of that hope, which spoke volumes to her vanity and her love, that she might one day be Mrs Weir of Hermiston; swift, also, to recognize in his stumbling or throttled utterance the death-knell of these expectations, and constant, poor girl! in her large-minded madness, to go on and to reck nothing of the future. But these unfinished references, these blinks in which his heart spoke, and his memory and reason rose up to silence it before the words were well uttered, gave her unqualifiable agony. She was raised up and dashed down again bleeding. The recurrence of the subject forced her, for however short a time, to open her eyes on what she did not wish to see; and it had invariably ended in another disappointment. So now again, at the mere wind of its coming, at the mere mention of his father's name—who might seem indeed to have accompanied them in their whole moorland courtship, an awful figure in a wig with an ironical and bitter smile, present to guilty consciousness—she fled from it head down.

'Ye havena told me yet,' she said, 'who was it spoke?'

'Your aunt for one,' said Archie.

'Auntie Kirstie?' she cried. 'And what do I care for my Auntie Kirstie?'

She cares a great deal for her niece,' replied Archie, in kind reproof.

'Troth, and it's the first I've heard of it,' retorted the girl.

'The question here is not who it is, but what they say, what they have noticed,' pursued the lucid schoolmaster. 'That is what we have to think of in self-defence.'

'Auntie Kirstie, indeed! A bitter, thrawn auld maid that's fomented trouble in the country before I was born, and will be doing it still, I daur say, when I'm deid! It's in her nature; it's as natural for her as it's for a sheep to eat.'

'Pardon me, Kirstie, she was not the only one,' interposed Archie. 'I had two warnings, two sermons, last night, both most kind and considerate. Had you been there, I promise you you would have grat, my dear! And they opened my eyes. I saw we were going a wrong way.'

'Who was the other one?' Kirstie demanded.

By this time Archie was in the condition of a hunted beast. He had come, braced and resolute; he was to trace out a line of conduct for the pair of them in a few cold, convincing sentences; he had now been there some time, and he was still staggering round the outworks and undergoing what he felt to be a savage cross-examination.

'Mr Frank!' she cried. 'What nex', I would like to ken?'

'He spoke most kindly and truly.'

'What like did he say?'

'I am not going to tell you; you have nothing to do with that,' cried Archie, startled to find he had admitted so much.

'O, I have naething to do with it!' she repeated, springing to her feet. 'A'body at Hermiston's free to pass their opinions upon me, but I have naething to do wi' it! Was this at prayers like? Did ye ca' the grieve into the consultation? Little wonder if a'body's talking, when ye make a'body yer confidants! But as you say, Mr Weir—most kindly, most considerately, most truly, I'm sure—I have naething to do with it. And I think I'll better be going. I'll be wishing you good evening, Mr Weir.' And she made him a stately curtsey, shaking as she did so from head to foot, with the barren ecstasy of temper.

Poor Archie stood dumbfounded. She had moved some steps away from him before he recovered the gift of articulate speech.

'Kirstie!' he cried. 'O, Kirstie woman!'

There was in his voice a ring of appeal, a clang of mere astonishment that showed the schoolmaster was vanquished.

She turned round on him. 'What do ye Kirstie me for?' she retorted. 'What have ye to do wi' me! Gang to your ain freends and deave them!'

He could only repeat the appealing 'Kirstie!'

'Kirstie, indeed!' cried the girl, her eyes blazing in her white face. 'My name is Miss Christina Elliott, I would have ye to ken, and I daur ye to ca' me out of it. If I canna get love, I'll have respect, Mr Weir. I'm come of decent people, and I'll have respect. What have I done that ye should lightly me? What have I done? What have I done? O, what have I done?' and her voice rose upon the third repetition. 'I thocht—I thocht—I thocht I was sae happy!' and the first sob broke from her like the paroxysm of some mortal sickness.

Archie ran to her. He took the poor child in his arms, and she nestled to his breast as to a mother's, and clasped him in hands that were strong like vices. He felt her whole body shaken by the throes of distress, and had pity upon her beyond speech. Pity, and at the same time a bewildered fear of this explosive engine in his arms, whose works he did not understand, and yet had been tampering with. There arose from before him the curtains of boyhood, and he saw for the first time the ambiguous face of woman as she is. In vain he looked back over the interview; he saw not where he had offended. It seemed unprovoked, a wilful convulsion of brute nature. . . .